PREFACE

This Student Solutions Guide has been developed as a supplement to *Thermodynamics: An Engineering Approach,* by Yunus A. Çengel and Michael A. Boles and is intended to provide students with additional resources to help them solve thermodynamics problems. The guide provides **60 new worked-out examples** to help students build confidence. By studying solutions that are representative of the key problem types, students learn to master the skills necessary to succeed in a given chapter. These examples, along with the existing ones in the book, have been carefully selected to foster mature understanding of the fundamental concepts and principles. This solutions guide also offers **learning objectives and a glossary for all chapters** in the text.

For the instructor, this guide offers a new supply of homework problems to assign for each chapter of the text. These problems have been carefully crafted to emphasize real-world applications and to add a new dimension to existing problems. The supplement provides **120 new supplemental homework problems** with the opportunity to easily create many more problems. Instructors should go to the Instructor Center of the book Online Learning Center (www.mhhe.com/cengel) for solutions to the supplemental problems and for additional information on how EES (Engineering Equation Solver) can be used to easily create even more new homework problems.

The authors hope that this supplement will prove useful to both students and instructors. Since this student guide is a work in progress that we would like to improve upon for our next edition, we welcome your comments and suggestions. Comments may be submitted to our editor, Debra Matteson, at debra_matteson@mcgraw-hill.com.

We would also like to acknowledge our gratitude to Mehmet Kanaglu, William Beckman, Sanford Klein, and Mohamed S. El-Morsi for their assistance in preparing this supplement and reviewing the material.

Yunus A. Çengel
Michael A. Boles

3

Student Solutions Guide

for use with

Thermodynamics
An Engineering Approach

Fourth Edition

Yunus A. Çengel
University of Nevada, Reno

Michael A. Boles
North Carolina State University

Boston   Burr Ridge, IL   Dubuque, IA   Madison, WI   New York   San Francisco   St. Louis
Bangkok   Bogotá   Caracas   Kuala Lumpur   Lisbon   London   Madrid   Mexico City
Milan   Montreal   New Delhi   Santiago   Seoul   Singapore   Sydney   Taipei   Toronto

The McGraw·Hill Companies

Student Solutions Guide for use with
THERMODYNAMICS: AN ENGINEERING APPROACH, FOURTH EDITION
YUNUS A. ÇENGEL AND MICHAEL A. BOLES

Published by McGraw-Hill Higher Education, an imprint of The McGraw-Hill Companies, Inc.,
1221 Avenue of the Americas, New York, NY 10020. Copyright © 2002 by The McGraw-Hill
Companies, Inc. All rights reserved.

This book is printed on acid-free paper.

1 2 3 4 5 6 7 8 9 0 QPD/QPD 0 9 8 7 6 5 4 3

ISBN 0-07-293570-7

www.mhhe.com

CONTENTS

CHAPTER 1: BASIC CONCEPTS OF THERMODYNAMICS
Educational Objectives and Glossary
Example 1.1 Sulfur emission by a diesel engine
Example 1.2 Operation of a hydraulic lift
Supplement 1.1 Lead emission by cars using leaded gasoline
Supplement 1.2 Expressing specific heat in different units
Supplement 1.3 Increasing pressure in a cylinder by putting weights on piston
Supplement 1.4 Calculating atmospheric pressure using airplane data
Supplement 1.5 Losing weight by changing diet

Chapter 2: PROPERTIES OF PURE SUBSTANCES
Educational Objectives and Glossary
Example 2.1 Properties of saturated steam mixture
Example 2.2 Properties of R.134a during a cooling process in a cylinder
Example 2.3 Combustion in a diesel engine
Example 2.4 Use of compressibility factor for CO2
Example 2.5 Using gas constant to determine expansion work in a cylinder
Supplement 2.1 Calculating atmospheric pressure using boiling water data
Supplement 2.2 Properties of water during a heating process
Supplement 2.3 Properties of water during a cooling process in a cylinder
Supplement 2.4 Combustion in a gasoline engine
Supplement 2.5 Withdrawing an ideal gas from a tank
Supplement 2.6 Mass and volume flow rates of CO2 in a pipe
Supplement 2.7 The use of compressibility factor for steam
Supplement 2.8 Using compression work to determine R, Cv, and Cp of an ideal gas
Supplement 2.9 Comparison of internal, kinetic, and potential energies

CHAPTER 3: ENERGY TRANSFER BY HEAT, WORK, AND MASS
Educational Objectives and Glossary
Example 3.1 Boundary work during polytropic expansion of nitrogen
Example 3.2 Compression work in a cylinder with stops
Example 3.3 Mass balance for air flowing in a pipe
Example 3.4 Mass balance and boundary work for charging steam into a balloon
Example 3.5 Conversion of flow energy of steam into sensible energy
Supplement 3.1 Boundary work during isentropic expansion of nitrogen
Supplement 3.2 Boundary work during isothermal expansion of nitrogen
Supplement 3.3 Net boundary work of a cycle
Supplement 3.4 Mass balance for R.134a flowing in a pipe
Supplement 3.5 Mass balance for a solar water storage tank
Supplement 3.6 Mass balance and boundary work during discharging air from a cylinder
Supplement 3.7 Flow work of steam in a pipe
Supplement 3.8 Flow work and energy transport by mass
Supplement 3.9 Conversion of flow work of helium into sensible energy
Supplement 3.10 Conduction heat transfer to an LNG tank

CHAPTER 4: THE FIRST LAW OF THERMODYNAMICS
Educational Objectives and Glossary
Example 4.1 Mixing of steam at different states
Example 4.2 Heating of a room by electrical radiator containing oil
Example 4.3 Turbocharger of an internal combustion engine

Example 4.4 Throttling an ideal gas vs. a real gas
Example 4.5 Mixing of warm and cold air in an AC system
Example 4.6 Flow of steam inside a pipe
Example 4.7 Discharging refrigerant from a cylinder
Supplement 4.1 Electrical heating of water in a tank
Supplement 4.2 Isothermal compression of a gas in a cylinder
Supplement 4.3 Cooling water in a cylinder with stops
Supplement 4.4 Accelerating steam in a nozzle
Supplement 4.5 A flash chamber serving steam to turbine
Supplement 4.6 A hot water tank used for shower
Supplement 4.7 A heat exchanger with heat loss to surroundings
Supplement 4.8 Flow of air inside a pipe
Supplement 4.9 Heat transfer balance on a solar collector
Supplement 4.10 Charging of a rigid tank by steam
Supplement 4.11 Charging of a cylinder by steam
Supplement 4.12 Withdrawing R.134a from a cylinder
Supplement 4.13 Withdrawing air from a cylinder

CHAPTER 5: THE SECOND LAW OF THERMODYNAMICS
Educational Objectives and Glossary
Example 5.1 COP of a heat pump with R22 as the refrigerant
Example 5.2 Thermal efficiency of a geothermal power plant
Example 5.3 Minimum power requirement for a commercial refrigerator
Supplement 5.1 Coal consumption in a power plant
Supplement 5.2 Efficiency of a wind turbine
Supplement 5.3 Efficiency of a cryogenic turbine
Supplement 5.4 Heat rejection by a refrigerator
Supplement 5.5 Maximum COP of an air-conditioner
Supplement 5.6 Minimum power requirement for a heat pump

CHAPTER 6: ENTROPY
Educational Objectives and Glossary
Example 6.1 A reversible cycle in a closed system with air
Example 6.2 Various expressions of reversible work in a pump
Example 6.3 Entropy generation during heating of a room by hot water
Example 6.4 Entropy generation during expansion of R.134a
Example 6.5 Entropy generation in a steam turbine
Example 6.6 Entropy analysis of a compressor with air
Example 6.7 Entropy generation during discharging of water from a tank
Supplement 6.1 A reversible cycle in a closed system with steam
Supplement 6.2 Work input and entropy generation in a pump and a compressor
Supplement 6.3 An alternative expression of reversible work in a turbine
Supplement 6.4 A constant-entropy process for water
Supplement 6.5 A cylinder with two compartments containing N_2 and He
Supplement 6.6 Entropy generation during electrical heating of CO_2
Supplement 6.7 Entropy generation during expansion of helium
Supplement 6.8 Entropy analysis of a compressor with R.134a
Supplement 6.9 Isentropic efficiency and entropy generation in a nozzle
Supplement 6.10 Turbocharger of an internal combustion engine
Supplement 6.11 Isothermal efficiency and entropy generation during compression of air
Supplement 6.12 Entropy generation during charging of air into a cylinder

CHAPTER 7: EXERGY: A MEASURE OF WORK POTENTIAL
Educational Objectives and Glossary
Example 7.1 Exergy destroyed during heat exchange between water and air

Example 7.2 Exergy analysis of a steam turbine
Example 7.3 Exergy analysis of an air compressor
Example 7.4 Exergy analysis of an expansion valve
Example 7.5 Exergy analysis of a steam nozzle
Supplement 7.1 Exergy analysis of a geothermal power plant
Supplement 7.2 Exergy destruction during heating of R.134a in a cylinder
Supplement 7.3 Exergy destruction during heating of a room by an electrical radiator
Supplement 7.4 Exergy analysis of a mixing chamber
Supplement 7.5 Exergy analysis of a heat exchanger
Supplement 7.6 Exergy analysis of a gas turbine
Supplement 7.7 Exergy analysis of a R.134a compressor
Supplement 7.8 Exergy analysis of a water pump
Supplement 7.9 Exergy analysis of an expansion valve
Supplement 7.10 Exergy analysis of a diffuser

CHAPTER 8: GAS POWER CYCLES

Educational Objectives and Glossary
Example 8.1 Carnot heat engine in a closed system
Example 8.2 Otto cycle with constant specific heats
Example 8.3 A diesel.fuel burning gas-turbine cycle
Supplement 8.1 Otto cycle with variable specific heats
Supplement 8.2 Power output and fuel consumption of a diesel engine
Supplement 8.3 Energy and exergy analyses of a dual cycle
Supplement 8.4 An actual gas-turbine cycle
Supplement 8.5 Energy and exergy analyses of a regenerative gas-turbine cycle
Supplement 8.6 A regenerative gas-turbine cycle with reheating and intercooling
Supplement 8.7 A gas-turbine cogeneration plant
Supplement 8.8 An actual jet propulsion cycle

CHAPTER 9: VAPOR AND COMBINED POWER CYCLES

Educational Objectives and Glossary
Example 9.1 Comparison of Carnot and Rankine cycles
Example 9.2 A binary geothermal power plant
Example 9.3 A combined gas-steam power cycle
Supplement 9.1 A single-flash geothermal power plant
Supplement 9.2 A double-flash geothermal power plant
Supplement 9.3 A combined flash-binary geothermal power plant
Supplement 9.4 An actual reheat Rankine cycle
Supplement 9.5 A Rankine cycle with reheating and regeneration
Supplement 9.6 A cogeneration plant
Supplement 9.7 Exergy analysis of a single-flash geothermal power plant

CHAPTER 10: REFRIGERATION CYCLES

Educational Objectives and Glossary
Example 10.1 Actual vs. ideal cycle operation for a heat pump with R22
Example 10.2 Analysis of a commercial refrigerator with heat rejection to water
Example 10.3 Gas refrigeration cycle with regeneration, variable specific heats
Supplement 10.1 The ideal vapor-compression refrigeration cycle
Supplement 10.2 Analysis of an air-conditioner
Supplement 10.3 Analysis of a geothermal heat pump
Supplement 10.4 A two-stage cascade refrigeration cycle
Supplement 10.5 A two-stage refrigeration cycle with a flash chamber
Supplement 10.6 Gas refrigeration cycle with regeneration, constant specific heats
Supplement 10.7 A reversible absorption refrigeration cycle

CHAPTER 11: THERMODYNAMIC PROPERTY RELATIONS
Educational Objectives and Glossary
Example 11.1 Enthalpy of Vaporization
Example 11.2 Generalized Chart Solution
Supplement 11.1 Estimate Sublimation Pressure
Supplement 11.2 Generalized Chart Solution
Supplement 11.3 Generalized Chart Solution

CHAPTER 12: GAS MIXTURES
Educational Objectives and Glossary
Example 12.1 Properties of Products of Combustion
Example 12.2 Determine Mass Fractions, Enthalpy Change Per Unit Mass
Example 12.3 Constant Pressure Adiabatic Mixing
Supplement 12.1 Determine Mass Fractions
Supplement 12.2 Mixture Flow Through a Converging Nozzle
Supplement 12.3 Work Done By Products of Combustion in a Piston-Cylinder
Supplement 12.4 Work to Compress Fuel-Air Mixture
Supplement 12.5 Work Done By Mixture Expanding In Turbine
Supplement 12.6 Mixing Between Tanks

CHAPTER 13: GAS—VAPOR MIXTURES AND AIR-CONDITIONING
Educational Objectives and Glossary
Example 13.1 Determine Properties of Atmospheric Air
Example 13.2   Automobile Air Conditioner
Example 13.3 Air Conditioner Refrigerant Flow Rate
Supplement 13.1 Unsteady Flow of Air-vapor Mixture into a Tank
Supplement 13.2 Adiabatic Saturation Process
Supplement 13.3 Nozzle Flow with Atmospheric Air
Supplement 13.4 Cooling of Atmospheric Air in a Workspace
Supplement 13.5 Determine Chilled Water Flow Rate for Air Conditioner
Supplement 13.6 Determine Volume Flow Rate of Air to Auto A/C
Supplement 13.7 Cooling Tower

CHAPTER 14: CHEMICAL REACTIONS
Educational Objectives and Glossary
Example 14.1 Combustion of an Alcohol
Example 14.2 Water Supply to Combustion Process
Example 14.3 Find Required Volume Flow Rate of a Fuel
Supplement 14.1 Mass Flow Rate of Air for Combustion of Fuel Mixture
Supplement 14.2 Water Condensed in High Efficiency Gas Furnace
Supplement 14.3 Water Condensed during Combustion Process
Supplement 14.4 Properties of Products of Combustion
Supplement 14.5 Determine Moles of Gas Components in Combustion Process
Supplement 14.6 Lower Heating Value of a Fuel Mixture

CHAPTER 15: CHEMICAL AND PHASE EQUILIBRIUM
Educational Objectives and Glossary
Example 15.1 Equilibrium Constant
Example 15.2 Single Chemical Equilibrium Reaction
Example 15.3 Adiabatic flame temperature, single equilibrium reaction
Supplement 15.1 Tabulate lnKp
Supplement 15.2 Estimate equilibrium constant
Supplement 15.3 Estimate Enthalpy of Reaction
Supplement 15.4 Adiabatic flame temperature, simultaneous equilibrium reactions
Supplement 15.5 Constant volume adiabatic combustion and equilibrium
Supplement 15.6 Control CO in products of combustion

CHAPTER 16: THERMODYNAMICS OF HIGH-SPEED GAS FLOW

Educational Objectives and Glossary
Example 16.1 Inlet Temperature for Choked Converging Nozzle
Example 16.2 Converging -Diverging Nozzle
Example 16.3 Normal Shock Wave
Supplement 16.1 Inlet Temperature, Pressure for Choked Converging Nozzle
Supplement 16.2 Turbojet with Converging Nozzle
Supplement 16.3 Turbojet with Converging-Diverging Nozzle
Supplement 16.4 Non-Isentropic Converging Nozzle
Supplement 16.5 Non-Isentropic Converging-Diverging Nozzle
Supplement 16.6 Normal Shock Wave

Chapter 1 Educational Objectives and Glossary

The Educational Objectives of Chapter 1 are to:

- Identify the unique vocabulary associated with thermodynamics through the precise definition of basic concepts to form a sound foundation for the development of the scientific principles to follow and to prevent possible misunderstandings.
- Review the English and the metric SI unit systems that will be used throughout the text.
- Explain the basic concepts of thermodynamics such as system, state, state postulate, equilibrium, process, cycle, energy, and various forms of energy.
- Review concepts of temperature, temperature scales, pressure, and absolute and gage pressure.
- Introduce an intuitive systematic problem-solving technique that can be used as a model in solving engineering problems.

Chapter 1 Glossary

Absolute pressure is the actual pressure at a given position and it is measured relative to absolute vacuum (i.e., absolute zero pressure). Throughout this text, the pressure P will denote absolute pressure unless specified otherwise.

Bar is the unit of pressure equal to 10^5 pascal.

Barometer is a device that measures the atmospheric pressure; thus, the atmospheric pressure is often referred to as the barometric pressure.

Boundary is the real or imaginary surface that separates the system from its surroundings. The boundary of a system can be *fixed* or *movable*.

Bourdon tube, named after the French inventor Eugene Bourdon, is a type of commonly used mechanical pressure measurement device which consists of a hollow metal tube bent like a hook whose end is closed and connected to a dial indicator needle.

British thermal unit (Btu) is the energy unit in the English system needed to raise the temperature of 1 lbm of water at 68 °F by 1°F.

Calorie (cal) is the amount of energy in the metric system needed to raise the temperature of 1 g of water at 15 °C by 1°C.

Celsius scale (formerly called the *centigrade scale;* in 1948 it was renamed after the Swedish astronomer A. Celsius, 1701–1744, who devised it) is the temperature scale used in the SI system. On the Celsius scale, the ice and steam points are assigned the values of 0 and 100 °C, respectively.

Chemical energy is the internal energy associated with the atomic bonds in a molecule.

Chemical equilibrium is established in a system when its chemical composition does not change with time.

Classical thermodynamics is the macroscopic approach to the study of thermodynamics that does not require knowledge of the behavior of individual particles.

Closed system (also known as a **control mass**) consists of a fixed amount of mass, and no mass can cross its boundary. But energy, in the form of heat or work, can cross the boundary.

Continuum is a view of mass as continuous, homogeneous matter with no holes. Matter is made up of atoms that are widely spaced in the gas phase. Yet it is very convenient to disregard the atomic nature of a substance. The continuum idealization allows us to treat properties as point functions, and to assume the properties to vary continually in space with no jump discontinuities. This idealization is valid as long as the size of the system we deal with is large relative to the space between the molecules. This is the case practically in all problems, except some specialized ones.

Control surface is the boundary of a control volume, and it can be real or imaginary.

Control volume, or **open system,** is any arbitrary region in space through which mass and energy can pass across the boundary. Most control volumes have fixed boundaries and thus do not involve any moving boundaries. A control volume may also involve heat and work interactions just as a closed system, in addition to mass interaction.

Cycle is a process, or series of processes, that allows a system to undergo state changes and returns the system to the initial state at the end of the process. That is, for a cycle the initial and final states are identical.

Density is defined as *mass per unit volume*.

Dimensionally homogeneous means that every term in an equation must have the same unit. To make sure that all terms in an engineering equation have the same units is the simplest error check one can perform.

Dimensions are any physical characterizations of a quantity.

English system, which is also known as the *United States Customary System* (USCS), has the respective units the pound-mass (lbm), foot (ft), and second (s). The pound symbol *lb* is actually the abbreviation of *libra,* which was the ancient Roman unit of weight.

Equilibrium implies a state of balance. In an equilibrium state there are no unbalanced potentials (or driving forces) within the system. A system in equilibrium experiences no changes when it is isolated from its surroundings.

Extensive properties are those whose values depend on the size—or extent—of the system. Mass m, volume V, and total energy E are some examples of extensive properties.

Fahrenheit scale (named after the German instrument maker G. Fahrenheit, 1686–1736) is the temperature scale in the English system. On the Fahrenheit scale, the ice and steam points are assigned 32 and 212 °F.

Gage pressure is the difference between the absolute pressure and the local atmospheric pressure.

Gravitational acceleration g is 9.807 m/s^2 at sea level and varies by less than 1 percent up to 30,000 m. Therefore, g can be assumed to be constant at 9.81 m/s^2.

Ideal gas temperature scale is a temperature scale that turns out to be identical to the Kelvin scale. The temperatures on this scale are measured using a **constant-volume gas thermometer,** which is basically a rigid vessel filled with a gas, usually hydrogen or helium, at low pressure.

Incompressible substances, such as liquids and solids, have densities that have negligible variation with pressure.

Independent properties exist when one property can be varied while another property is held constant.

Intensive properties are those that are independent of the size of a system, such as temperature, pressure, and density.

Internal energy U of a system is the sum of all the microscopic forms of energy.

Iso- prefix is often used to designate a process for which a particular property remains constant.

Isobaric process is a process during which the pressure P remains constant.

Isochoric (or isometric) process is a process during which the specific volume v remains constant.

Isolated system is a closed system in which energy is not allowed to cross the boundary.

Isothermal process is a process during which the temperature T remains constant.

Joule (J) is a unit of energy and has the unit "newton-meter (N·m)."

Kelvin scale is the thermodynamic temperature scale in the SI and is named after Lord Kelvin (1824–1907). The temperature unit on this scale is the kelvin, which is designated by K (not °K; the degree symbol was officially dropped from kelvin in 1967). The lowest temperature on the Kelvin scale is 0 K.

Kilojoule (1 kJ) is 1000 joules.

Kilopascal (kPa) is the unit of pressure equal to 1000 pascal or 1000 N/m^2.

Kinetic energy KE is energy that a system possesses as a result of its motion relative to some reference frame. When all parts of a system move with the same velocity, the kinetic energy is expressed as KE = m V^2/2.

Latent energy is the internal energy associated with the phase of a system.

Macroscopic forms of energy are those a system possesses as a whole with respect to some outside reference frame, such as kinetic and potential energies.

Manometer is a device based on the principle that an elevation change of Δz of a fluid corresponds to a pressure change of ΔP/ ρg, which suggests that a fluid column can be used to measure pressure differences. The manometer is commonly used to measure small and moderate pressure differences.

Mechanical equilibrium is related to pressure, and a system is in mechanical equilibrium if there is no change in pressure at any point of the system with time.

Megapascal (MPa) is the unit of pressure equal to 10^6 pascal.

Metric SI (from *Le Système International d' Unités*), which is also known as the *International System*, is based on six fundamental dimensions. Their units, adopted in 1954 at the Tenth General Conference of Weights and Measures, are: *meter* (m) for length, *kilogram* (kg) for mass, *second* (s) for time, *ampere* (A) for electric current, *degree Kelvin* (K) for temperature, *candela* (cd) for luminous intensity (amount of light), and *mole* (mol) for the amount of matter.

Microscopic forms of energy are those related to the molecular structure of a system and the degree of the molecular activity, and they are independent of outside reference frames.

Newton (N), in SI, is the force unit defined as the force required to accelerate a mass of 1 kg at a rate of 1 m/s^2.

Nuclear energy is the tremendous amount of energy associated with the strong bonds within the nucleus of the atom itself.

Open system, or **control volume,** is any arbitrary region in space through which mass and energy can pass across the boundary.

Pascal (Pa) is the unit of pressure defined as newtons per square meter (N/m^2).

Pascal's law allows us to "jump" from one fluid column to the next in manometers without worrying about pressure change as long as we don't jump over a different fluid, and the fluid is at rest.

Pascal's principle, after Blaise Pascal (1623–1662), states that the consequence of the pressure in a fluid remaining constant in the horizontal direction is that the pressure applied to a confined fluid increases the pressure throughout by the same amount.

Path of a process is the series of states through which a system passes during a process.

Phase equilibrium when a system involves two phases is established when the mass of each phase reaches an equilibrium level and stays there.

Piezoelectric (or press-electric) **effect** is the emergence of an electric potential in a crystalline substance when subjected to mechanical pressure. This phenomenon, first discovered by brothers Pierre and Jacques Curie in 1880, forms the basis for the widely used **strain-gage** pressure transducers.

Potential energy PE is the energy that a system possesses as a result of its elevation in a gravitational field and is expressed as PE = mgz.

Pound-force (lbf), in the English system, is the force unit defined as the force required to accelerate a mass of 32.174 lbm (1 slug) at a rate of 1 ft/s^2.

Pressure is defined as the force exerted by a fluid per unit area.

Pressure transducers are made of semiconductor materials such as silicon and convert the pressure effect to an electrical effect such as a change in voltage, resistance, or capacitance. Pressure transducers are smaller and faster, and they are more sensitive, reliable, and precise than their mechanical counterparts.

Primary or **fundamental dimensions,** such as mass m, length L, time t, and temperature *T*, are the basis for the derivation of secondary dimensions.

Problem-solving technique is a step-by-step approach to problem solving discussed in Chapter 1.

Process is any change that a system undergoes from one equilibrium state to another. To describe a process completely, one should specify the initial and final states of the process, as well as the path it follows, and the interactions with the surroundings.

Property is any characteristic of a system. Some familiar properties are pressure P, temperature T, volume V, and mass m. The list can be extended to include less familiar ones such as viscosity, thermal conductivity, modulus of elasticity, thermal expansion coefficient, electric resistivity, and even velocity and elevation.

Quasi-static, or **quasi-equilibrium, process** is a process which proceeds in such a manner that the system remains infinitesimally close to an equilibrium state at all times. A quasi-equilibrium process can be viewed as a sufficiently slow process that allows the system to adjust itself internally so that properties in one part of the system do not change any faster than those at other parts.

Rankine scale, named after William Rankine (1820–1872) is the thermodynamic temperature scale in the English system. The temperature unit on this scale is the rankine, which is designated by R.

Secondary dimensions, or **derived dimensions**, such as velocity, energy E, and volume V, are expressed in terms of the primary dimensions.

Sensible energy is the portion of the internal energy of a system associated with the kinetic energies of the molecules.

Simple compressible system is a system in which there is the absence of electrical, magnetic, gravitational, motion, and surface tension effects. These effects are due to external force fields and are negligible for most engineering problems.

Specific gravity, or **relative density,** is defined as the ratio of the density of a substance to the density of some standard substance at a specified temperature (usually water at 4°C, for which the density is 1000 kg/m^3).

Specific properties are extensive properties per unit mass. Some examples of specific properties are specific volume ($v=V/$m) and specific total energy ($e= E/$m).

Specific volume is the reciprocal of density and is defined as the volume per unit mass.

Specific weight w is the weight of a unit volume of a substance and is determined from the product of the local acceleration of gravity and the substance density.

State of a system not undergoing any change gives a set of properties that completely describes the condition of a system. At this point, all the properties can be measured or calculated throughout the entire system.

State postulate specifies the number of properties required to fix the state of a system: The state of a simple compressible system is completely specified by two independent, intensive properties.

Stationary systems are closed systems whose velocity and elevation of the center of gravity remain constant during a process.

Statistical thermodynamics, an approach to thermodynamics more elaborate than classical thermodynamics, is based on the average behavior of large groups of individual particles.

Steady implies no change with time. The opposite of steady is unsteady, or transient.

Steady-flow devices operate for long periods of time under the same conditions.

Steady-flow process is defined as a process during which a fluid flows through a control volume steadily. That is, the fluid properties can change from point to point within the control volume, but at any fixed point they remain the same during the entire process.

Surroundings is the mass or region outside the thermodynamic system.
Thermal energy is the sensible and latent forms of internal energy.

Thermal equilibrium means that the temperature is the same throughout the entire system.

Thermodynamic equilibrium is a condition of a system in which all the relevant types of equilibrium are satisfied.

Thermodynamics can be defined as the science of *energy*. Energy can be viewed as the ability to cause changes. The name *thermodynamics* stems from the Greek words *therme* (heat) and *dynamis* (power), which is most descriptive of the early efforts to convert heat into power. Today the same name is broadly interpreted to include all aspects of energy and energy transformations, including power production, refrigeration, and relationships among the properties of matter.

Thermodynamic system, or simply a **system,** is defined as a quantity of matter or a region in space chosen for study.

Thermodynamic temperature scale is a temperature scale that is independent of the properties of any substance or substances.

Total energy E of a system is the sum of the numerous forms of energy such as thermal, mechanical, kinetic, potential, electric, magnetic, chemical, and nuclear, and their constituents. The total energy of a system on a unit mass basis is denoted by e and is defined as E/m.

Triple point of water is the state at which all three phases of water coexist in equilibrium.

Uniform implies no change with location over a specified region.

Units are the arbitrary magnitudes assigned to the dimensions.

Vacuum pressure is the pressure below atmospheric pressure and is measured by a vacuum gage that indicates the difference between the atmospheric pressure and the absolute pressure.

Weight is the gravitational force applied to a body, and its magnitude is determined from Newton's second law.

Work, which is a form of energy, can simply be defined as force times distance.

Zeroth law of thermodynamics states that if two bodies are in thermal equilibrium with a third body, they are also in thermal equilibrium with each other. By replacing the third body with a thermometer, the zeroth law can be restated as two bodies are in thermal equilibrium if both have the same temperature reading even if they are not in contact.

EXAMPLE 1-1 Sulfur emission by a diesel engine

A diesel engine with an engine volume of 4.0 liter and an engine speed of 2500 rpm operates on an air-fuel ratio of 18 kg air/kg fuel. The engine uses light diesel fuel that contains 750 ppm (part per million) of sulfur by mass. All of this sulfur is exhausted to the environment where the sulfur is converted to sulfurous acid (H_2SO_3). If the rate of the air entering the engine is 336 kg/h, determine the mass flow rate of sulfur in the exhaust. Also, determine the mass flow rate of sulfurous acid added to the environment if for one kmol of sulfur in the exhaust, one kmol sulfurous acid will be added to the environment. The molar mass of the sulfur is 32 kg/kmol.

Equations

GIVEN

$$Vol_{engine} = 4 \text{ [liter]} \cdot \left| 0.001 \ \frac{m^3}{\text{liter}} \right| \tag{1}$$

$$\dot{N} = 2500 \text{ [rpm]} \cdot \left| 0.016667 \ \frac{\text{rps}}{\text{rpm}} \right| \tag{2}$$

$$AF = 18 \tag{3}$$

$$Sulfur_{PPM} = 750 \times 10^{-6} \tag{4}$$

$$\dot{m}_{air} = 336 \text{ [kg/h]} \tag{5}$$

$$MM_{sulfur} = 32 \text{ [kg/kmol]} \tag{6}$$

PROPERTIES

$$MM_{O2} = MW\,(O2\,) \tag{7}$$

$$MM_{H2} = MW\,(H2\,) \tag{8}$$

$$MM_{H2SO3} = MM_{H2} + MM_{sulfur} + 1.5 \cdot MM_{O2} \quad \textbf{Sulfurous acid molar mass} \tag{9}$$

ANALYSIS

$$AF = \dot{m}_{air}/\dot{m}_{fuel} \quad \textbf{Air-fuel ratio} \tag{10}$$

$$\dot{m}_{sulfur} = Sulfur_{PPM} \cdot \dot{m}_{fuel} \quad \textbf{Sulfur mass flow rate} \tag{11}$$

$$\dot{m}_{H2SO3} = MM_{H2SO3}/MM_{sulfur} \cdot \dot{m}_{sulfur} \quad \textbf{Sulfurous acid mass flow rate} \tag{12}$$

Solution

$AF = 18$ [kg/kg]	$MM_{H2} = 2.016$ [kg/kmol]	$MM_{H2SO3} = 82.01$ [kg/kmol]	$MM_{O2} = 32$ [kg/kmol]
$MM_{sulfur} = 32$ [kg/kmol]	$\dot{m}_{air} = 336$ [kg/h]	$\dot{m}_{fuel} = 18.67$ [kg/h]	$\boxed{\dot{m}_{H2SO3} = 0.03588 \text{ [kg/h]}}$
$\boxed{\dot{m}_{sulfur} = 0.014 \text{ [kg/h]}}$	$\dot{N} = 41.67$ [rps]	$Sulfur_{PPM} = 0.00075$	$Vol_{engine} = 0.004$ [m³]

EXAMPLE 1-2   Operation of a hydraulic lift

A hydraulic lift is to be used to lift a 2500 kg weight by putting a weight of 25 kg on a piston with a diameter of 10 cm. Determine the diameter of the piston on which the weight is to be placed.

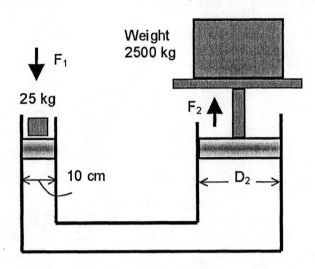

Equations

GIVEN

$$m_2 = 2500 \ [\text{kg}] \tag{1}$$

$$m_1 = 25 \ [\text{kg}] \tag{2}$$

$$D_1 = 0.10 \ [\text{m}] \tag{3}$$

ANALYSIS

$g = 9.81 \ [\text{m/s}^2] \quad$ **Gravitational acceleration** $\tag{4}$

$F_1 = m_1 \cdot g \quad$ **Newton's 2nd law** $\tag{5}$

$A_1 = \pi \cdot \dfrac{D_1^2}{4} \quad$ **Piston area** $\tag{6}$

$P_1 = F_1/A_1 \tag{7}$

$P_2 = P_1 \quad$ **From the force balance, since A$_1$=A$_2$** $\tag{8}$

$F_2 = m_2 \cdot g \quad$ **Newton's 2nd law** $\tag{9}$

$P_2 = F_2/A_2 \tag{10}$

$A_2 = \pi \cdot \dfrac{D_2^2}{4} \quad$ **Piston area** $\tag{11}$

Solution

$A_1 = 0.007854 \ [\text{m}^2]$

$A_2 = 0.7854 \ [\text{m}^2]$

$D_1 = 0.1 \ [\text{m}]$

$\boxed{D_2 = 1 \ [\text{m}]}$

$F_1 = 245.3 \ [\text{N}]$

$F_2 = 24525 \ [\text{N}]$

$g = 9.81 \ [\text{m/s}^2]$

$m_1 = 25 \ [\text{kg}]$

$m_2 = 2500 \ [\text{kg}]$

$P_1 = 31226 \ [\text{Pa}]$

$P_2 = 31226 \ [\text{Pa}]$

Chapter 1 Supplemental Problems

Supplement 1.1 Lead emission by cars using leaded gasoline

Leaded gasoline contains lead that ends up in the engine exhaust. Lead is a very toxic engine emission. The use of leaded gasoline in the U.S. is unlawful for most vehicles since the 1980s. However, the leaded gasoline is still used in many parts of the world. Consider a city with 10,000 cars using leaded gasoline. The gasoline contains 0.15 g/liter of lead and 35% of lead is exhausted to the environment. Assuming that an average car travels 15,000 km per year with a gasoline consumption of 10 liter/100 km, determine the amount of lead put into the atmosphere per year in that city. *Answer*: 788 kg

Supplement 1.2 Expressing specific heat in different units

Specific heat is defined as the amount of energy needed to increase the temperature of a unit mass of a substance by one degree. The specific heat of water at the room temperature is 4.18 kJ/kg-°C in SI unit system. Using the unit conversion function capability of EES, express the specific heat of water in (a) kJ/kg-K, (b) Btu/lbm-F, (c) Btu/lbm-R, and (d) kCal/kg-°C units. *Answers*: (a) 4.18, (b) (c) (d) 0.9984

Supplement 1.3 Increasing pressure in a cylinder by putting weights on piston

A vertical piston-cylinder device contains a gas at a pressure of 100 kPa. The piston has a mass of 5 kg and a diameter of 12 cm. Pressure of the gas is to be increased by placing some weights on the piston. Determine the local atmospheric pressure and the mass of the weights that will double the pressure of the gas inside the cylinder. *Answers*: 95.7 kPa, 115.3 kg

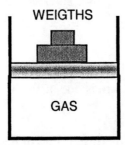

WEIGTHS

GAS

Supplement 1.4 Calculating atmospheric pressure using airplane data

The pilot of an airplane reads the altitude 3000 m and the absolute pressure 58 kPa when flying over a city. Calculate the local atmospheric pressure in that city in kPa and in mmHg. Take the densities of air and mercury to be 1.15 kg/m^3 and 13,600 kg/m^3, respectively. *Answers*: 91.8 kPa, 688 mmHg

Altitude: 3 km
P = 58 kPa

Supplement 1.5 Losing weight by changing diet

The body mass index (BMI) of a 1.7.m tall person is 30. This person normally has three slices of large size cheese pizza and a 400.ml Coke in his lunch hour. A change diet results in two slices of the same pizza and a 200.ml Coke. Assuming that the deficit in the calorie intake is made up by burning body fat, determine how long it will take for the BMI of this person to drop to 25. Use the data in Table 1.3 of the text for calories and take the metabolizable energy content of 1 kg of body fat to be 33,100 kJ. *Answer*: 262 days

Chapter 2 Educational Objectives and Glossary

The Educational Objectives of Chapter 2 are to:

- Introduce the concept of a pure substance.
- Discuss the physics of phase-change processes.
- Illustrate the *P-v*, *T-v*, and *P-T* property diagrams and *P-v-T* surfaces of pure substances.
- Demonstrate the procedures for determining thermodynamic properties of pure substances from tables of property data.
- Describe the hypothetical substance "ideal gas" and the ideal-gas equation of state.
- Apply the ideal-gas equation of state in the solution of typical problems.
- Introduce the compressibility factor, which accounts for the deviation of real gases from ideal-gas behavior, and to illustrate its use.
- Present some of the best-known equations of state such as the van der Waals, Beattie-Bridgeman, and Benedict-Webb-Rubin equations.
- Define the specific heat at constant volume and the specific heat at constant pressure.
- Relate the specific heats to the calculation of the changes in internal energy and enthalpy of ideal gases.
- Describe the incompressible substance such as solids and liquids and how to determine the changes in internal energy and enthalpy for these substances.

Chapter 2 Glossary

Beattie-Bridgeman equation of state is one of the best known and is a reasonably accurate equation of state.

Benedict-Webb-Rubin equation of state is one of the more recent and very accurate equations of state.

Compressed liquid has a pressure greater than the saturation pressure corresponding to the temperature.

Compressed liquid region is all compressed liquid states located in the region to the left of the saturated liquid line and below the critical temperature line. In the absence of compressed liquid data, a general approximation is to treat compressed liquid as saturated liquid at the given temperature.

Compressibility factor Z is a correction factor to account for deviation from ideal-gas behavior at a given temperature and pressure. $Z = Pv/RT$.

Critical point is defined as the point at which the saturated liquid and saturated vapor states are identical.

Critical pressure P_{cr} is the pressure of a substance at the critical point.

Critical temperature T_{cr} is the temperature of a substance at the critical point.

Critical volume v_{cr} is the volume of a substance at the critical point.

Dome is the saturation states located beneath the joined saturated liquid line and saturated vapor line.

Enthalpy H (from the Greek word *enthalpien*, which means *to heat*) is a property and is defined as the sum of the internal energy U and the PV product.

Enthalpy change of an ideal gas is given as $\Delta h = \int C_P(T)dT \cong C_{P,\,av}(T_2 - T_1)$.

Enthalpy of vaporization (or latent heat of vaporization) is the quantity h_{fg} listed in the saturation tables.

Equation of state is any equation that relates the pressure, temperature, and specific volume of a substance. Property relations that involve other properties of a substance at equilibrium states are also referred to as equations of state.

Gas constant R is different for each gas and is determined from $R = R_u/M$.

Gas phase of a substance has molecules that are far apart from each other, and a molecular order is nonexistent. Gas molecules move about at random, continually colliding with each other and the walls of the container they are in.

Generalized compressibility chart shows that by curve-fitting all the data, gases seem to obey the principle of corresponding states reasonably well.

Ideal gas is a gas that obeys the ideal-gas equation of state.

Ideal-gas equation of state (or ideal-gas relation) predicts the P-v-T behavior of a gas quite accurately within some properly selected region where $Pv = RT$.

Ideal gas specific heat relation is $C_p = C_v + R$.

Internal energy change of an ideal gas is given as $\Delta u = \int C_v(T)dT \cong C_{v,\,av}(T_2 - T_1)$.

Latent heat is the amount of energy absorbed or released during a phase-change process.

Latent heat of fusion is the amount of energy absorbed during melting and is equivalent to the amount of energy released during freezing.

Latent heat of vaporization is the amount of energy absorbed during vaporization and is equivalent to the energy released during condensation.

Liquid phase has a molecular spacing not much different from that of the solid phase, except the molecules are no longer at fixed positions relative to each other. In a liquid, chunks of molecules float about each other; however, the molecules maintain an orderly structure within each chunk and retain their original positions with respect to one another. The distances between molecules generally experience a slight increase as a solid turns liquid, with water being a rare exception.

Liquid–vapor saturation curve is a plot of saturation temperature T_{sat} versus saturation pressure P_{sat}.

Mass of a system is equal to the product of its molar mass M and the mole number N.

Melting line separates the solid and liquid regions on the phase diagram.

Molar mass M can simply be defined as the *mass of one mole* (also called a *gram-mol*e, abbreviated gmol) *of a substance in grams*, or the *mass of one kmol* (also called a *kilogram-mol*e, abbreviated kgmol) *in kilograms*. In English units, it is the mass of 1 lbmol in lbm. Notice that the molar mass of a substance has the same numerical value in both unit systems because of the way it is defined.

Phase diagram is the *P-T* diagram of a pure substance and shows all three phases separated from each other by the sublimation line, vaporization line, and melting line.

Principle of corresponding states is the fact that compressibility factor Z for all gases is approximately the same at the same reduced pressure and temperature.

Pseudo-reduced specific volume v_R is used with the generalized compressibility chart to determine the third property when P and v, or T and v, are given instead of P and T.

***P-v-T* surface** is a three-dimensional surface in space which represents the *P-v-T* behavior of a substance. All states along the path of a quasi-equilibrium process lie on the *P-v-T* surface since such a process must pass through equilibrium states. The single-phase regions appear as curved surfaces on the *P-v-T* surface, and the two-phase regions as surfaces perpendicular to the *P-T* plane.

Pure substance is a substance that has a fixed chemical composition throughout.

Quality x is the ratio of the mass of vapor to the total mass of a saturated mixture. The quality lies in the range $0 \le x \le 1$.

Reduced pressure P_R is the ratio of the pressure to the critical pressure.

Reduced temperature T_R is the ratio of the temperature to the critical temperature

Reference state is chosen to assign a value of zero for a convenient property or properties at that state.

Saturated liquid is a liquid that is about to vaporize.

Saturated liquid line is the saturated liquid states connected by a line that meets the saturated vapor line at the critical point, forming a dome.

Saturated liquid–vapor mixture is a mixture of the liquid and vapor phases that coexist in equilibrium.

Saturated liquid–vapor mixture region, or the **wet region** is all the states that involve both the liquid and vapor phases in equilibrium and are located under the dome.

Saturated vapor is a vapor that is about to condense.

Saturated vapor line is the saturated vapor states connected by a line that meets the saturated liquid line at the critical point, forming a dome.

Saturation pressure P_{sat} is called the pressure at which a pure substance changes phase at a given temperature.

Saturation temperature T_{sat} is the temperature at which a pure substance changes phase at a given pressure.

Solid phase has molecules arranged in a three-dimensional pattern (lattice) that is repeated throughout. Because of the small distances between molecules in a solid, the attractive forces of molecules on each other are large and keep the molecules at fixed positions.

Specific heat is defined as the energy required to raise the temperature of a unit mass of a substance by one degree. In general, this energy will depend on how the process is executed.

Specific heat at constant pressure C_p as the energy required to raise the temperature of the unit mass of a substance by one degree as the pressure is maintained constant. C_p is a mea-sure of the variation of enthalpy of a substance with temperature. C_p can be defined as the change in the enthalpy of a substance per unit change in temperature at constant pressure.

Specific heat at constant volume C_v is the energy required to raise the temperature of the unit mass of a substance by one degree as the volume is maintained constant. C_v is related to the changes in internal energy. It would be more proper to define C_v as the change in the internal energy of a substance per unit change in temperature at constant volume.

Specific heats for solids and liquids, or incompressible substances, are equal.

Subcooled liquid has a temperature less than the saturation temperature corresponding to the pressure.

Specific heat ratio k, is defined as the ratio C_p/C_v.

Sublimation is the process of passing from the solid phase directly into the vapor phase.

Sublimation line separates the solid and vapor regions on the phase diagram.

Superheated vapor is a vapor that is not about to condense (not a saturated vapor). A superheated vapor has a temperature greater than the saturation temperature for the pressure.

Superheated vapor region is all the superheated states located to the right of the saturated vapor line and above the critical temperature line.

Triple line is the locus of the conditions where all three phases of a pure substance coexist in equilibrium. The states on the triple line of a substance have the same pressure and temperature but different specific volumes.

Triple point is a point on the *P-T* diagram that represents the triple line.

Universal gas constant R_u is the same for all substances and its value is 8.314 kJ/kmol·K and 1.986 Btu/lbmol·R.

Vacuum cooling is a way to cool a substance by reducing the pressure of the sealed cooling chamber to the saturation pressure at the desired low temperature and evaporating some water from the products to be cooled. The heat of vaporization during evaporation is absorbed from the products, which lowers the product temperature.

Vacuum freezing is the application of vacuum cooling when the pressure (actually, the vapor pressure) in the vacuum chamber is dropped below 0.6 kPa, the saturation pressure of water at 0°C.

van der Waals equation of state is one of the earliest attempts to correct the ideal gas equation for real gas behavior.

Vapor implies a gas that is not far from a state of condensation.

Vaporization line separates the liquid and vapor regions on the phase diagram.

Virial equations of state is an equation of state of a substance expressed in a series form as

$$P = RT/v + a(T)/v^2 + b(T)/v^3 + c(T)/v^4 + d(T)/v^5 + \ldots$$

where the coefficients a(T), b(T), c(T), and so on, are functions of temperature alone and are called *virial coefficients*.

EXAMPLE 2-1   Properties of saturated steam mixture

A 1.8-m³ rigid tank contains steam at 220°C. The one-third of the volume is in the liquid phase and the rest is in the vapor form. Determine (a) the pressure of the steam, (b) the quality of the saturated mixture, and (c) the density of the mixture.

Steam
1.8 m³
220°C

Equations

GIVEN

$$Vol = 1.8 \ [\text{m}^3] \tag{1}$$

$$Vol_f = 1/3 \cdot Vol \tag{2}$$

$$Vol_g = 2/3 \cdot Vol \tag{3}$$

$$T = 220 \ [\text{C}] \tag{4}$$

ANALYSIS

$$Fluid\$ = \text{'Steam\_iapws'} \tag{5}$$

$$P_{sat} = \text{P (Fluid\$}, \ T = T, \ x = 1) \quad \textbf{x can be chosen any value between 0 and 1} \tag{6}$$

$$v_f = \text{v (Fluid\$}, \ T = T, \ x = 0) \quad \textbf{Saturated liquid specific volume} \tag{7}$$

$$v_g = \text{v (Fluid\$}, \ T = T, \ x = 1) \quad \textbf{Saturated vapor specific volume} \tag{8}$$

$$v_f = Vol_f / m_f \tag{9}$$

$$v_g = Vol_g / m_g \tag{10}$$

$$m = m_f + m_g \quad \textbf{Total mass of the steam in the tank} \tag{11}$$

$$x = \frac{m_g}{m} \quad \textbf{Quality} \tag{12}$$

$$v = v_f + x \cdot (v_g - v_f) \quad \textbf{Specific volume of the steam in the tank} \tag{13}$$

$$\rho = \frac{1}{v} \quad \textbf{Density} \tag{14}$$

Solution

$Fluid\$ = \text{'Steam\_iapws'}$ $m = 518.1 \ [\text{kg}]$ $m_f = 504.2 \ [\text{kg}]$ $m_g = 13.94 \ [\text{kg}]$

$\boxed{P_{sat} = 2320 \ [\text{kPa}]}$ $\boxed{\rho = 287.8 \ [\text{kg/m}^3]}$ $T = 220 \ [\text{C}]$ $v = 0.003474 \ [\text{m}^3/\text{kg}]$

$Vol = 1.8 \ [\text{m}^3]$ $Vol_f = 0.6 \ [\text{m}^3]$ $Vol_g = 1.2 \ [\text{m}^3]$ $v_f = 0.00119 \ [\text{m}^3/\text{kg}]$

$v_g = 0.08609 \ [\text{m}^3/\text{kg}]$ $\boxed{x = 0.0269}$

EXAMPLE 2-2   Properties of R-134a during a cooling process in a cylinder

A piston-cylinder device contains 0.85 kg of refrigerant-134a at -10°C. The piston that is free to move has a mass of 12 kg and a diameter of 25 cm. The local atmospheric pressure is 88 kPa. Now, heat is transferred to R-134a until the temperature is 15°C. Determine (a) the final pressure, (b) the change in the volume of the cylinder, and (c) the change in the enthalpy of the R-134a.

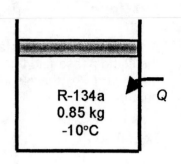

R-134a
0.85 kg
-10°C

Q

Equations

GIVEN

$$m = 0.85 \ [\text{kg}] \tag{1}$$

$$T_1 = -10 \ [\text{C}] \tag{2}$$

$$m_p = 12 \ [\text{kg}] \tag{3}$$

$$D = 0.25 \ [\text{m}] \tag{4}$$

$$P_{atm} = 88 \ [\text{kPa}] \tag{5}$$

$$T_2 = 15 \ [\text{C}] \tag{6}$$

ANALYSIS

$$Fluid\$ = \text{'R134a'} \tag{7}$$

$$g = 9.81 \ \left[\text{m/s}^2\right] \quad \textbf{Gravitational acceleration} \tag{8}$$

$$A_c = \pi \cdot \frac{D^2}{4} \quad \textbf{Piston cross sectional area} \tag{9}$$

$$P_1 = P_{atm} + \left(\frac{m_p \cdot g}{A_c} \cdot \left| 0.001 \ \frac{kPa}{Pa} \right| \right) \quad \textbf{Absolute pressure of R-134a} \tag{10}$$

$$v_1 = \text{v} \, (Fluid\$, \ T = T_1, \ P = P_1) \quad \textbf{Specific volume} \tag{11}$$

$$h_1 = \text{h} \, (Fluid\$, \ T = T_1, \ P = P_1) \quad \textbf{Specific enthalpy} \tag{12}$$

$$P_2 = P_1 \quad \textbf{Final pressure} \tag{13}$$

$$v_2 = \text{v} \, (Fluid\$, \ T = T_2, \ P = P_2) \quad \textbf{Specific volume} \tag{14}$$

$$h_2 = \text{h} \, (Fluid\$, \ T = T_2, \ P = P_2) \quad \textbf{Specific enthalpy} \tag{15}$$

$$v_1 = Vol_1/m \tag{16}$$

$$v_2 = Vol_2/m \tag{17}$$

$$\Delta Vol = Vol_2 - Vol_1 \quad \textbf{Volume change} \tag{18}$$

$$\Delta H = m \cdot (h_2 - h_1) \quad \textbf{Enthalpy change} \tag{19}$$

Solution

$A_c = 0.04909 \left[\mathrm{m}^2\right]$

$D = 0.25 \left[\mathrm{m}\right]$

$\boxed{\Delta H = 17.35 \left[\mathrm{kJ}\right]}$

$\boxed{\Delta Vol = 0.0205 \left[\mathrm{m}^3\right]}$

$Fluid\$ = \text{'R134a'}$

$g = 9.81 \left[\mathrm{m/s}^2\right]$

$h_1 = 247.8 \left[\mathrm{kJ/kg}\right]$

$h_2 = 268.2 \left[\mathrm{kJ/kg}\right]$

$m = 0.85 \left[\mathrm{kg}\right]$

$m_p = 12 \left[\mathrm{kg}\right]$

$P_1 = 90.4 \left[\mathrm{kPa}\right]$

$\boxed{P_2 = 90.4 \left[\mathrm{kPa}\right]}$

$P_{atm} = 88 \left[\mathrm{kPa}\right]$

$T_1 = -10 \left[\mathrm{C}\right]$

$T_2 = 15 \left[\mathrm{C}\right]$

$Vol_1 = 0.1957 \left[\mathrm{m}^3\right]$

$Vol_2 = 0.2162 \left[\mathrm{m}^3\right]$

$v_1 = 0.2302 \left[\mathrm{m}^3/\mathrm{kg}\right]$

$v_2 = 0.2544 \left[\mathrm{m}^3/\mathrm{kg}\right]$

EXAMPLE 2-3   Combustion in a diesel engine

Combustion in a diesel engine may be approximated by a constant-pressure heat addition process. The cylinder contains air before the combustion and the combustion gases after it, and both may be approximated by air, an ideal gas. In a diesel engine, the cylinder conditions are 950 K and 75 cm^3 before the combustion and 150 cm^3 after it. The engine operates with an air-fuel ratio of 22 kg air/kg fuel (the mass of the air divided by the mass of the fuel). Determine the temperature after the combustion process.

Combustion
chamber
950 K
75 cm^3

Equations

GIVEN

$T_1 = 950 \ [\text{K}]$ (1)

$V_1 = 75 \ [\text{cm}^3]$ (2)

$V_2 = 150 \ [\text{cm}^3]$ (3)

$m_f = 1$ **Assumed fuel mass** (4)

$AF = 22$ **Air-fuel ratio** (5)

ANALYSIS

$AF = m_a / m_f$ (6)

$m_1 = m_a$ **Mass of air in the cylinder before combustion** (7)

$m_2 = m_a + m_f$ **Mass of combustion gases in the cylinder after combustion** (8)

$\dfrac{m_1 \cdot T_1}{V_1} = (m_2 \cdot T_2)/V_2$ **Ideal gas relation, pressure is constant** (9)

Solution

$AF = 22$
$m_1 = 22 \ [\text{kg}]$
$m_2 = 23 \ [\text{kg}]$
$m_a = 22 \ [\text{kg}]$
$m_f = 1 \ [\text{kg}]$
$T_1 = 950 \ [\text{K}]$
$\boxed{T_2 = 1817 \ [\text{K}]}$
$V_1 = 75 \ [\text{cm}^3]$
$V_2 = 150 \ [\text{cm}^3]$

EXAMPLE 2-4   The use of compressibiliy factor for CO2

Carbon dioxide gas enters a pipe at 3 MPa and 500 K at a rate of 2 kg/s. CO_2 is cooled at constant pressure as it flows in the pipe and the temperature of CO_2 drops to 450 K at the exit. Determine the volume flow rate and the density of carbon dioxide at the inlet and the volume flow rate at the exit of the pipe using (a) the ideal gas equation and (b) the generalized compressibility chart. Also, determine (c) the error involved in each case.

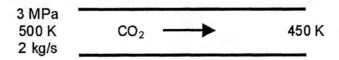

3 MPa
500 K
2 kg/s

CO_2 →

450 K

Equations

GIVEN

$$P_1 = 3000 \ [kPa] \tag{1}$$

$$T_1 = 500 \ [K] \tag{2}$$

$$\dot{m} = 2 \ [kg/s] \tag{3}$$

$$T_2 = 450 \ [K] \tag{4}$$

PROPERTIES

$$Fluid\$ = \text{'CO2'} \tag{5}$$

$$R = R_u/MM \quad \textbf{Gas constant} \tag{6}$$

$$R_u = 8.314 \ [kJ/kmol \cdot K] \quad \textbf{Universal gas constant} \tag{7}$$

$$MM = \text{MW (Fluid\$)} \tag{8}$$

$$P_{crit} = \text{P}_{crit} \text{ (Fluid\$)} \tag{9}$$

$$T_{crit} = \text{T}_{crit} \text{ (Fluid\$)} \tag{10}$$

ANALYSIS

(a) Ideal gas solution

$$P_1 \cdot \dot{V}_{1,a} = (\dot{m} \cdot R \cdot T_1) \tag{11}$$

$$\rho_{1,a} = \frac{P_1}{R \cdot T_1} \tag{12}$$

$$P_2 = P_1 \tag{13}$$

$$P_2 \cdot \dot{V}_{2,a} = (\dot{m} \cdot R \cdot T_2) \tag{14}$$

(b) Compressibility chart solution

$P_R = P_1/P_{crit}$ **Reduced pressure** $\qquad\qquad$ (15)

$T_{R,1} = T_1/T_{crit}$ **Reduced temperature** $\qquad\qquad$ (16)

$T_{R,2} = T_2/T_{crit}$ $\qquad\qquad$ (17)

$Z_1 = \text{Compress}(T_{R,1},\ P_R)$ **EES function for compressibility factor** $\qquad\qquad$ (18)

$Z_2 = \text{Compress}(T_{R,2},\ P_R)$ $\qquad\qquad$ (19)

$P_1 \cdot \dot{V}_{1,b} = (Z_1 \cdot \dot{m} \cdot R \cdot T_1)$ $\qquad\qquad$ (20)

$\rho_{1,b} = \dfrac{P_1}{Z_1 \cdot R \cdot T_1}$ $\qquad\qquad$ (21)

$P_2 \cdot \dot{V}_{2,b} = (Z_2 \cdot \dot{m} \cdot R \cdot T_2)$ $\qquad\qquad$ (22)

Percent errors

$Error_{V1} = \dfrac{\dot{V}_{1,a} - \dot{V}_{1,b}}{\dot{V}_{1,b}} \cdot |100\ \%|$ $\qquad\qquad$ (23)

$Error_{\rho,1} = \dfrac{\rho_{1,b} - \rho_{1,a}}{\rho_{1,b}} \cdot |100\ \%|$ $\qquad\qquad$ (24)

$Error_{V2} = \dfrac{\dot{V}_{2,a} - \dot{V}_{2,b}}{\dot{V}_{2,b}} \cdot |100\ \%|$ $\qquad\qquad$ (25)

Solution

$\boxed{Error_{\rho,1} = 2.091\ [\%]}$ $\quad$ $\boxed{Error_{V1} = 2.136\ [\%]}$ $\quad$ $\boxed{Error_{V2} = 3.563\ [\%]}$ $\quad$ $Fluid\$ = \text{'CO2'}$

$MM = 44.01\ [\text{kg/kmol}]$ $\quad$ $\dot{m} = 2\ [\text{kg/s}]$ $\quad$ $P_1 = 3000\ [\text{kPa}]$ $\quad$ $P_2 = 3000\ [\text{kPa}]$

$P_{crit} = 7377\ [\text{kPa}]$ $\quad$ $P_R = 0.4067$ $\quad$ $R = 0.1889\ [\text{kJ/kg-K}]$ $\quad$ $\boxed{\rho_{1,a} = 31.76\ [\text{kg/m}^3]}$

$\boxed{\rho_{1,b} = 32.44\ [\text{kg/m}^3]}$ $\quad$ $R_u = 8.314\ [\text{kJ/kmol-K}]$ $\quad$ $T_1 = 500\ [\text{K}]$ $\quad$ $T_2 = 450\ [\text{K}]$

$T_{crit} = 304.1\ [\text{K}]$ $\quad$ $T_{R,1} = 1.644$ $\quad$ $T_{R,2} = 1.48$ $\quad$ $\boxed{\dot{V}_{1,a} = 0.06297\ [\text{m}^3/\text{s}]}$

$\boxed{\dot{V}_{1,b} = 0.06165\ [\text{m}^3/\text{s}]}$ $\quad$ $\boxed{\dot{V}_{2,a} = 0.05667\ [\text{m}^3/\text{s}]}$ $\quad$ $\boxed{\dot{V}_{2,b} = 0.05472\ [\text{m}^3/\text{s}]}$ $\quad$ $Z_1 = 0.9791$

$Z_2 = 0.9656$

EXAMPLE 2-5 **Using gas constant to determine expansion work in a cylinder**

A piston-cylinder device contains 0.5 kg air. Now, heat is added to the air at constant pressure and the air temperature increases by 5°C. Determine the expansion work done during this process.

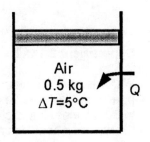

Air
0.5 kg
ΔT=5°C

Q

Equations

GIVEN

$m = 0.5$ [kg]   (1)

$\Delta T = 5$ [C]   (2)

ANALYSIS

$R_u = 8.314$ [kJ/kmol·K]   **Universal gas constant**   (3)

$MM = \text{MW (air)}$ (4)

$R = R_u/MM$ **Gas constant**   (5)

$W_b = m \cdot \Delta T \cdot R$ **Expansion work**   (6)

Gas constant, R, represents the boundary work for a unit mass and a unit temperature change

Solution

$\Delta T = 5$ [C]
$m = 0.5$ [kg]
$MM = 28.97$ [kg/kmol]
$R = 0.287$ [kJ/kg-C]
$R_u = 8.314$ [kJ/kmol-K]
$\boxed{W_b = 0.7175 \text{ [kJ]}}$

Chapter 2 Supplemental Problems

Supplement 2.1 Calculating atmospheric pressure using boiling water data

Water is boiled in a pan covered with a poorly-fitting lid in a specified location. Heat is supplied to the pan by a 2.kW resistance heater. The amount of water in the pan is observed to decrease by 1.19 kg in 30 minutes. If it is estimated that 75 percent of electricity consumed by the heater is transferred to the water as heat, determine the local atmospheric pressure in that location. *Answer:* 85.4 kPa

Supplement 2.2 Properties of water during a heating process

A rigid tank initially contains 1.4 kg saturated liquid water at 200°C. At this state, 25 percent of the volume is occupied by water and the rest by air. Now heat is supplied to the water until the tank contains saturated vapor only. Determine (a) the volume of the tank, (b) the final temperature and pressure, and (c) the internal energy change of the water. *Answers:* (a) 0.00648 m³, (b) 371°C, 21.4 MPa, (c) 1892 kJ

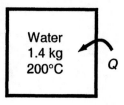

Supplement 2.3 Properties of water during a cooling process in a cylinder

A piston-cylinder device initially contains steam at 3.5 MPa, superheated by 5°C. Now, steam loses heat to the surroundings and piston moves down hitting a set of stops at which point the cylinder contains saturated liquid water. The cooling continues until the cylinder contains water at 200°C. Determine (a) the initial temperature, (b) the enthalpy change per unit mass of the steam by the time the piston first hit the stops, and (c) the final pressure and the quality (if mixture). *Answers:* (a) 248°C, (b) –1771 kJ/kg, (c) 1.56 MPa, 0.0006

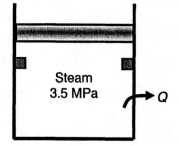

Supplement 2.4 Combustion in a gasoline engine

The combustion in a gasoline engine may be approximated by a constant volume heat addition process. There exists the air-fuel mixture in the cylinder before the combustion and the combustion gases after it, and both may be approximated as air, an ideal gas. In a gasoline engine, the cylinder conditions are 1.8 MPa and 450°C before the combustion and 1300°C after it. Determine the pressure at the end of the combustion process. *Answer :* 3916 kPa

Supplement 2.5 Withdrawing an ideal gas from a tank

A rigid tank contains an ideal gas at 300 kPa and 600 K. Now half of the gas is withdrawn from the tank and the gas is found at 100 kPa at the end of the process. Determine (a) the final temperature of the gas. Also, determine (b) the final pressure if no mass was withdrawn from the tank and the same final temperature was reached at the end of the process. *Answers:* (a) 400 K, (b) 200 kPa

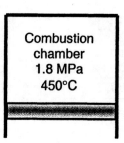

Supplement 2.6 Mass and volume flow rates of CO2 in a pipe

Carbon dioxide gas at 3 MPa and 500 K flows steadily in a pipe at a rate of 0.4 kmol/s. Determine (a) the volume and mass flow rates and the density of carbon dioxide at this state. If CO_2 is cooled at constant pressure as it flows in the pipe so that the temperature of CO_2 drops to 450 K at the exit of the pipe, determine (b) the volume flow rate at the exit of the pipe. *Answers*: (a) 0.554 m^3/s, 17.6 kg/s, 31.8 kg/m^3, (b) 0.499 m^3/s

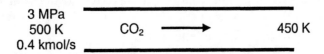

3 MPa
500 K
0.4 kmol/s

CO_2 →

450 K

Supplement 2.7 The use of compressibility factor for steam

A piston-cylinder device initially contains 0.2 kg of steam at 200 kPa and 300°C. The steam is cooled at constant pressure until it is at 150°C. Determine the volume change of the cylinder during this process using the compressibility factor and compare the result to the actual value. *Answers*: 0.07006 m^3, 0.07128 m^3 actual, 1.71% error.

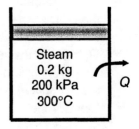

Steam
0.2 kg
200 kPa
300°C

Q

Supplement 2.8 Using compression work to determine R, Cv, and Cp of an ideal gas

A piston-cylinder device contains 0.8 kg of an ideal gas. Now, the gas is cooled at constant pressure and the gas temperature decreases by 10°C. If 16.6 kJ of compression work is done during this process, determine the gas constant and the molar mass of the gas. Also, determine the constant-volume and constant-pressure specific heats of the gas if its specific heat ratio is 1.667. *Answers*: 2.075 kJ/kg-°C, 4.007 kg/kmol, 3.111 kJ/kg-°C, 5.186 kJ/kg-°C

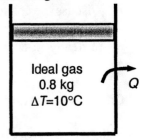

Ideal gas
0.8 kg
ΔT=10°C

Q

Supplement 2.9 Comparison of internal, kinetic, and potential energies

The temperature of air changes from 0°C to 10°C while its velocity changes from zero velocity to a final velocity, and its elevation changes from zero to a final elevation. At which values of final air velocity and final elevation, the internal, kinetic, and potential energy changes will be equal? *Answers*: 119.9 m/s, 733.3 m

AIR
0°C → 10°C
0 m/s→Vel_2
0 m → z_2
$\Delta U = \Delta KE = \Delta PE$

Chapter 3 Educational Objectives and Glossary

The Educational Objectives of Chapter 3 are to:

- Identify the types of energy that may be transferred to or from a thermodynamic system.
- Define the meaning of heat transfer and work.
- Determine that energy in the form of heat or work may cross the boundaries of a closed (fixed mass) system.
- Examine the various forms of work, with particular emphasis on the moving boundary work or PdV work commonly encountered in reciprocating devices such as automotive engines and compressors.
- Determine that a fluid flowing across a control surface of a control volume carries energy across the control surface in addition to any energy transfer across the control surface that may be in the form of heat and/or work.
- Identify the energy carried by a fluid stream crossing a control surface as the sum of internal energy, flow work, kinetic energy and potential energy of the fluid and to relate the combination of the internal energy and the flow work to the property enthalpy.
- Discuss the conservation of mass principle.
- Apply the conservation of mass principle to various systems including steady- and unsteady-flow control volumes.

Chapter 3 Glossary

Adiabatic process is a process during which there is no heat transfer. The word adiabatic comes from the Greek word *adiabatos*, which means not to be passed.

Boundary work (PdV work) is the work associated with the expansion or compression of a gas in a piston-cylinder device. Boundary work is the area under the process curve on a P-V diagram equal, in magnitude, to the work done during a quasi-equilibrium expansion or compression process of a closed system.

Conduction is the transfer of energy from the more energetic particles of a substance to the adjacent less energetic ones as a result of interaction between particles.

Conservation of mass principle is expressed as net mass transfer to or from a system during a process equal to the net change (increase or decrease) in the total mass of the system during that process.

Continuity equation is the conservation of mass equation as it is often referred to in fluid mechanics.

Convection is the transfer of energy between a solid surface and the adjacent fluid that is in motion, and it involves the combined effects of conduction and fluid motion.

Electrical work is work done on a system as electrons in a wire move under the effect of electromotive forces while crossing the system boundary.

Energy transport by mass is the product of the mass of the flowing fluid and its total energy. The rate of energy transport by mass is the product of the mass flow rate and the total energy of the flow.

Flow work, or **flow energy** is work required to push mass into or out of control volumes. On a unit mass basis this energy is equivalent to the product of the pressure and specific volume of the mass Pv.

Formal sign convention (classical thermodynamics sign convention) for heat and work interactions is as follows: heat transfer to a system and work done by a system are positive; heat transfer from a system and work done on a system are negative.

Heat is defined as the form of energy that is transferred between two systems (or a system and its surroundings) by virtue of a temperature difference.

Mass flow rate is the amount of mass flowing through a cross section per unit time.

Polytropic process is a process in which pressure and volume are often related by $PV^n = C$, where n and C are constants, during expansion and compression processes of real gases.

Radiation is the transfer of energy due to the emission of electromagnetic waves (or photons).

Rate of heat transfer is the amount of heat transferred per unit time.

Shaft work is energy transmitted by a rotating shaft and is the related to the torque **T** applied to the shaft and the number of revolutions of the shaft per unit time.

Spring work is the work done to change the length of a spring.

Surface tension is the force per unit length used to overcome the microscopic forces between molecules at the liquid–air interfaces.

Total energy of a flowing fluid is the sum of the enthalpy, kinetic, and potential energies of the flowing fluid.

Volume flow rate is the volume of the fluid flowing through a cross section per unit time.

Work is the energy transfer associated with a force acting through a distance.

EXAMPLE 3-1   Boundary work during polytropic expansion of nitrogen

A piston-cylinder device initially contains 0.07 m³ of nitrogen gas at 130 kPa and 120°C. The nitrogen is now expanded polytropically to a state of 100 kPa and 100°C. Determine the boundary work done during this process.

N₂ 130 kPa 120°C

Equations

GIVEN

$$V_1 = 0.07 \ [\text{m}^3] \tag{1}$$

$$P_1 = 130 \ [\text{kPa}] \tag{2}$$

$$T_1 = ConvertTemp \left(C, \ K, \ 120 \right) \tag{3}$$

$$P_2 = 100 \ [\text{kPa}] \tag{4}$$

$$T_2 = ConvertTemp \left(C, \ K, \ 100 \right) \tag{5}$$

PROPERTIES

$$R = R_u / MM \quad \textbf{Gas constant} \tag{6}$$

$$R_u = 8.314 \ [\text{kJ/kmol} \cdot \text{K}] \quad \textbf{Universal gas constant} \tag{7}$$

$$MM = \text{MW} \left(\text{N2} \right) \tag{8}$$

ANALYSIS

$$P_1 \cdot V_1 = m \cdot R \cdot T_1 \quad \textbf{Equation of state on mass basis, assuming ideal gas} \tag{9}$$

$$P_2 \cdot V_2 = m \cdot R \cdot T_2 \tag{10}$$

$$P_1 \cdot V_1^n = P_2 \cdot V_2^n \quad \textbf{Get the polytropic index (n) from this equation} \tag{11}$$

$$W_b = \frac{P_2 \cdot V_2 - P_1 \cdot V_1}{1 - n} \quad \textbf{Boundary work} \tag{12}$$

Solution

$m = 0.07799 \ [\text{kg}]$	$MM = 28.01 \ [\text{kg/kmol}]$	$n = 1.248$	$P_1 = 130 \ [\text{kPa}]$
$P_2 = 100 \ [\text{kPa}]$	$R = 0.2968 \ [\text{kJ/kg-K}]$	$R_u = 8.314 \ [\text{kJ/kmol-K}]$	$T_1 = 393.2 \ [\text{K}]$
$T_2 = 373.1 \ [\text{K}]$	$V_1 = 0.07 \ [\text{m}^3]$	$V_2 = 0.08637 \ [\text{m}^3]$	$\boxed{W_b = 1.863 \ [\text{kJ}]}$

EXAMPLE 3-2   Compression work in a cylinder with stops

A piston-cylinder device with a set of stops initially contains 0.3 kg of steam at 1.0 MPa and 400°C. The location of the stops corresponds to 60% of the initial volume. Now the steam is cooled. Determine the compression work if the final state is (a) 1.0 MPa and 250°C and (b) 500 kPa. Also, determine (c) the temperature at the final state in part (b).

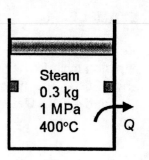

Equations

GIVEN

$$m = 0.3 \ [\text{kg}] \tag{1}$$

$$P_1 = 1 \ [\text{MPa}] \cdot \left| 1000 \ \frac{\text{kPa}}{\text{MPa}} \right| \tag{2}$$

$$T_1 = 400 \ [\text{C}] \tag{3}$$

$$P_{2,a} = P_1 \tag{4}$$

$$T_{2,a} = 250 \ [\text{C}] \tag{5}$$

$$P_{2,b} = 500 \ [\text{kPa}] \tag{6}$$

$$f = 0.60 \tag{7}$$

ANALYSIS

$$Fluid\$ = \text{'Steam'} \tag{8}$$

(a)

$$v_1 = v \left(Fluid\$, \ P = P_1, \ T = T_1 \right) \quad \textbf{initial specific volume} \tag{9}$$

$$v_2 = v \left(Fluid\$, \ P = P_{2,a}, \ T = T_{2,a} \right) \tag{10}$$

$$v_1 = Vol_1/m \quad \textbf{initial volume V}_1 \tag{11}$$

$$v_2 = Vol_2/m \tag{12}$$

$$W_{b,a} = P_1 \cdot (Vol_1 - Vol_2) \tag{13}$$

(b)

$$Vol_{stop} = f \cdot Vol_1 \tag{14}$$

$$W_{b,b} = P_1 \cdot (Vol_1 - Vol_{stop}) \quad \textbf{Compression work} \tag{15}$$

$$v_{stop} = Vol_{stop}/m \tag{16}$$

$$T_{2,b} = T \left(Fluid\$, \ P = P_{2,b}, \ v = v_{stop} \right) \quad \textbf{Final temperature} \tag{17}$$

Solution

$f = 0.6$

$Fluid\$ = $ 'Steam'

$m = 0.3 \ [\text{kg}]$

$P_1 = 1000 \ [\text{kPa}]$

$P_{2,a} = 1000 \ [\text{kPa}]$

$P_{2,b} = 500 \ [\text{kPa}]$

$T_1 = 400 \ [\text{C}]$

$T_{2,a} = 250 \ [\text{C}]$

$\boxed{T_{2,b} = 151.8 \ [\text{C}]}$

$Vol_1 = 0.09198 \ [\text{m}^3]$

$Vol_2 = 0.06979 \ [\text{m}^3]$

$Vol_{stop} = 0.05519 \ [\text{m}^3]$

$v_1 = 0.3066 \ [\text{m}^3/\text{kg}]$

$v_2 = 0.2326 \ [\text{m}^3/\text{kg}]$

$v_{stop} = 0.184 \ [\text{m}^3/\text{kg}]$

$\boxed{W_{b,a} = 22.18 \ [\text{kJ}]}$

$\boxed{W_{b,b} = 36.79 \ [\text{kJ}]}$

EXAMPLE 3-3   Mass balance for air flowing in a pipe

Air enters a 28-cm diameter pipe steadily at 200 kPa and 20°C with a velocity of 5 m/s. Heat is supplied to the pipe and air leaves the pipe at 180 kPa and 40°C. Determine (a) the volume flow rate of the air at the inlet, (b) the mass flow rate of the air, and (c) the velocity and volume flow rate at the exit.

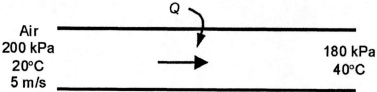

Equations

GIVEN

$$D = 0.28 \ [\text{m}] \tag{1}$$

$$P_1 = 200 \ [\text{kPa}] \tag{2}$$

$$T_1 = ConvertTemp \left(C, \ K, \ 20 \right) \tag{3}$$

$$Vel_1 = 5 \ [\text{m/s}] \tag{4}$$

$$P_2 = 180 \ [\text{kPa}] \tag{5}$$

$$T_2 = ConvertTemp \left(C, \ K, \ 40 \right) \tag{6}$$

PROPERTIES

$$R = R_u / MM \qquad \textbf{Gas constant} \tag{7}$$

$$R_u = 8.314 \ [\text{kJ/kmol} \cdot \text{K}] \qquad \textbf{Universal gas constant} \tag{8}$$

$$MM = MW \left(Air \right) \tag{9}$$

ANALYSIS

$$A = \pi \cdot \frac{D^2}{4} \qquad \textbf{Cross sectional area} \tag{10}$$

$$\rho_1 = \frac{P_1}{\left(R \cdot T_1 \right)} \qquad \textbf{Density of air at inlet} \tag{11}$$

$$\dot{Vol}_1 = A \cdot Vel_1 \qquad \textbf{Volume flow rate at inlet} \tag{12}$$

$$\dot{m} = \rho_1 \cdot A \cdot Vel_1 \qquad \textbf{Mass flow rate} \tag{13}$$

$$\rho_2 = \frac{P_2}{\left(R \cdot T_2 \right)} \qquad \textbf{Density of air at exit} \tag{14}$$

$$\dot{m} = \rho_2 \cdot \dot{Vol}_2 \tag{15}$$

$$\dot{Vol}_2 = A \cdot Vel_2 \qquad \textbf{Volume flow rate at exit} \tag{16}$$

Solution

$A = 0.06158 \ [\mathrm{m^2}]$

$D = 0.28 \ [\mathrm{m}]$

$MM = 28.97 \ [\mathrm{kg/kmol}]$

$\boxed{\dot{m} = 0.7318 \ [\mathrm{kg/s}]}$

$P_1 = 200 \ [\mathrm{kPa}]$

$P_2 = 180 \ [\mathrm{kPa}]$

$R = 0.287 \ [\mathrm{kJ/kg\text{-}K}]$

$\rho_1 = 2.377 \ [\mathrm{kg/m^3}]$

$\rho_2 = 2.003 \ [\mathrm{kg/m^3}]$

$R_u = 8.314 \ [\mathrm{kJ/kmol\text{-}K}]$

$T_1 = 293.2 \ [\mathrm{K}]$

$T_2 = 313.2 \ [\mathrm{K}]$

$Vel_1 = 5 \ [\mathrm{m/s}]$

$\boxed{Vel_2 = 5.935 \ [\mathrm{m/s}]}$

$\boxed{\dot{Vol}_1 = 0.3079 \ [\mathrm{m^3/s}]}$

$\boxed{\dot{Vol}_2 = 0.3654 \ [\mathrm{m^3/s}]}$

EXAMPLE 3-4   Mass balance and boundary work for charging steam into a balloon

A balloon initially contains 50 m³ of steam at 100 kPa and 150°C. The balloon is connected by a valve to a large reservoir that supplies steam at 150 kPa and 200°C. Now the valve is opened, and steam is allowed to enter the balloon until the pressure equilibrium with the steam at the supply line is reached. The material of the balloon is such that its volume increases linearly with pressure. If some heat transfer also takes place between the balloon and the surroundings and the mass of the steam in the balloon doubles at the end of the process, determine the final temperature and the boundary work during this process.

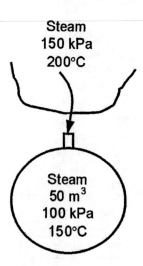

Steam
150 kPa
200°C

Steam
50 m³
100 kPa
150°C

Equations

GIVEN

$$Vol_1 = 50 \ [\text{m}^3] \tag{1}$$

$$P_1 = 100 \ [\text{kPa}] \tag{2}$$

$$T_1 = 150 \ [\text{C}] \tag{3}$$

$$P_i = 150 \ [\text{kPa}] \tag{4}$$

$$T_i = 200 \ [\text{C}] \tag{5}$$

$$P_2 = P_i \tag{6}$$

$$m_2 = 2 \cdot m_1 \tag{7}$$

ANALYSIS

$$Fluid\$ = \text{'Steam\_iapws'} \tag{8}$$

$$v_1 = v \,(Fluid\$, \ P = P_1, \ T = T_1) \quad \textbf{Initial specific volume} \tag{9}$$

$$v_1 = Vol_1/m_1 \quad \textbf{Initial volume, V}_1 \tag{10}$$

$$Vol_2 = (Vol_1/P_1) \cdot P_2 \quad \textbf{Volume changes linearly with pressure} \tag{11}$$

$$v_2 = Vol_2/m_2 \quad \textbf{Final specific volume} \tag{12}$$

$$T_2 = T \,(Fluid\$, \ P = P_2, \ v = v_2) \tag{13}$$

$$W_b = \frac{P_1 + P_2}{2} \cdot (Vol_2 - Vol_1) \quad \textbf{Boundary work} \tag{14}$$

Solution

$Fluid\$ = $ 'Steam_iapws'

$m_1 = 25.82$ [kg]

$m_2 = 51.64$ [kg]

$P_1 = 100$ [kPa]

$P_2 = 150$ [kPa]

$P_i = 150$ [kPa]

$T_1 = 150$ [C]

$\boxed{T_2 = 202.5 \text{ [C]}}$

$T_i = 200$ [C]

$Vol_1 = 50 \ \left[\text{m}^3\right]$

$Vol_2 = 75 \ \left[\text{m}^3\right]$

$v_1 = 1.937 \ \left[\text{m}^3/\text{kg}\right]$

$v_2 = 1.452 \ \left[\text{m}^3/\text{kg}\right]$

$\boxed{W_b = 3125 \text{ [kJ]}}$

EXAMPLE 3-5   Conversion of flow energy of steam into sensible energy

A rigid, insulated tank that is initially evacuated is connected through a valve to a supply line that carries steam at 4 MPa. Now the valve is opened, and steam is allowed to flow into the tank until the pressure reaches 4 MPa, at which point the valve is closed. If the final temperature of the steam in the tank is 550°C, determine the temperature of the steam in the supply line and the flow work per unit mass of the steam. Hint: Flow work of the steam in the supply line is converted to sensible internal energy in the tank.

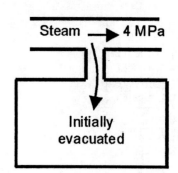

Steam → 4 MPa

Initially evacuated

Equations

GIVEN

$$P_{line} = 4000 \ [kPa] \tag{1}$$

$$P_{tank} = 4000 \ [kPa] \tag{2}$$

$$T_{tank} = 550 \ [C] \tag{3}$$

ANALYSIS

$$Fluid\$ = \text{'Steam\_iapws'} \tag{4}$$

$$u_{tank} = u \,(Fluid\$, \ T = T_{tank}, \ P = P_{tank}) \quad \textbf{Specific internal energy} \tag{5}$$

$$h_{line} = u_{tank} \tag{6}$$

$$T_{line} = T \,(Fluid\$, \ P = P_{line}, \ h = h_{line}) \quad \textbf{Line temperature} \tag{7}$$

$$u_{line} = u \,(Fluid\$, \ P = P_{line}, \ h = h_{line}) \quad \textbf{Specific internal energy} \tag{8}$$

$$w_{flow} = h_{line} - u_{line} \quad \textbf{Flow work} \tag{9}$$

Solution

$Fluid\$ = \text{'Steam\_iapws'}$
$h_{line} = 3190 \ [kJ/kg]$
$P_{line} = 4000 \ [kPa]$
$P_{tank} = 4000 \ [kPa]$
$\boxed{T_{line} = 389.5 \ [C]}$
$T_{tank} = 550 \ [C]$
$u_{line} = 2902 \ [kJ/kg]$
$u_{tank} = 3190 \ [kJ/kg]$
$\boxed{w_{flow} = 288 \ [kJ/kg]}$

Supplement 3.1 Boundary work during isentropic expansion of nitrogen

A piston-cylinder device initially contains 0.07 m^3 of nitrogen gas at 130 kPa and 120°C. The nitrogen is now expanded isentropically to a pressure of 100 kPa. Determine the final temperature and the boundary work done during this process. Note that during an isentropic process the polytropic constant takes the value of the specific heat ratio. *Answers*: 365 K, 1.65 kJ

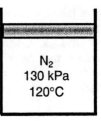

N₂
130 kPa
120°C

Supplement 3.2 Boundary work during isothermal expansion of nitrogen

A piston-cylinder device initially contains 0.25 kg of nitrogen gas at 130 kPa and 120°C. The nitrogen is now expanded isothermally to a pressure of 100 kPa. Determine the boundary work done during this process. *Answer:* 7.65 kJ

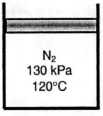

N₂
130 kPa
120°C

Supplement 3.3 Net boundary work of a cycle

A piston-cylinder device contains 0.15 kg of air initially at 2 MPa and 350°C. The air is first expanded isothermally to 500 kPa, then compressed polytropically to the initial pressure, and finally compressed at the constant pressure to the initial state. Determine the boundary work for each process and the net work of the cycle. The polytropic constant is 1.2. *Answers*: 37.18 kJ, .34.86 kJ, .6.97 kJ, .4.65 kJ

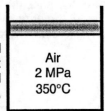

Air
2 MPa
350°C

Supplement 3.4 Mass balance for R.134a flowing in a pipe

Refrigerant.134a enters a 28.cm diameter pipe steadily at 200 kPa and 20°C with a velocity of 5 m/s. Heat is supplied to the pipe and the refrigerant leaves the pipe at 180 kPa and 40°C. Determine (a) the volume flow rate of the refrigerant at the inlet, (b) the mass flow rate of the refrigerant, and (c) the velocity and volume flow rate at the exit. *Answers*: (a) 0.308 m^3/s, (b) 2.70 kg/s, (c) 6.02 m/s, 0.371 m^3/s

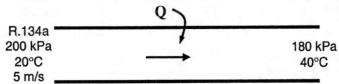

R.134a
200 kPa
20°C
5 m/s

180 kPa
40°C

Supplement 3.5 Mass balance for a solar water storage tank

Consider a 300 liter storage tank of a solar water collector initially filled with warm water at 45°C. Warm water is withdrawn from the tank through a 2.cm hose at a velocity of 0.5 m/s while cold water enters the tank at 20°C at a rate of 15 liter/min. Determine the amount of water in the tank after a 20.minute period. *Answer.* 184.2 kg

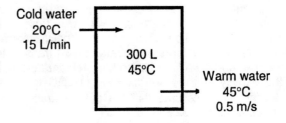

Cold water
20°C
15 L/min

300 L
45°C

Warm water
45°C
0.5 m/s

Supplement 3.6 Mass balance and boundary work during discharging air from a cylinder

A vertical piston-cylinder device initially contains 0.25 m³ of air at 600 kPa and 300°C. A valve connected to the cylinder is now opened, and air is allowed to escape until three quarters of the mass leave the cylinder at which point the volume is 0.05 m³. Determine the final temperature in the cylinder and the boundary work during this process. *Answers*: 458.4 K, 120 kJ

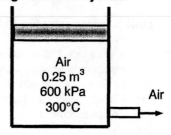

Supplement 3.7 Flow work of steam in a pipe

Steam flows in a pipe at 150°C at a rate of 18 kg/min and the power needed to maintain the flow is 58 kW. Determine the pressure and the internal energy of the steam. *Answers*: 120 kPa, 2582 kJ/kg

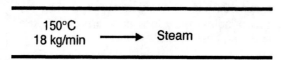

Supplement 3.8 Flow work and energy transport by mass

Air flows steadily in a pipe at 300 kPa, 77°C, and 25 m/s at a rate of 18 kg/min. Determine (a) the diameter of the pipe, (b) the rate of flow energy, and (c) the rate of energy transport by mass. Also, determine (d) the error involved in part (c) if the kinetic energy is neglected. *Answers*: (a) 7.15 cm, (b) 30.14 kW, (c) 105.3 kW, (d) 0.09%

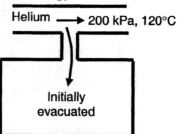

Supplement 3.9 Conversion of flow work of helium into sensible energy

A rigid, insulated tank that is initially evacuated is connected through a valve to a supply line that carries helium at 200 kPa and 120°C. Now the valve is opened, and helium is allowed to flow into the tank until the pressure reaches 200 kPa, at which point the valve is closed. Determine the flow work of the helium in the supply line and the final temperature of the helium in the tank. Hint: Flow work of the helium in the supply line is converted to sensible internal energy in the tank. *Answers*: 816 kJ/kg, 655 K

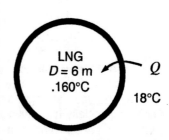

Supplement 3.10 Conduction heat transfer to an LNG tank

When the transportation of natural gas in a pipeline is not feasible for economic reasons, it is first liquefied using non-conventional refrigeration cycles to a temperature of about .160°C, and then transported in specially insulated tanks placed in marine ships. Consider a 6.m.diameter spherical tank that is filled with liquefied natural gas (LNG) at .160°C. The tank is exposed to ambient air at 18°C. The tank is thin-shelled and its temperature can be taken to be the same as the temperature of LNG. The tank is insulated with 5.cm.thick super insulation which has an effective thermal conductivity of 0.00008 W/m-°C. Determine the rate of heat transfer to the tank and estimate how long it will take for the LNG temperature to rise to .150°C. Take the density and the specific heat of LNG to be 425 kg/m³ and 3.475 kJ/kg·°C and assume that the outer surface is at the ambient temperature. *Answers*: 32.8 W, 590 days

Chapter 4 Educational Objectives and Glossary

The Educational Objectives of Chapter 4 are to:

- Identify the first law of thermodynamics as simply a statement of the conservation of energy principle, and it asserts that total energy is a thermodynamic property.
- Develop the general energy balance, which is expressed as $E_{in} - E_{out} = \Delta E_{system}$ and is developed in a step-by-step manner using an intuitive approach.
- Solve energy balance problems for closed (fixed mass) systems that involve heat and work interactions for general pure substances, ideal gases, and incompressible substances.
- Solve energy balance problems for steady flow systems and common steady-flow devices such as nozzles, compressors, turbines, throttling valves, mixers, and heat exchangers.
- Apply the energy balance to general unsteady-flow processes with particular emphasis on the uniform-flow process, which is the model process for commonly encountered charging and discharging processes.

Chapter 4 Glossary

Compressor is a device that increases the pressure of a gas to very high pressures.

Conservation of energy principle or energy balance based on the first law of thermodynamics may be expressed as follows: Energy can be neither created nor destroyed; it can only change forms. The net change (increase or decrease) in the total energy of the system during a process is equal to the difference between the total energy entering and the total energy leaving the system during that process. The energy balance can be written explicitly as

$$E_{in} - E_{out} = (Q_{in} - Q_{out}) + (W_{in} - W_{out}) + (E_{mass,\,in} - E_{mass,\,out}) = \Delta E_{system}$$

Diffuser is a device that increases the pressure of a fluid by decreasing the fluid velocity.

Fan is a device that increases the pressure of a gas slightly and is mainly used to mobilize a gas.

First law of thermodynamics is simply a statement of the conservation of energy principle, and it asserts that total energy is a thermodynamic property. Joule's experiments indicate the following: For all adiabatic processes between two specified states of a closed system, the net work done is the same regardless of the nature of the closed system and the details of the process.

First law of thermodynamics for a closed system using the classical thermodynamics sign convention is

$$Q_{net,\,in} - W_{net,\,out} = \Delta E_{system} \quad \text{or} \quad Q - W = \Delta E$$

where $Q = Q_{net,\,in} = Q_{in} - Q_{out}$ is the net heat input and $W = W_{net,\,out} = W_{out} - W_{in}$ is the net work output. Obtaining a negative quantity for Q or W simply means that the assumed direction for that quantity is wrong and should be reversed.

Heat exchangers are devices where two moving fluid streams exchange heat without mixing. Heat exchangers are widely used in various industries, and they come in various designs. The simplest form of a heat exchanger is a double-tube (also called tube-and-shell) heat exchanger composed of two concentric pipes of different diameters. One fluid flows in the inner pipe, and the other in the annular space between the two pipes. Heat is transferred from the hot fluid to the cold one through the wall separating them. Sometimes the inner tube makes a couple of turns inside the shell to increase the heat transfer area, and thus the rate of heat transfer.

Mixing chamber is the section of a control volume where mixing process takes place for two or more streams of fluids. The mixing chamber does not have to be a distinct "chamber." Mixing chambers are sometimes classified as direct-contact heat exchangers.

Nozzle is a device that increases the velocity of a fluid at the expense of decreasing pressure.

Pump is a device that increases the pressure of liquids very much as compressors increase the pressure of gases.

Stationary systems are systems that do not involve any changes in their velocity or elevation during a process

Steady means no change with time.

Steady-flow process, which was defined in Chapter 1, is a process during which a fluid flows through a control volume steadily.

Throttling valves are any kind of flow-restricting devices that cause a significant pressure drop in the fluid. Some familiar examples are ordinary adjustable valves, capillary tubes, and porous plugs. Unlike turbines, they produce a pressure drop without involving any work. The pressure drop in the fluid is often accompanied by a large drop in temperature, and for that reason throttling devices are commonly used in refrigeration and air-conditioning applications. The magnitude of the temperature drop (or, sometimes, the temperature rise) during a throttling process is governed by a property called the Joule-Thomson coefficient, which is discussed in Chapter 11.

Total energy E of a system is the sum of the numerous forms of energy that can exist within the system such as internal (sensible, latent, chemical, and nuclear), kinetic, potential, electrical, and magnetic.

Turbine is a device that produces shaft work due to a decrease of enthalpy, kinetic, and potential energies of a flowing fluid.

Uniform-flow process involves the following idealization: The fluid flow at any inlet or exit is uniform and steady, and thus the fluid properties do not change with time or position over the cross section of an inlet or exit. If they do change with time, the fluid properties are averaged and treated as constants for the entire process.

Unsteady-flow, or transient-flow, processes are processes that involve changes within a control volume with time.

EXAMPLE 4-1 Mixing of steam at different states

Two tanks (Tank A and Tank B) are separated by a partition. Initially Tank A contains 2 kg steam at 1 MPa and 300°C while Tank B contains 3 kg saturated steam mixture with a mass fraction of 50 percent. Now the partition is removed and they are allowed to mix until the mechanical and thermal equilibrium are established. If the pressure at the final state is 300 kPa, determine (a) the temperature and quality of the steam (if mixture) at the final state and (b) the amount of heat lost from the tanks.

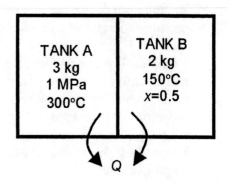

Equations

GIVEN

$$m_A = 2 \ [\text{kg}] \tag{1}$$

$$T_{1A} = 300 \ [\text{C}] \tag{2}$$

$$P_{1A} = 1000 \ [\text{kPa}] \tag{3}$$

$$m_B = 3 \ [\text{kg}] \tag{4}$$

$$T_{1B} = 150 \ [\text{C}] \tag{5}$$

$$x_{1B} = 0.5 \tag{6}$$
$$P_2 = 300 \ [\text{kPa}] \tag{7}$$

PROPERTIES

$$Fluid\$ = \text{'Steam\_iapws'} \tag{8}$$
$$u_{1A} = u \, (Fluid\$, \ T = T_{1A}, \ P = P_{1A}) \tag{9}$$
$$v_{1A} = v \, (Fluid\$, \ T = T_{1A}, \ P = P_{1A}) \tag{10}$$
$$u_{1B} = u \, (Fluid\$, \ T = T_{1B}, \ x = x_{1B}) \tag{11}$$
$$v_{1B} = v \, (Fluid\$, \ T = T_{1B}, \ x = x_{1B}) \tag{12}$$

ANALYSIS

$$Vol_{1A} = m_A \cdot v_{1A} \quad \textbf{Volume of Tank A} \tag{13}$$
$$Vol_{1B} = m_B \cdot v_{1B} \quad \textbf{Volume of Tank B} \tag{14}$$
$$Vol_t = Vol_{1A} + Vol_{1B} \quad \textbf{Total volume} \tag{15}$$
$$m_t = m_A + m_B \quad \textbf{Total mass} \tag{16}$$
$$v_2 = Vol_t / m_t \quad \textbf{Final specific volume} \tag{17}$$
$$T_2 = T \, (Fluid\$, \ P = P_2, \ v = v_2) \quad \textbf{Final temperature} \tag{18}$$
$$x_2 = x \, (Fluid\$, \ P = P_2, \ v = v_2) \quad \textbf{Final quality} \tag{19}$$
$$u_2 = u \, (Fluid\$, \ P = P_2, \ v = v_2) \quad \textbf{Final internal energy} \tag{20}$$
$$-Q_{out} = m_A \cdot (u_2 - u_{1A}) + m_B \cdot (u_2 - u_{1B}) \quad \textbf{Energy balance} \tag{21}$$

Solution

$Fluid\$ = $ 'Steam_iapws'

$m_A = 2$ [kg]

$m_B = 3$ [kg]

$m_t = 5$ [kg]

$P_{1A} = 1000$ [kPa]

$P_2 = 300$ [kPa]

$\boxed{Q_{out} = 3959 \text{ [kJ]}}$

$T_{1A} = 300$ [C]

$T_{1B} = 150$ [C]

$\boxed{T_2 = 133.5 \text{ [C]}}$

$u_{1A} = 2794$ [kJ/kg]

$u_{1B} = 1595$ [kJ/kg]

$u_2 = 1283$ [kJ/kg]

$Vol_{1A} = 0.516 \left[\text{m}^3\right]$

$Vol_{1B} = 0.5904 \left[\text{m}^3\right]$

$Vol_t = 1.106 \left[\text{m}^3\right]$

$v_{1A} = 0.258 \left[\text{m}^3/\text{kg}\right]$

$v_{1B} = 0.1968 \left[\text{m}^3/\text{kg}\right]$

$v_2 = 0.2213 \left[\text{m}^3/\text{kg}\right]$

$x_{1B} = 0.5$

$\boxed{x_2 = 0.3641}$

EXAMPLE 4-2   Heating of a room by electrical radiator containing oil

A 30-liter electrical radiator containing heating oil is placed in a 50-m³ room. Both the room and the oil in the radiator are initially at 10°C. The radiator with a rating of 1.8 kW is now turned on. Heat is also lost from the room at an average rate of 0.35 kW. It is measured after a while that the room is at 20°C and the oil in the radiator is at 50°C. Taking the density and the specific heat of oil to be 950 kg/m³ and 2.2 kJ/kg-°C, respectively, determine how long it has been since the heater was first turned on. Assume the room is well sealed.

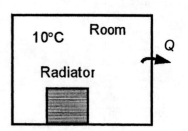

Equations

GIVEN

$$Vol_{oil} = 0.030 \ \left[\text{m}^3\right] \tag{1}$$

$$Vol_{room} = 50 \ \left[\text{m}^3\right] \tag{2}$$

$$\dot{W}_{in} = 1.8 \ [\text{kW}] \tag{3}$$

$$\dot{Q}_{out} = 0.35 \ [\text{kW}] \tag{4}$$

$$T_1 = 10 \ [\text{C}] \tag{5}$$

$$T_{oil,2} = 50 \ [\text{C}] \tag{6}$$

$$T_{air,2} = 20 \ [\text{C}] \tag{7}$$

$$\rho_{oil} = 950 \ \left[\text{kg/m}^3\right] \tag{8}$$

$$C_{p,oil} = 2.2 \ [\text{kJ/kg·C}] \tag{9}$$

$$P = 101.3 \ [\text{kPa}] \quad \textbf{Assumed} \tag{10}$$

PROPERTIES

$$Fluid\$ = \text{'Air'} \tag{11}$$

$$C_{p,air} = c_p \ (Fluid\$, \ T = T_{ave}) \quad \textbf{Specific heat at constant pressure} \tag{12}$$

$$C_{v,air} = c_v \ (Fluid\$, \ T = T_{ave}) \quad \textbf{Specific heat at constant volume} \tag{13}$$

$$T_{ave} = \text{Average}(T_1, \ T_{air,2}) \quad \textbf{Average temperature of air} \tag{14}$$

$$R = C_{p,air} - C_{v,air} \quad \textbf{Gas constant} \tag{15}$$

ANALYSIS

$$P \cdot Vol_{room} = m_{air} \cdot R \cdot ConvertTemp \ (C, \ K, \ T_1) \quad \textbf{Equation of state} \tag{16}$$

$$\rho_{oil} = m_{oil}/Vol_{oil} \quad \textbf{Heating oil density} \tag{17}$$

$$\left(\dot{W}_{in} - \dot{Q}_{out}\right) \cdot time = m_{air} \cdot C_{v,air} \cdot (T_{air,2} - T_1) + m_{oil} \cdot C_{p,oil} \cdot (T_{oil,2} - T_1) \quad \textbf{Energy balance} \tag{18}$$

Solution

$C_{p,air} = 1.007 \ [\text{kJ/kg-K}]$

$C_{p,oil} = 2.2 \ [\text{kJ/kg-C}]$

$C_{v,air} = 0.7195 \ [\text{kJ/kg-K}]$

$Fluid\$ = \text{'Air'}$

$m_{air} = 62.32 \ [\text{kg}]$

$m_{oil} = 28.5 \ [\text{kg}]$

$P = 101.3 \ [\text{kPa}]$

$\dot{Q}_{out} = 0.35 \ [\text{kW}]$

$R = 0.287 \ [\text{kJ/kg-K}]$

$\rho_{oil} = 950 \ [\text{kg/m}^3]$

$\boxed{time = 2039 \ [\text{s}]}$

$T_1 = 10 \ [\text{C}]$

$T_{air,2} = 20 \ [\text{C}]$

$T_{ave} = 15 \ [\text{C}]$

$T_{oil,2} = 50 \ [\text{C}]$

$Vol_{oil} = 0.03 \ [\text{m}^3]$

$Vol_{room} = 50 \ [\text{m}^3]$

$\dot{W}_{in} = 1.8 \ [\text{kW}]$

EXAMPLE 4-3 Turbocharger of an internal combustion engine

The turbocharger of an internal combustion engine consists of a turbine and a compressor. Hot exhaust gases flow through the turbine to produce work and the work output from the turbine is used as the work input to the compressor. The pressure of ambient air is increased as it flows through the compressor before it enters the engine cylinders. Thus, the purpose of a turbocharger is to increase the pressure of air so that more air gets into the cylinder. Consequently, more fuel can be burned and more power can be obtained from the engine.

Exhaust gases enter the turbine at 400°C and 120 kPa at a rate of 0.02 kg/s and leaves at 350°C. Air enters the compressor at 50°C and 100 kPa and leaves at 130 kPa at a rate of 0.018 kg/s. The compressor increases the air pressure with a side effect: It also increases the air temperature, which increases the possibility of a gasoline engine to experience an engine knock. To avoid this, an aftercooler is placed after the compressor to cool the warm air by cold ambient air before it enters the engine cylinders. It is estimated that the aftercooler must decrease the air temperature below 80°C if knock is to be avoided. The cold ambient air enters the aftercooler at 30°C and leaves at 40°C. Assuming the mechanical efficiency between the turbine and compressor to be 100 percent and using air properties for the exhaust gases, determine (a) the temperature of the air at the compressor outlet and (b) the minimum volume flow rate of ambient air required to avoid knock.

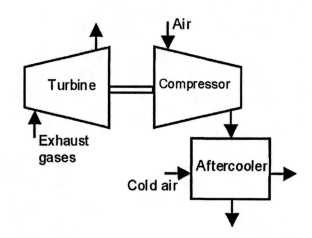

Equations

GIVEN

$$T_{exh,1} = 400 \ [C] \tag{1}$$

$$P_{exh,1} = 120 \ [kPa] \tag{2}$$

$$T_{exh,2} = 350 \ [C] \tag{3}$$

$$\dot{m}_{exh} = 0.02 \ [kg/s] \tag{4}$$

$$T_{air,1} = 50 \ [C] \tag{5}$$

$$P_{air,1} = 100 \ [kPa] \tag{6}$$

$$P_{air,2} = 130 \ [\text{kPa}] \tag{7}$$

$$\dot{m}_{air} = 0.018 \ [\text{kg/s}] \tag{8}$$

$$T_{air,3} = 80 \ [\text{C}] \tag{9}$$

$$T_{coldair,1} = 30 \ [\text{C}] \tag{10}$$

$$T_{coldair,2} = 40 \ [\text{C}] \tag{11}$$

$$\eta_{mec} = 1.0 \tag{12}$$

PROPERTIES

$Fluid\$ = $ 'Air' $\tag{13}$

$C_{p,exh} = \text{c}_\text{p}\,(Fluid\$, \ T = T_{exh,ave})$ **Exhaust specific heat at constant pressure** $\tag{14}$

$T_{exh,ave} = \text{Average}(T_{exh,1}, \ T_{exh,2}) \tag{15}$

$C_{p,air} = \text{c}_\text{p}\,(Fluid\$, \ T = T_{air,ave})$ **Air specific heat at constant pressure** $\tag{16}$

$T_{air,ave} = \text{Average}(T_{air,1}, \ T_{air,2}) \tag{17}$

$C_{p,coldair} = \text{c}_\text{p}\,(Fluid\$, \ T = T_{coldair,ave})$ **Cold air specific heat at constant pressure** $\tag{18}$

$T_{coldair,ave} = \text{Average}(T_{coldair,1}, \ T_{coldair,2}) \tag{19}$

$R_{air} = R_u/MM_{air}$ **Gas constant** $\tag{20}$

$R_u = 8.314 \ [\text{kPa}\cdot\text{m}^3/\text{kmol}\cdot\text{K}]$ **Universal gas constant** $\tag{21}$

$MM_{air} = \text{MW}\,(Fluid\$) \tag{22}$

ANALYSIS

$\dot{W}_T = \dot{m}_{exh} \cdot C_{p,exh} \cdot (T_{exh,1} - T_{exh,2})$ **Turbine power output** $\tag{23}$

$\dot{W}_C = \eta_{mec} \cdot \dot{W}_T$ **Compressor input power** $\tag{24}$

$\dot{W}_C = \dot{m}_{air} \cdot C_{p,air} \cdot (T_{air,2} - T_{air,1}) \tag{25}$

$\dot{m}_{air} \cdot C_{p,air} \cdot (T_{air,2} - T_{air,3}) = \dot{m}_{coldair} \cdot C_{p,coldair} \cdot (T_{coldair,2} - T_{coldair,1})$ **Energy balance on the aftercooler** $\tag{26}$

$\dot{V}ol_{coldair} = \dot{m}_{coldair} \cdot v_{coldair}$ **Volume flow rate of ambient air at the inlet of aftercooler** $\tag{27}$

$P_{air,1} \cdot v_{coldair} = R_{air} \cdot ConvertTemp\,(C, \ K, \ T_{coldair,1})$ **Ideal gas equation for ambient air at the inlet of aftercooler** $\tag{28}$

$T_{air,2} = T_{air,2} \tag{29}$

Solution

$C_{p,air} = 1.008$ [kJ/kg-C]
$C_{p,coldair} = 1.007$ [kJ/kg-K]
$C_{p,exh} = 1.062$ [kJ/kg-K]
$\eta_{mec} = 1$
$Fluid\$ = $ 'Air'
$MM_{air} = 28.97$ [kg/kmol]
$\dot{m}_{air} = 0.018$ [kg/s]
$\dot{m}_{coldair} = 0.05147$ [kg/s]
$\dot{m}_{exh} = 0.02$ [kg/s]
$P_{exh,1} = 120$ [kPa]
$R_{air} = 0.287$ [kJ/kg-K]
$R_u = 8.314$ [kPa-m^3/kmol-K]

$\boxed{T_{air,2} = 108.6 \text{ [C]}}$

$T_{air,ave} = 79.28$ [C]
$T_{coldair,ave} = 35$ [C]
$T_{exh,ave} = 375$ [C]

$\boxed{\dot{V}ol_{coldair} = 0.04478 \left[\text{m}^3/\text{s}\right]}$

$v_{coldair} = 0.8701$ [m^3/kg]
$\dot{W}_C = 1.062$ [kW]
$\dot{W}_T = 1.062$ [kW]

EXAMPLE 4-4   Throttling an ideal gas vs. a real gas

Carbon dioxide gas enters a throttling valve at 5 MPa and 100°C and leaves at 100 kPa. Determine the temperature change during this process if CO2 is assumed (a) an ideal gas and (b) a real gas.

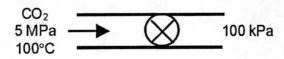

Equations

GIVEN

$$P_1 = 5000 \ [\text{kPa}] \tag{1}$$

$$T_1 = 100 \ [\text{C}] \tag{2}$$

$$P_2 = 100 \ [\text{kPa}] \tag{3}$$

ANALYSIS

(a)

$$Fluid_{Ideal\$} = \text{`CO2'} \tag{4}$$

$$h_{1,a} = \text{h}\,(Fluid_{Ideal\$},\ T = T_1) \quad \textbf{Specific enthalpy} \tag{5}$$

$$h_{2,a} = h_{1,a} \quad \textbf{Energy balance} \tag{6}$$

$$T_{2,a} = \text{T}\,(Fluid_{Ideal\$},\ h = h_{2,a}) \quad \textbf{Temperature at exit} \tag{7}$$

$$\Delta T_a = T_1 - T_{2,a} \quad \textbf{Temperature difference} \tag{8}$$

(b)

$$Fluid_{Real\$} = \text{`Carbondioxide'} \tag{9}$$

$$h_{1,b} = \text{h}\,(Fluid_{Real\$},\ T = T_1,\ P = P_1) \tag{10}$$

$$h_{2,b} = h_{1,b} \tag{11}$$

$$T_{2,b} = \text{T}\,(Fluid_{Real\$},\ h = h_{2,b},\ P = P_2) \tag{12}$$

$$\Delta T_b = T_1 - T_{2,b} \tag{13}$$

Solution

$\boxed{\Delta T_a = -0.00 \text{ [C]}}$

$\boxed{\Delta T_b = 33.98 \text{ [C]}}$

$Fluid_{Ideal}\$ = \text{'CO2'}$

$Fluid_{Real}\$ = \text{'Carbondioxide'}$

$h_{1,a} = -8876 \text{ [kJ/kg]}$

$h_{1,b} = 34.77 \text{ [kJ/kg]}$

$h_{2,a} = -8876 \text{ [kJ/kg]}$

$h_{2,b} = 34.77 \text{ [kJ/kg]}$

$P_1 = 5000 \text{ [kPa]}$

$P_2 = 100 \text{ [kPa]}$

$T_1 = 100 \text{ [C]}$

$T_{2,a} = 100 \text{ [C]}$

$T_{2,b} = 66.02 \text{ [C]}$

EXAMPLE 4-5   Mixing of warm and cold air in an AC system

An air conditioning system involves the mixing of cold air and warm ambient air before the mixture is routed to the cooled room. The cold air enters the mixing chamber at 5°C at a rate of 1.25 m³/s and the warm air enters at 34°C. The ratio of the mass flow rates of the hot to cold water is 1.6. Air is withdrawn from the cooled room at 24°C at the same rate as the mixture. Using variable specific heats, determine (a) the mixture temperature at the inlet of the room and (b) the rate of cooling supplied to the room. Assume the heat gains to the mixing chamber to be negligible and the mixing to take place at a pressure of 120 kPa.

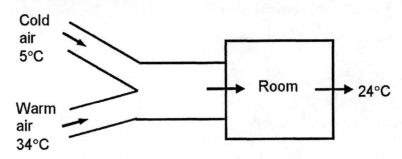

Equations

GIVEN

$$T_1 = 5 \ [\text{C}] \tag{1}$$

$$T_2 = 34 \ [\text{C}] \tag{2}$$

$$\dot{Vol}_1 = 1.25 \ \left[\text{m}^3/\text{s}\right] \tag{3}$$

$$\dot{m}_2/\dot{m}_1 = 1.6 \tag{4}$$

$$T_{room} = 24 \ [\text{C}] \tag{5}$$

$$P = 120 \ [\text{kPa}] \tag{6}$$

PROPERTIES

$$Fluid\$ = \text{'Air'} \tag{7}$$

$h_1 = \text{h} \,(Fluid\$, \ T = T_1)$ **Specific enthalpy for the cold air**   (8)

$h_2 = \text{h} \,(Fluid\$, \ T = T_2)$ **Specific enthalpy for the warm air**   (9)

$h_{room} = \text{h} \,(Fluid\$, \ T = T_{room})$ (10)

$R = R_u/MM$ **Gas constant**   (11)

$R_u = 8.314 \ [\text{kJ/kmol} \cdot \text{K}]$ **Universal gas constant**   (12)

$$MM = \text{MW (Fluid\$)} \tag{13}$$

ANALYSIS

$$P \cdot v_1 = R \cdot ConvertTemp\,(C,\ K,\ T_1) \qquad \textbf{Equation of state per mass basis for the cold air} \tag{14}$$

$$v_1 = \dot{Vol}_1/\dot{m}_1 \qquad \textbf{Cold air specific volume} \tag{15}$$

$$\dot{m}_3 = \dot{m}_1 + \dot{m}_2 \qquad \textbf{Mass balance} \tag{16}$$

$$\dot{m}_1 \cdot h_1 + \dot{m}_2 \cdot h_2 = \dot{m}_3 \cdot h_3 \qquad \textbf{Energy balance} \tag{17}$$

$$T_3 = \text{T}\,(\text{Fluid\$},\ h = h_3) \qquad \textbf{Mixture temperature} \tag{18}$$

$$\dot{Q}_{cooling} = \dot{m}_3 \cdot (h_{room} - h_3) \qquad \textbf{Rate of cooling to room} \tag{19}$$

Solution

$Fluid\$ = \text{'Air'}$
$h_1 = 278.4\ [\text{kJ/kg}]$
$h_2 = 307.6\ [\text{kJ/kg}]$
$h_3 = 296.4\ [\text{kJ/kg}]$
$h_{room} = 297.6\ [\text{kJ/kg}]$
$MM = 28.97\ [\text{kg/kmol}]$
$\dot{m}_1 = 1.879\ [\text{kg/s}]$
$\dot{m}_2 = 3.006\ [\text{kg/s}]$
$\dot{m}_3 = 4.885\ [\text{kg/s}]$
$P = 120\ [\text{kPa}]$
$\boxed{\dot{Q}_{cooling} = 5.669\ [\text{kW}]}$
$R = 0.287\ [\text{kJ/kg-K}]$
$R_u = 8.314\ [\text{kJ/kmol-K}]$
$T_1 = 5\ [\text{C}]$
$T_2 = 34\ [\text{C}]$
$\boxed{T_3 = 22.85\ [\text{C}]}$
$T_{room} = 24\ [\text{C}]$
$\dot{Vol}_1 = 1.25\ [\text{m}^3/\text{s}]$
$v_1 = 0.6653\ [\text{m}^3/\text{kg}]$

EXAMPLE 4-6   Flow of steam inside a pipe

Steam enters an insulated pipe at 200 kPa and 200°C and leaves at 150 kPa and 150°C. The diameter ratio for the pipe is D_1/D_2=1.80. Determine the inlet and exit velocities for the steam.

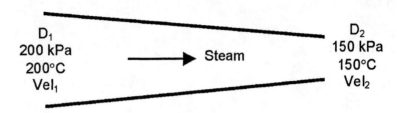

Equations

GIVEN

$$P_1 = 200 \ [kPa] \tag{1}$$

$$T_1 = 200 \ [C] \tag{2}$$

$$P_2 = 150 \ [kPa] \tag{3}$$

$$T_2 = 150 \ [C] \tag{4}$$

$$D_1 = 1.8 \ [m] \quad \textbf{Assumed, it does not matter what value is assumed} \tag{5}$$

$$D_2 = 1 \ [m] \tag{6}$$

PROPERTIES

$$Fluid\$ = \text{'Steam\_iapws'} \tag{7}$$

$$h_1 = h \, (Fluid\$, \ T = T_1, \ P = P_1) \quad \textbf{Specific enthalpy at inlet} \tag{8}$$

$$v_1 = v \, (Fluid\$, \ T = T_1, \ P = P_1) \quad \textbf{Specific volume at inlet} \tag{9}$$

$$h_2 = h \, (Fluid\$, \ T = T_2, \ P = P_2) \quad \textbf{Specific enthalpy at exit} \tag{10}$$

$$v_2 = v \, (Fluid\$, \ T = T_2, \ P = P_2) \quad \textbf{Specific volume at exit} \tag{11}$$

ANALYSIS

$$h_1 + \left(\frac{Vel_1^2}{2} \right) \cdot \left| 0.001 \, \frac{kJ/kg}{m^2/s^2} \right| = h_2 + \left(Vel_2^2/2 \right) \cdot \left| 0.001 \, \frac{kJ/kg}{m^2/s^2} \right| \quad \textbf{Energy balance} \tag{12}$$

$$\left(\pi/4 \cdot D_1^2 \right) \cdot Vel_1/v_1 = \left(\pi/4 \cdot D_2^2 \right) \cdot Vel_2/v_2 \quad \textbf{Mass balance} \tag{13}$$

Solution

$D_1 = 1.8 \ [\text{m}]$

$D_2 = 1 \ [\text{m}]$

$Fluid\$ = \text{'Steam\_iapws'}$

$h_1 = 2871 \ [\text{kJ/kg}]$

$h_2 = 2773 \ [\text{kJ/kg}]$

$P_1 = 200 \ [\text{kPa}]$

$P_2 = 150 \ [\text{kPa}]$

$T_1 = 200 \ [\text{C}]$

$T_2 = 150 \ [\text{C}]$

$\boxed{Vel_1 = 118.8 \ [\text{m/s}]}$

$\boxed{Vel_2 = 458 \ [\text{m/s}]}$

$v_1 = 1.08 \ [\text{m}^3/\text{kg}]$

$v_2 = 1.286 \ [\text{m}^3/\text{kg}]$

EXAMPLE 4-7 Discharging refrigerant from a cylinder

An insulated vertical piston-cylinder device initially contains 0.8 m³ of refrigerant-134a at 1.2 MPa and 120°C. A linear spring at this point applies full force to the piston. A valve connected to the cylinder is now opened, and refrigerant is allowed to escape. As the piston moves down, the spring unwinds, and at the final state the pressure drops to 0.6 MPa and the volume to 0.5 m³. Determine (a) the amount of refrigerant that has escaped and (b) the final temperature of the refrigerant.

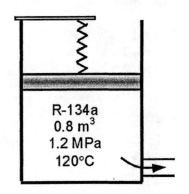

Equations

GIVEN

$$P_1 = 1.2 \ [\text{MPa}] \cdot \left| 1000 \ \frac{kPa}{\text{MPa}} \right| \tag{1}$$

$$T_1 = 120 \ [\text{C}] \tag{2}$$

$$Vol_1 = 0.8 \ [\text{m}^3] \tag{3}$$

$$P_2 = 0.6 \ [\text{MPa}] \cdot \left| 1000 \ \frac{kPa}{\text{MPa}} \right| \tag{4}$$

$$Vol_2 = 0.5 \ [\text{m}^3] \tag{5}$$

PROPERTIES

$$Fluid\$ = \text{'R134a'} \tag{6}$$

$$v_1 = \text{v} (Fluid\$, \ T = T_1, \ P = P_1) \quad \textbf{Initial specific volume} \tag{7}$$

$$u_1 = \text{u} (Fluid\$, \ T = T_1, \ P = P_1) \quad \textbf{Initial specific internal energy} \tag{8}$$

$$h_1 = \text{h} (Fluid\$, \ T = T_1, \ P = P_1) \quad \textbf{Initial specific enthalpy} \tag{9}$$

ANALYSIS

$$v_2 = \text{v} (Fluid\$, \ T = T_2, \ P = P_2) \quad \textbf{Final specific volume} \tag{10}$$

$$u_2 = \text{u} (Fluid\$, \ T = T_2, \ P = P_2) \quad \textbf{Final specific internal energy} \tag{11}$$

$$h_2 = \text{h} (Fluid\$, \ T = T_2, \ P = P_2) \quad \textbf{Final specific enthalpy} \tag{12}$$

$$h_e = \text{Average}(h_1, \ h_2) \quad \textbf{Approximate specific enthalpy of the refrigerant escaping from the cylinder} \tag{13}$$

$$v_1 = Vol_1/m_1 \tag{14}$$

$$v_2 = Vol_2/m_2 \tag{15}$$

$$m_e = m_1 - m_2 \quad \textbf{Mass of refrigerant escaped} \tag{16}$$

$$W_{b,in} - m_e \cdot h_e = m_2 \cdot u_2 - m_1 \cdot u_1 \quad \textbf{Energy balance} \tag{17}$$

$$W_{b,in} = \frac{P_1 + P_2}{2} \cdot (Vol_1 - Vol_2) \quad \textbf{Boundary work, pressure changes with volume linearly} \tag{18}$$

Solution

$Fluid\$ = $ 'R134a'

$h_1 = 354.1$ [kJ/kg]

$h_2 = 336.2$ [kJ/kg]

$h_e = 345.2$ [kJ/kg]

$m_1 = 33.02$ [kg]

$m_2 = 10.55$ [kg]

$\boxed{m_e = 22.47 \text{ [kg]}}$

$P_1 = 1200$ [kPa]

$P_2 = 600$ [kPA]

$T_1 = 120$ [C]

$\boxed{T_2 = 96.75 \text{ [C]}}$

$u_1 = 325$ [kJ/kg]

$u_2 = 307.8$ [kJ/kg]

$Vol_1 = 0.8$ [m^3]

$Vol_2 = 0.5$ [m^3]

$v_1 = 0.02423$ [m^3/kg]

$v_2 = 0.04739$ [m^3/kg]

$W_{b,in} = 270$ [kJ]

Chapter 4 Supplemental Problems

Supplement 4.1 Electrical heating of water in a tank

An insulated rigid tank initially contains 1.4 kg saturated liquid water at 200°C. At this state, 25 percent of the volume is occupied by water and the rest by air. Now an electric resistor placed in the tank is turned on for 20 minutes after which the tank contains saturated water vapor. Determine (a) the volume of the tank, (b) the final temperature, and (c) the power rating of the resistor. *Answers*: (a) 0.00648 m3, (b) 371°C, (c) 1.58 kW

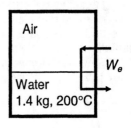

Supplement 4.2 Isothermal compression of a gas in a cylinder

A vertical piston-cylinder device contains an ideal gas at the ambient conditions of 1 bar and 24°C. The piston has a diameter of 12 cm and the face of the piston is 20 cm from the base of the cylinder. Now an external shaft connected to the piston exerts a force corresponding to a work input of 0.1 kJ. The mass of the piston is negligible and the temperature of the gas remains constant during the process. Determine (a) the amount of heat transfer, (b) the final pressure in the cylinder, and (c) the distance that the piston is displaced. *Answers*: (a) 0.1 kJ, (b) 156 kPa, (c) 7.1 cm

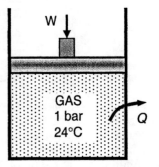

Supplement 4.3 Cooling water in a cylinder with stops

A piston-cylinder device initially contains 0.15 kg steam at 3.5 MPa, superheated by 5°C. Now, steam loses heat to the surroundings and piston moves down hitting a set of stops at which point the cylinder contains saturated liquid water. The cooling continues until the cylinder contains water at 200°C. Determine (a) the final pressure and the quality (if mixture), (b) the boundary work, and (c) the heat transfer until the piston first hit the stops and the total heat transfer. *Answers*: (a) 1.56 MPa, 0.0006, (b) 29.9 kJ, (c) 266 kJ, 295 kJ

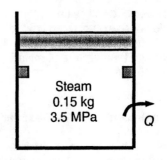

Supplement 4.4 Accelerating steam in a nozzle

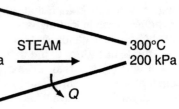

Steam enters a nozzle at 400°C and 800 kPa with a velocity of 10 m/s and leaves at 300°C and 200 kPa. The inlet area of the nozzle is 800 cm². Heat is also lost from the steam at a rate of 25 kW. Determine the velocity and the volume flow rate of the steam at the nozzle exit. *Answers*: 606 m/s, 2.74 m³/s

Supplement 4.5 A flash chamber serving steam to turbine

In a single-flash geothermal power plant, geothermal water enters the flash chamber (a throttling valve) at 230°C as a saturated liquid at a rate of 50 kg/s. The steam resulting from the flashing process enters a turbine and leaves at 20 kPa with a moisture content of 5 percent. Determine the temperature of the steam after the flashing process and the power output from the turbine if the pressure of the steam at the exit of the flash chamber is (a) 1 MPa, (b) 500 kPa, (c) 100 kPa, (d) 50 kPa. *Answers*: (a) 179.9°C, 1616 kW, (b) 151.8°C, 2134 kW, (c) 99.6°C, 2333 kW, (d) 81.3°C, 2173 kW

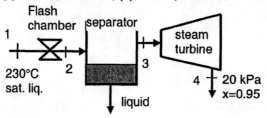

Supplement 4.6 A hot water tank used for shower

The 60 liter water tank of a house is heated by electricity with a rating of 1.6 kW. The tank is initially full of hot water at 80°C. Somebody takes a shower by mixing a constant flow of hot water from the tank with cold water at 20°C at a rate of 0.06 kg/s. After a shower period of 8 minutes, the water temperature in the tank is measured to drop to 60°C. The heater is on during shower and hot water withdrawn from the tank is replaced by cold water at the same flow rate. Determine the mass flow rate of hot water withdrawn from the tank during shower and the average temperature of mixed water used for shower. *Answers*: 0.0575 kg/s, 44.5°C

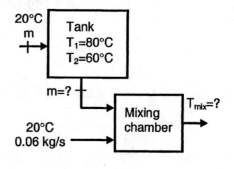

Supplement 4.7 A heat exchanger with heat loss to surroundings

Hot exhaust gases of an internal combustion engine is to be used to produce saturated water vapor at 2 MPa pressure. The exhaust gases enter the heat exchanger at 400°C at a rate of 32 kg/min and water enters at 15°C. The heat exchanger is not well insulated and it is estimated that 10 percent of heat given up by the exhaust gases is lost to the surroundings. If the mass flow rate of the exhaust gases is 15 times that of the water, determine (a) the temperature of the exhaust gases at the heat exchanger exit and (b) the rate of heat transfer to the water. Use the constant specific heat properties of air for the exhaust gases. *Answers*: (a) 206.1°C, (b) 97.26 kW

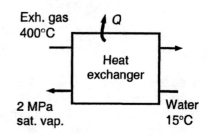

Supplement 4.8 Flow of air inside a pipe

Air enters a pipe at 50°C and 200 kPa and leaves at 40°C and 150 kPa. It is estimated that heat is lost from the pipe in the amount of 3.3 kJ per kg of air flowing in the pipe. The diameter ratio for the pipe is $D_1/D_2=1.8$. Using constant specific heats for air, determine the inlet and exit velocities of the air. *Answers*: 27.7 m/s, 120 m/s

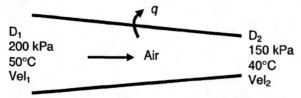

Supplement 4.9 Heat transfer balance on a solar collector

Consider a flat plate solar collector placed at the roof of a house. The temperatures at the inner and outer surfaces of glass window are measured to be 30°C and 25°C, respectively. The glass window has a surface area of 2.2 m² and a thickness of 1.2 cm and a thermal conductivity of 0.7 W/m-°C. Heat is lost from the outer surface of the window by convection and radiation with a convection heat transfer coefficient of 10 W/m².°C and an ambient temperature of 15°C. Determine the fraction of heat lost from the glass window by radiation under steady conditions. *Answer*: 0.657

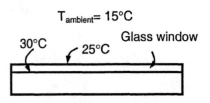

Supplement 4.10 Charging of a rigid tank by steam

A 2.m³ rigid insulated tank initially containing saturated water vapor at 1 MPa is connected through a valve to a supply line that carries steam at 400°C. Now the valve is opened, and steam is allowed to flow slowly into the tank until the pressure in the tank builds up to 2 MPa. At this instant the tank temperature is measured to be 300°C. Determine the mass of the steam that has entered and the pressure of the steam in the supply line. *Answers*: 5.65 kg, 8.93 MPa

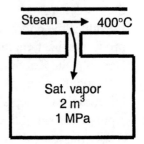

Supplement 4.11 Charging of a cylinder by steam

A piston-cylinder device initially contains 0.6 kg of steam with a volume of 0.1 m³. The mass of the piston is such that it maintains a constant pressure of 800 kPa. The cylinder is connected through a valve to a supply line that carries steam at 5 MPa and 500°C. Now the valve is opened and steam is allowed to flow slowly into the cylinder until the volume of the cylinder doubles and the temperature in the cylinder reaches 250°C, at which point the valve is closed. Determine (a) the amount of mass that has entered and (b) the amount of heat transfer. *Answers*: 0.082 kg, 448 kJ

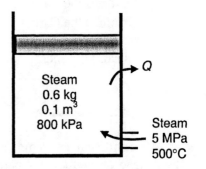

Supplement 4.12 Withdrawing R.134a from a cylinder

A piston-cylinder device initially contains 2 kg of refrigerant.134a at 800 kPa and 80°C. At this state, the piston is touching on a pair of stops. The mass of the piston is such that a 500.kPa pressure is required to move it. A valve at the bottom of the tank is opened, and R.134a is withdrawn from the cylinder. After a while, the piston is observed to move and the valve is closed when half of the refrigerant is withdrawn from the tank and the temperature in the tank is 20°C. Determine (a) the work done and (b) the heat transfer. *Answers*: (a) 11.6 kJ, (b) 60.7 kJ

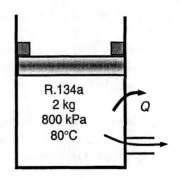

Supplement 4.13 Withdrawing air from a cylinder

A piston-cylinder device initially contains 1.2 kg of air at 700 kPa and 200°C. At this state, the piston is touching on a pair of stops. The mass of the piston is such that a 600.kPa pressure is required to move it. A valve at the bottom of the tank is opened, and air is withdrawn from the cylinder. The valve is closed when the volume of the cylinder decreases to the 80% of the initial volume. If it is estimated that 40 kJ of heat is lost from the cylinder, determine (a) the final temperature of the air in the cylinder, (b) the amount of mass that has escaped from the cylinder, and (c) the work done. Use constant specific heats at the average temperature. *Answers*: (a) 415 K, (b) 0.262 kg, (c) 27.9 kJ

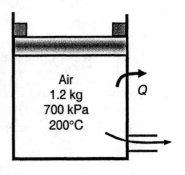

Chapter 5 Educational Objectives and Glossary

The Educational Objectives of Chapter 5 are to:

- Introduce the second law of thermodynamics, which asserts that processes occur in a certain direction and that energy has quality as well as quantity.
- Identify valid processes as those that satisfy both the first and second laws of thermodynamics.
- Introduce the concepts of thermal energy reservoirs, reversible and irreversible processes, heat engines, refrigerators, and heat pumps.
- Describe the Kelvin-Planck and Clausius statements of the second law of thermodynamics.
- Discuss the concepts of perpetual-motion machines.
- Apply the second law of thermodynamics to cycles and cyclic devices.
- Apply the second law to determine the absolute thermodynamic temperature scale.
- Describe the Carnot cycle.
- Examine the Carnot principles, idealized Carnot heat engines, refrigerators, and heat pumps.
- Discuss the energy conservation associated with the use of household refrigerators.

Chapter 5 Glossary

Air conditioners are refrigerators whose refrigerated space is a room or a building instead of the food compartment.

Air-source heat pumps use the cold outside air as the heat source in winter.

Annual fuel utilization efficiency, or AFUE, accounts for the combustion efficiency as well as other losses such as heat losses to unheated areas and start-up and cool-down losses in buildings.

Carnot cycle was first proposed in 1824 by French engineer Sadi Carnot, is composed of four reversible processes—two isothermal and two adiabatic, and can be executed either in a closed or a steady-flow system.

Carnot efficiency is the highest efficiency a heat engine operating between the two thermal energy reservoirs at temperatures T_L and T_H can have, $\eta_{th, rev} = 1 - T_L / T_H$.

Carnot heat engine is the theoretical heat engine that operates on the Carnot cycle.

Carnot heat pump is a heat pump that operates on the reversed Carnot cycle. When operating between the two thermal energy reservoirs at temperatures T_L and T_H the Carnot heat pump can have a coefficient of performance of $COP_{HP, rev} = 1/ (1- T_L / T_H) = T_H /(T_H - T_L)$.

Carnot principles are two conclusions that pertain to the thermal efficiency of reversible and irreversible (i.e., actual) heat engines and are expressed as follows:

1. The efficiency of an irreversible heat engine is always less than the efficiency of a reversible one operating between the same two reservoirs.

2. The efficiencies of all reversible heat engines operating between the same two reservoirs are the same.

Carnot refrigerator is a refrigerator that operates on the reversed Carnot cycle. When operating between the two thermal energy reservoirs at temperatures T_L and T_H the Carnot refrigerator can have a coefficient of performance of $COP_{R, rev} = 1/(T_H/T_L - 1) = T_L/(T_H - T_L)$.

Clausius statement of the second law is expressed as follows: It is impossible to construct a device that operates in a cycle and produces no effect other than the transfer of heat from a lower-temperature body to a higher-temperature body.

Coefficient of performance (COP) is the efficiency of a refrigerator or heat pump.

Combustion efficiency combustion equipment is defined as the amount of heat released during combustion divided by the heating value of the fuel. A combustion efficiency of 100 percent indicates that the fuel is burned completely and the stack gases leave the combustion chamber at room temperature, and thus the amount of heat released during a combustion process is equal to the heating value of the fuel.

Condenser is a heat exchanger in which the working fluid condenses as it rejects heat to the surroundings.

Efficiency is one of the most frequently used terms in thermodynamics, and it indicates how well an energy conversion or transfer process is accomplished.

Efficiency of a cooking appliance can be defined as the ratio of the useful energy transferred to the food to the energy consumed by the appliance.

Efficiency of a water heater is defined as the ratio of the energy delivered to the house by hot water to the energy supplied to the water heater.

Efficiency of resistance heaters is 100 percent as they convert all the electrical energy they consume into heat.

Energy efficiency rating (EER) is the performance of refrigerators and air conditioners, and is the amount of heat removed from the cooled space in Btu's for 1 Wh (watt-hour) of electricity consumed.

Evaporator is a heat exchanger in which the working fluid evaporates as it receives heat from the surroundings.

Externally reversible process has no irreversibilities to occur outside the system boundaries during the process. Heat transfer between a reservoir and a system is an externally reversible process if the surface of contact between the system and the reservoir is at the temperature of the reservoir.

Generator is a device that converts mechanical energy to electrical energy.

Generator efficiency is the ratio of the electrical power output to the mechanical power input.

Geothermal heat pumps (also called ground-source heat pumps) use the ground as the heat source.

Heat engines are devices that convert heat to work. Heat engines differ considerably from one another, but all can be characterized by the following:
  1. They receive heat from a high-temperature source (solar energy, oil furnace, nuclear reactor, etc.).
  2. They convert part of this heat to work (usually in the form of a rotating shaft).
  3. They reject the remaining waste heat to a low-temperature sink (the atmosphere, rivers, etc.).
  4. They operate on a cycle.

Heating value of a fuel is the amount of heat released when a specified amount of fuel (usually a unit mass) at room temperature is completely burned and the combustion products are cooled to the room temperature.

Heat pumps are cyclic devices which operate on the refrigeration cycle and discharge energy to a heated space to maintain the heated space at a high temperature.

Heat pump coefficient of performance is the efficiency of a heat pump, denoted by COP_{HP}, and expressed as desired output divided by required input or $COP_{HP} = Q_H/W_{net, in}$.

Heat reservoir is a thermal energy reservoir since it can supply or absorb energy in the form of heat.

Heat sink is a heat reservoir that absorbs energy in the form of heat.

Heat source is a heat reservoir that supplies energy in the form of heat.

Higher heating value, or HHV, is the heating value of the fuel when the water in the combustion gases is completely condensed and thus the heat of vaporization is also recovered. Efficiencies of furnaces are based on higher heating values.

Internally reversible process has no irreversibilities that occur within the boundaries of the system during the process. During an internally reversible process, a system proceeds through a series of equilibrium states, and when the process is reversed, the system passes through exactly the same equilibrium states while returning to its initial state.

Irreversible processes are processes which, once having taken place in a system, cannot spontaneously reverse themselves and restore the system to its initial state.

Irreversibilities are the factors that cause a process to be irreversible. They include friction, unrestrained expansion, mixing of two gases, heat transfer across a finite temperature difference, electric resistance, inelastic deformation of solids, and chemical reactions.

Kelvin-Planck statement of the second law of thermodynamics is expressed as follows: It is impossible for any device that operates on a cycle to receive heat from a single reservoir and produce a net amount of work. This statement can also be expressed as no heat engine can have a thermal efficiency of 100 percent, or as for a power plant to operate, the working fluid must exchange heat with the environment as well as the furnace.

Kelvin unit magnitude was established at the International Conference on Weights and Measures in 1954. The triple point of water (the state at which all three phases of water exist in equilibrium) was assigned the value 273.16 K (0.01°C). The magnitude of a kelvin is defined as 1/273.16 of the temperature interval between absolute zero and the triple-point temperature of water. The magnitudes of temperature units on the Kelvin and Celsius scales are identical (1 K, 1°C). The temperatures on these two scales differ by a constant 273.15.

Lighting efficacy is defined as the amount of light output in lumens per W of electricity consumed.

Lower heating value, or LHV, is the heating value of the fuel when the water in the combustion gases is a vapor. Efficiencies of cars and jet engines are normally based on lower heating values since water normally leaves as a vapor in the exhaust gases, and it is not practical to try to recuperate the heat of vaporization.

Motor efficiency is the ratio of the mechanical energy output of a motor to the electrical energy input. The full-load motor efficiencies range from about 35 percent for small motors to over 96 percent for large high-efficiency motors.

Overall efficiency for a power plant is the ratio of the net electrical power output to the rate of fuel energy input. Overall efficiencies are about 25 to 28 percent for gasoline automotive engines, 34 to 38 percent for diesel engines, and 40 to 60 percent for large power plants.

Perpetual-motion machine is any device that violates either the first or second law of thermodynamics.

Perpetual-motion machine of the first kind (PMM1) is a device that violates the first law of thermodynamics (by creating energy).

Perpetual-motion machine of the second kind (PMM2) is a device that violates the second law of thermodynamics.

Refrigerant is the working fluid used in the refrigeration cycle.

Refrigerators are cyclic devices which allow the transfer of heat from a low-temperature medium to a high-temperature medium.

Refrigerator coefficient of performance is the efficiency of a refrigerator, denoted by COP_R, and expressed as desired output divided by required input or $COP_R = Q_L/W_{net, in}$.

Reversed Carnot cycle is the result of reversing all the process that comprise the reversible Carnot heat-engine cycle, in which case it becomes the Carnot refrigeration cycle.

Reversible process is defined as a process that can be reversed without leaving any trace on the surroundings. Reversible processes are idealized processes, and they can be approached but never reached in reality.

Steam power plant is an external-combustion engine in which steam (water) is the working fluid. That is, combustion takes place outside the engine, and the thermal energy released during this process is transferred to the steam as heat. A turbine in the power plant converts some of the energy of the steam into rotating shaft work.

Therm of natural gas is an amount of energy equal to 29.3 kWh.

Thermal efficiency is a measure of the performance of a heat engine and is the fraction of the heat input to the heat engine that is converted to net work output.

Thermal efficiency of a heat engine is the fraction of the thermal energy supplied to a heat engine that is converted to work.

Thermal efficiency of a power plant is defined as the ratio of the shaft work output of the turbine to the heat input to the working fluid.

Thermal energy reservoir, or just a reservoir is a hypothetical body with a relatively large thermal energy capacity (mass specific heat) that can supply or absorb finite amounts of heat without undergoing any change in temperature.

Thermodynamic temperature scale is a temperature scale that is independent of the properties of the substances that are used to measure temperature. This temperature scale is called the Kelvin scale, and the temperatures on this scale are called absolute temperatures. On the Kelvin scale, the temperature ratios depend on the ratios of heat transfer between a reversible heat engine and the reservoirs and are independent of the physical properties of any substance.

Ton of refrigeration is a measure of the rate of energy transfer in the amount of 12,000 Btu/h or 211 kJ/min.

Totally reversible process, or simply **reversible process,** involves no irreversibilities within the system or its surroundings. A totally reversible process involves no heat transfer through a finite temperature difference, no non-quasi-equilibrium changes, and no friction or other dissipative effects.

Vapor-compression refrigeration cycle is the most frequently used refrigeration cycle and involves four main components: a compressor, a condenser, an expansion valve, and an evaporator.

Working fluid is the fluid to and from which heat and work is transferred while undergoing a cycle in heat engines and other cyclic devices.

EXAMPLE 5-1 COP of a heat pump with R22 as the refrigerant

Refrigerant-22 enters the condenser of a residential heat pump at 800 kPa and 35°C at a rate of 0.018 kg/s and leaves at 800 kPa as a saturated liquid. If the compressor consumes 1.2 kW of power, determine (a) the COP of the heat pump and (b) the rate of heat absorbed from the outside air.

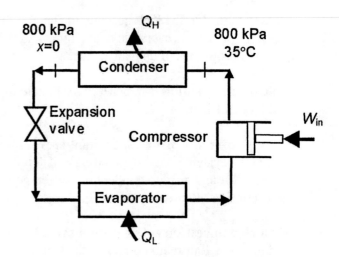

Equations

GIVEN

$$P_1 = 800 \ [\text{kPa}] \tag{1}$$

$$T_1 = 35 \ [\text{C}] \tag{2}$$

$$\dot{m} = 0.018 \ [\text{kg/s}] \tag{3}$$

$$P_2 = 800 \ [\text{kPa}] \tag{4}$$

$$x_2 = 0 \tag{5}$$

$$\dot{W}_{in} = 1.2 \ [\text{kW}] \tag{6}$$

ANALYSIS

$$Fluid\$ = \text{'R22'} \tag{7}$$

$$h_1 = \text{h} \, (\text{Fluid}\$, \ P = P_1, \ T = T_1) \quad \textbf{Specific enthalpy at condenser inlet} \tag{8}$$

$$h_2 = \text{h} \, (\text{Fluid}\$, \ P = P_2, \ x = x_2) \quad \textbf{Specific enthalpy at condenser exit} \tag{9}$$

$$\dot{Q}_H = \dot{m} \cdot (h_1 - h_2) \quad \textbf{Rate of energy transfer from the refrigerant} \tag{10}$$

$$COP = \dot{Q}_H / \dot{W}_{in} \tag{11}$$

$$\dot{Q}_L = \dot{Q}_H - \dot{W}_{in} \quad \textbf{Heat absorbed from outside air} \tag{12}$$

Solution

$\boxed{COP = 3.108}$

$Fluid\$ = \text{'R22'}$

$h_1 = 425.8 \text{ [kJ/kg]}$

$h_2 = 218.6 \text{ [kJ/kg]}$

$\dot{m} = 0.018 \text{ [kg/s]}$

$P_1 = 800 \text{ [kPa]}$

$P_2 = 800 \text{ [kPa]}$

$\dot{Q}_H = 3.73 \text{ [kW]}$

$\boxed{\dot{Q}_L = 2.53 \text{ [kW]}}$

$T_1 = 35 \text{ [C]}$

$\dot{W}_{in} = 1.2 \text{ [kW]}$

$x_2 = 0$

EXAMPLE 5-2   Thermal efficiency of a geothermal power plant

A geothermal power plant uses geothermal liquid water extracted at 160°C at a rate of 440 kg/s as the heat source and produces 22 MW of net power. The waste heat is rejected to the ambient air at 25°C. Determine (a) the actual thermal efficiency, (b) the maximum possible thermal efficiency, and (c) the rate of heat rejection from this power plant.

Equations

GIVEN

$$T_{geo} = 160 \ [C] \tag{1}$$

$$\dot{m}_{geo} = 440 \ [kg/s] \tag{2}$$

$$\dot{W}_{net} = 22 \ [MW] \tag{3}$$

$$T_{ambient} = 25 \ [C] \tag{4}$$

ANALYSIS

$$Fluid\$ = \text{'Steam\_iapws'} \tag{5}$$

$$h_{geo} = \text{h}\,(Fluid\$, \ T = T_{geo}, \ x = 0) \quad \textbf{Assumed saturated liquid} \tag{6}$$

$$h_{dead} = \text{h}\,(Fluid\$, \ T = T_{ambient}, \ x = 0) \quad \textbf{Dead state enthalpy} \tag{7}$$

$$\dot{Q}_{in} = \dot{m}_{geo} \cdot (h_{geo} - h_{dead}) \cdot \left| 0.001 \ \frac{MW}{kW} \right| \quad \textbf{Energy of geothermal source} \tag{8}$$

$$\eta_{th} = \dot{W}_{net}/\dot{Q}_{in} \quad \textbf{Thermal efficieincy} \tag{9}$$

$$\eta_{th,max} = 1 - \frac{ConvertTemp\,(C, \ K, \ T_{ambient})}{(ConvertTemp\,(C, \ K, \ T_{geo}))} \quad \textbf{Max thermal efficieincy} \tag{10}$$

$$\dot{Q}_{out} = \dot{Q}_{in} - \dot{W}_{net} \quad \textbf{Cycle, energy balance} \tag{11}$$

Solution

$$\boxed{\eta_{th} = 0.08762}$$
$$\boxed{\eta_{th,max} = 0.3117}$$
$$Fluid\$ = \text{'Steam\_iapws'}$$
$$h_{dead} = 104.8 \ [kJ/kg]$$
$$h_{geo} = 675.5 \ [kJ/kg]$$
$$\dot{m}_{geo} = 440 \ [kg/s]$$
$$\dot{Q}_{in} = 251.1 \ [MW]$$
$$\boxed{\dot{Q}_{out} = 229.1 \ [MW]}$$
$$T_{ambient} = 25 \ [C]$$
$$T_{geo} = 160 \ [C]$$
$$\dot{W}_{net} = 22 \ [MW]$$

EXAMPLE 5-3   Minimum power requirement for a commercial refrigerator

A commercial refrigerator with refrigerant-134a as the working fluid is used to keep the refrigerated space at -35°C by rejecting its waste heat to cooling water that enters the condenser at 18°C at a rate of 0.25 kg/s and leaves at 26°C. The refrigerant enters the condenser at 1.2 MPa and 50°C and leaves at the same pressure subcooled by 5°C. If the compressor consumes 3.3 kW of power, determine (a) the mass flow rate of the refrigerant, (b) the refrigeration load, (c) the COP, and (d) the minimum power input to the compressor for the same refrigeration load.

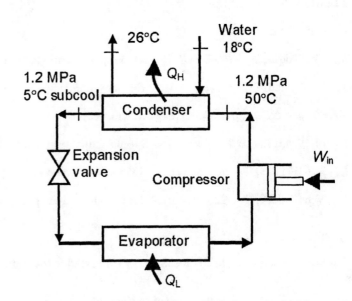

Equations

GIVEN

$$T_L = ConvertTemp\,(C,\ K,\ -35) \tag{1}$$

$$T_H = ConvertTemp\,(C,\ K,\ 18) \tag{2}$$

$$T_{w1} = 18\ [C] \tag{3}$$

$$\dot{m}_w = 0.25\ [kg/s] \tag{4}$$

$$T_{w2} = 26\ [C] \tag{5}$$

$$P_1 = 1.2\ [MPa] \cdot \left|1000\ \frac{kPa}{MPa}\right| \tag{6}$$

$$T_1 = 50\ [C] \tag{7}$$

$$P_2 = 1.2\ [MPa] \cdot \left|1000\ \frac{kPa}{MPa}\right| \tag{8}$$

$$\Delta T_{subcool} = 5\ [C] \tag{9}$$

$$\dot{W}_{in} = 3.3\ [kW] \tag{10}$$

PROPERTIES

$Fluid1\$ = $ 'R134a' \hfill (11)

$Fluid2\$ = $ 'Steam_iapws' \hfill (12)

$h_1 = $ h (Fluid1\$, $P = P_1$, $T = T_1$)   **R134a specific enthalpy at condenser inlet** \hfill (13)

$T_{sat} = $ T (Fluid1\$, $P = P_2$, $x = 0$)   **Condensation temperature** \hfill (14)

$T_2 = T_{sat} - \Delta T_{subcool}$ **Condenser exit temperature** \hfill (15)

$h_2 = $ h (Fluid1\$, $P = P_2$, $T = T_2$)   **Specific enthalpy at condenser exit** \hfill (16)

$h_{w1} = $ h (Fluid2\$, $T = T_{w1}$, $x = 0$)   **Inlet cooling water specific enthalpy** \hfill (17)

$h_{w2} = $ h (Fluid2\$, $T = T_{w2}$, $x = 0$)   **Exit cooling water specific enthalpy** \hfill (18)

ANALYSIS

$\dot{Q}_H = \dot{m}_w \cdot (h_{w2} - h_{w1})$ **Rate of energy transfered to the water** \hfill (19)

$\dot{m}_R = \dfrac{\dot{Q}_H}{(h_1 - h_2)}$ **Mass flow rate of refrigerant** \hfill (20)

$\dot{Q}_L = \dot{Q}_H - \dot{W}_{in}$ **Refrigeration load** \hfill (21)

$COP = \dot{Q}_L / \dot{W}_{in}$ **Actual COP** \hfill (22)

$COP_{max} = \dfrac{1}{(T_H/T_L - 1)}$ **Maximum COP** \hfill (23)

$\dot{W}_{in,min} = \dot{Q}_L / COP_{max}$ **Minimum power input** \hfill (24)

Solution

$\boxed{COP = 1.535}$	$COP_{max} = 4.493$	$\Delta T_{subcool} = 5$ [C]	$Fluid1\$ = $ 'R134a'
$Fluid2\$ = $ 'Steam_iapws'	$h_1 = 278.3$ [kJ/kg]	$h_2 = 110.2$ [kJ/kg]	$h_{w1} = 75.54$ [kJ/kg]
$h_{w2} = 109$ [kJ/kg]	$\boxed{\dot{m}_R = 0.04977 \text{ [kg/s]}}$	$\dot{m}_w = 0.25$ [kg/s]	$P_1 = 1200$ [kPa]
$P_2 = 1200$ [kPa]	$\dot{Q}_H = 8.367$ [kW]	$\boxed{\dot{Q}_L = 5.067 \text{ [kW]}}$	$T_1 = 50$ [C]
$T_2 = 41.29$ [C]	$T_H = 291.2$ [K]	$T_L = 238.2$ [K]	$T_{sat} = 46.29$ [C]
$T_{w1} = 18$ [C]	$T_{w2} = 26$ [C]	$\dot{W}_{in} = 3.3$ [kW]	$\boxed{\dot{W}_{in,min} = 1.128 \text{ [kW]}}$

Chapter 5 Supplemental Problems

Supplement 5.1 Coal consumption in a power plant

A coal-burning steam power plant produces a net power of 300 MW with an overall thermal efficiency of 32% (Net power divided by the rate of heat released from the burning of coal). The actual gravimetric air-fuel ratio in the furnace is calculated to be 12 kg air/kg-fuel. The heating value of the coal is 28,000 kJ/kg. Determine (a) the amount of coal consumed during a one-day period and (b) the rate of air flowing through the furnace. *Answers*: (a) 2.893×10^6 kg, (b) 401.8 kg/s

Supplement 5.2 Efficiency of a wind turbine

A wind turbine is rotating at 15 rpm under steady winds flowing through the turbine at 110 kPa and 20°C at a rate of 42,000 kg/s. The tip velocity of the turbine blade is measured to be 250 km/h. If 180 kW power is produced by the turbine, determine (a) the average velocity of the air and (b) the conversion efficiency of the turbine. *Answers*: (a) 5.3 m/s, (b) 31.3%

Supplement 5.3 Efficiency of a cryogenic turbine

When the transportation of natural gas in a pipeline is not feasible for economic reasons, it is first liquefied using non-conventional refrigeration cycles and then transported in super-insulated tanks. In a natural gas liquefaction plant, the liquefied natural gas (LNG) enters a cryogenic turbine at 40 bar and .160°C at a rate of 55 kg/s and leaves at 3 bar. If 350 kW power is produced by the turbine, determine the efficiency of the turbine. Use the properties of methane for natural gas. *Answer*: 72.9%

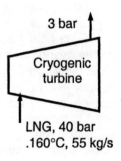

Supplement 5.4 Heat rejection by a refrigerator

Refrigerant.134a enters the evaporator coils of a household refrigerator placed at the back of the freezer section at 120 kPa with a quality of 20 percent and leaves at 120 kPa and .20°C. If the compressor consumes 450 W of power and the COP the refrigerator is 1.2, determine (a) the mass flow rate of the refrigerant and (b) the rate of heat rejected to the kitchen air. *Answers*: (a) 0.00311 kg/s, 990 W

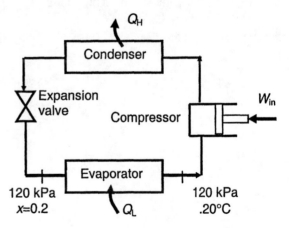

Supplement 5.5 Maximum COP of an air-conditioner

An air-conditioner with refrigerant.134a as the refrigerant is used to keep a room at 26°C by rejecting the waste heat to the outside air at 34°C. The room is gaining heat through the walls and the windows at a rate of 250 kJ/min while the heat generated by the computer, TV, and lights amounts to 900 W. The refrigerant enters the compressor at 500 kPa as a saturated vapor at a rate of 100 L/min and leaves at 1200 kPa and 50°C. Determine (a) the actual COP, (b) the maximum COP, and (c) the minimum volume flow rate of the refrigerant at the compressor inlet for the same compressor inlet and exit conditions. *Answers*: (a) 6.59, (b) 37.4, (c) 17.6 L/min

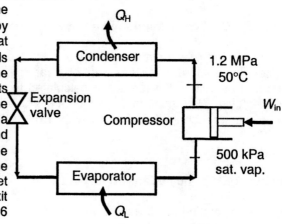

Supplement 5.6 Minimum power requirement for a heat pump

A heat pump with refrigerant.134a as the working fluid is used to keep a space at 25°C by absorbing heat from geothermal water that enters the evaporator at 50°C at a rate of 0.065 kg/s and leaves at 40°C. Refrigerant enters the evaporator at 20°C with a quality of 15 percent and leaves at the same pressure as saturated vapor. If the compressor consumes 1.2 kW of power, determine (a) the mass flow rate of the refrigerant, (b) the heating load, (c) the COP, and (d) the minimum power input to the compressor for the same heating load. *Answers*: (a) 0.0176 kg/s, (b) 3.92 kW, (c) 3.27, (d) 0.303 kW

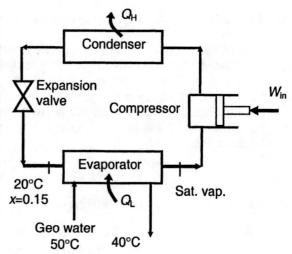

Chapter 6 Educational Objectives and Glossary

The Educational Objectives of Chapter 6 are to:

- Apply the second law to processes.
- Define a new property called entropy as it applies to commonly encountered engineering processes.
- Discuss the Clausius inequality, which forms the basis for the definition of entropy.
- Explain the increase of entropy principle.
- Calculate the entropy changes that take place during processes for pure substances, incompressible substances, and ideal gases.
- Examine a special class of idealized processes, called isentropic processes and develop the property relations for these processes.
- Derive the reversible steady-flow work relations.
- Develop the isentropic, or adiabatic, efficiencies of various steady-flow engineering devices and apply the definitions to turbines, compressors, and nozzles.
- Introduce and apply the entropy balance to various systems.

Chapter 6 Glossary

Absolute entropy is entropy calculated relative to the absolute reference point determined by the third law of thermodynamics.

Clausius inequality, first stated by the German physicist R. J. E. Clausius (1822–1888), is expressed as the cyclic integral of Q/T is always less than or equal to zero. This inequality is valid for all cycles, reversible or irreversible.

Entropy (from a classical thermodynamics point of view) is a property designated S and is defined as $dS = (\delta Q/T)_{\text{int rev}}$.

Entropy (from a statistical thermodynamics point of view) can be viewed as a measure of molecular disorder, or molecular randomness. The entropy of a system is related to the total number of possible microscopic states of that system, called thermodynamic probability p, by the Boltzmann relation, expressed as $S = k \ln p$ where k is the Boltzmann constant.

Entropy balance relation for a control volume is stated as the rate of entropy change within the control volume during a process is equal to the sum of the rate of entropy transfer through the control volume boundary by heat transfer, the net rate of entropy transfer into the control volume by mass flow, and the rate of entropy generation within the boundaries of the control volume as a result of irreversibilities.

Entropy balance relation in general is stated as the entropy change of a system during a process is equal to the net entropy transfer through the system boundary and the entropy generated within the system as a result of irreversibilities.

Entropy change of a closed system is due to the entropy transfer accompanying heat transfer and the entropy generation within the system boundaries.

Entropy generation S_{gen} is entropy generated or created during an irreversible process, is due entirely to the presence of irreversibilities, and is a measure of the magnitudes of the irreversibilities present during that process. Entropy generation is always a positive quantity or zero. Its value depends on the process, and thus it is not a property.

Heat transfer is the area under the process curve on a *T-S* diagram during an internally reversible process. The area has no meaning for irreversible processes.

Increase of entropy principle or second law of thermodynamics is expressed as the entropy of an isolated system during a process always increases or, in the limiting case of a reversible process, remains constant. In other words, the entropy of an isolated system never decreases.

Internally reversible process has no irreversibilities occurring within a system undergoing the process.

Isentropic efficiency of a compressor is defined as the ratio of the work input required to raise the pressure of a gas to a specified value in an isentropic manner to the actual work input.

Isentropic efficiency of a nozzle is defined as the ratio of the actual kinetic energy of the fluid at the nozzle exit to the kinetic energy value at the exit of an isentropic nozzle for the same inlet state and exit pressure.

Isentropic efficiency of a turbine is defined as the ratio of the actual work output of the turbine to the work output that would be achieved if the process between the inlet state and the exit pressure were isentropic.

Isentropic process is an internally reversible and adiabatic process. In such a process the entropy remains constant.

Isothermal efficiency of a compressor is defined as the ratio of the work input to a compressor for the reversible isothermal case and the work input to a compressor for the actual case.

Mechanisms of entropy transfer S_{in} and S_{out} are heat transfer and mass flow. Entropy transfer is recognized at the system boundary as it crosses the boundary, and it represents the entropy gained or lost by a system during a process. The only form of entropy interaction associated with a fixed mass or closed system is heat transfer, and thus the entropy transfer for an adiabatic closed system is zero.

Mollier diagram, after the German scientist R. Mollier (1863–1935), is the *h-s* diagram. The Mollier diagram is useful when solving isentropic, steady flow process problems dealing with nozzles, turbines, and compressors.

Multistage compression with intercooling is a compression process where a gas is compressed in stages and cooled between each stage by passing it through a heat exchanger called an intercooler.

Relative pressure P_r is defined as the quantity $\exp(s°/R)$ and is a dimensionless quantity that is a function of temperature only since $s°$ depends on temperature alone. Relative pressure is used in isentropic processes of ideal gases where variable specific heats are required.

Relative specific volume v_r is defined as the quantity T/P_r is a function of temperature only and P_r is the relative pressure. Relative specific volume is used in isentropic processes of ideal gases where variable specific heats are required.

Reversible steady-flow work is defined as the negative of the integral of the specific volume-pressure product. The larger the specific volume, the larger the reversible work produced or consumed by the steady-flow device. Therefore, every effort should be made to keep the specific volume of a fluid as small as possible during a compression process to minimize the work input and as large as possible during an expansion process to maximize the work output.

Second law distinction between heat transfer and work states that an energy interaction that is accompanied by entropy transfer is heat transfer, and an energy interaction that is not accompanied by entropy transfer is work.

***Tds* relations** relate the *Tds* product to other thermodynamic properties. The first Gibbs relation is $Tds = du + Pdv$. The second Gibbs relation is $Tds = dh - vdP$.

Third law of thermodynamics states that the entropy of a pure crystalline substance at absolute zero temperature is zero.

EXAMPLE 6-1   A reversible cycle in a closed system with air

A piston-cylinder device contains air that undergoes a reversible thermodynamic cycle. Initially the air is at 400 kPa and 300 K with a volume of 0.3 m³. The air is first expanded isothermally to 150 kPa, then compressed adiabatically to the initial pressure, and finally compressed at the constant pressure to the initial state. Accounting for the variation of specific heats with temperature, determine the work and heat transfer for each process.

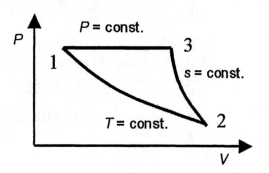

Equations

GIVEN

$$P_1 = 400 \ [\text{kPa}] \tag{1}$$

$$T_1 = 300 \ [\text{K}] \tag{2}$$

$$V_1 = 0.3 \ [\text{m}^3] \tag{3}$$

$$P_2 = 150 \ [\text{kPa}] \tag{4}$$

$$T_2 = T_1 \tag{5}$$

$$P_3 = P_1 \tag{6}$$

$$s_3 = s_2 \tag{7}$$

PROPERTIES

$$Fluid\$ = \text{'Air'} \tag{8}$$

$$R = R_u/MM \quad \textbf{Gas constant} \tag{9}$$

$$R_u = 8.314 \ [\text{kJ/kmol} \cdot \text{K}] \quad \textbf{Universal gas constant} \tag{10}$$

$$MM = \text{MW} (Fluid\$) \tag{11}$$

$$u_1 = \text{u} (Fluid\$, \ T = T_1) \quad \textbf{Specific internal energy} \tag{12}$$

$$s_1 = \text{s} (Fluid\$, \ T = T_1, \ P = P_1) \quad \textbf{Specific entropy} \tag{13}$$

$$u_2 = \text{u} (Fluid\$, \ T = T_2) \tag{14}$$

$$s_2 = \text{s} (Fluid\$, \ T = T_2, \ P = P_2) \tag{15}$$

$$u_3 = \text{u} (Fluid\$, \ P = P_3, \ s = s_3) \tag{16}$$

$$T_3 = \text{T} (Fluid\$, \ P = P_3, \ s = s_3) \tag{17}$$

EXAMPLE 6-2   Various expressions of reversible work in a pump

An adiabatic pump is to be used to compress saturated liquid water at 10 kPa to a pressure of 15 MPa in a reversible manner. Determine the work input using (a) entropy data from the compressed liquid table, (b) inlet specific volume and pressure values, (c) average specific volume and pressure values. Also, determine (d) the error involved in part *b* and part *c*.

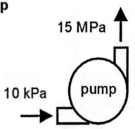

Equations

GIVEN

$$P_1 = 10 \ [\text{kPa}] \tag{1}$$

$$x_1 = 0 \tag{2}$$

$$P_2 = 15 \ [\text{MPa}] \cdot \left| 1000 \ \frac{\text{kPa}}{\text{MPa}} \right| \tag{3}$$

ANALYSIS

$$Fluid\$ = \text{'Steam\_iapws'} \tag{4}$$

(a)

$$h_1 = \text{h} \, (Fluid\$, \ P = P_1, \ x = x_1) \quad \textbf{Specific enthalpy} \tag{5}$$

$$s_1 = \text{s} \, (Fluid\$, \ P = P_1, \ x = x_1) \quad \textbf{Specific entropy} \tag{6}$$

$$s_2 = s_1 \quad \textbf{Isentropic process} \tag{7}$$

$$h_2 = \text{h} \, (Fluid\$, \ P = P_2, \ s = s_2) \tag{8}$$

$$w_{p,a} = h_2 - h_1 \quad \textbf{Energy balance} \tag{9}$$

(b)

$$v_1 = \text{v} \, (Fluid\$, \ P = P_1, \ x = x_1) \quad \textbf{Saturated vapor specific volume} \tag{10}$$

$$w_{p,b} = v_1 \cdot (P_2 - P_1) \quad \textbf{Pumping work} \tag{11}$$

(c)

$$v_2 = \text{v} \, (Fluid\$, \ P = P_2, \ s = s_2) \quad \textbf{Specific volume} \tag{12}$$

$$v_{ave} = \text{Average}(v_1, \ v_2) \quad \textbf{Average specific volume} \tag{13}$$

$$w_{p,c} = v_{ave} \cdot (P_2 - P_1) \tag{14}$$

(d)

$$Error_b = \frac{w_{p,b} - w_{p,a}}{w_{p,a}} \cdot |100\,\%| \tag{15}$$

$$Error_c = \frac{w_{p,c} - w_{p,a}}{w_{p,a}} \cdot |100\,\%| \tag{16}$$

ANALYSIS

$$P_1 \cdot V_1 = m \cdot R \cdot T_1 \quad \text{\textbf{Equation of state}} \tag{18}$$

$$P_2 \cdot V_2 = m \cdot R \cdot T_2 \tag{19}$$

$$P_3 \cdot V_3 = m \cdot R \cdot T_3 \tag{20}$$

$$Q_{12,in} - W_{12,out} = m \cdot (u_2 - u_1) \quad \text{\textbf{Energy balance, isothermal expansion, process 1-2}} \tag{21}$$

$$Q_{12,in} = T_1 \cdot \Delta S_{12} \quad \text{\textbf{Heat transfer , process 1-2}} \tag{22}$$

$$\Delta S_{12} = m \cdot (s_2 - s_1) \tag{23}$$

$$W_{23,in} = m \cdot (u_3 - u_2) \quad \text{\textbf{Energy balance, isentropic compression, process 2-3}} \tag{24}$$

$$Q_{23} = 0 \quad \text{\textbf{Adiabatic process}} \tag{25}$$

$$W_{31,in} - Q_{31,out} = m \cdot (u_1 - u_3) \quad \text{\textbf{Energy balance, constant pressure compression, process 3-1}} \tag{26}$$

$$W_{31,in} = P_1 \cdot (V_3 - V_1) \tag{27}$$

Solution

$\Delta S_{12} = 0.3923 \ [\text{kJ/K}]$
$Fluid\$ = \text{'Air'}$
$m = 1.394 \ [\text{kg}]$
$MM = 28.97 \ [\text{kg/kmol}]$
$\boxed{Q_{12,in} = 117.7 \ [\text{kJ}]}$
$\boxed{Q_{23} = 0 \ [\text{kJ}]}$
$\boxed{Q_{31,out} = 135.8 \ [\text{kJ}]}$
$R = 0.287 \ [\text{kJ/kg-K}]$
$R_u = 8.314 \ [\text{kJ/kmol-K}]$
$\boxed{W_{12,out} = 117.7 \ [\text{kJ}]}$
$\boxed{W_{23,in} = 97.13 \ [\text{kJ}]}$
$\boxed{W_{31,in} = 38.66 \ [\text{kJ}]}$

Solution

$Error_b = 0.3168 \, [\%]$

$Error_c = 0.002747 \, [\%]$

$Fluid\$ = \text{'Steam\_iapws'}$

$h_1 = 191.8 \, [\text{kJ/kg}]$

$h_2 = 206.9 \, [\text{kJ/kg}]$

$P_1 = 10 \, [\text{kPa}]$

$P_2 = 15000 \, [\text{kPa}]$

$s_1 = 0.6492 \, [\text{kJ/kg-K}]$

$s_2 = 0.6492 \, [\text{kJ/kg-K}]$

$v_1 = 0.00101 \, [\text{m}^3/\text{kg}]$

$v_2 = 0.001004 \, [\text{m}^3/\text{kg}]$

$v_{ave} = 0.001007 \, [\text{m}^3/\text{kg}]$

$w_{p,a} = 15.096 \, [\text{kJ/kg}]$

$w_{p,b} = 15.144 \, [\text{kJ/kg}]$

$w_{p,c} = 15.097 \, [\text{kJ/kg}]$

$x_1 = 0$

EXAMPLE 6-3   Entropy generation during heating of a room by hot water

A container filled with 45 kg of liquid water at 95°C is placed in a 90-m³ room that is initially at 12°C. Thermal equilibrium is established after a while as a result of heat transfer between the water and the air in the room. Using constant specific heats, determine (a) the final equilibrium temperature, (b) the amount of heat transfer between the water and the air in the room, and (c) the entropy generation. Assume the room is well-sealed and neglect heat losses from the room to the surroundings.

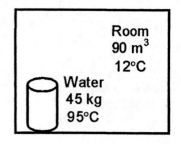

Equations

GIVEN

$$m_w = 45 \ [\text{kg}] \tag{1}$$

$$T_{w1} = ConvertTemp\,(C,\ K,\ 95) \tag{2}$$

$$V_{room} = 90 \ [\text{m}^3] \tag{3}$$

$$T_{a1} = ConvertTemp\,(C,\ K,\ 12) \tag{4}$$

$$P_1 = 101.3 \ [\text{kPa}] \quad \textbf{Assume atmospheric pressure} \tag{5}$$

PROPERTIES

$$Fluid\$ = \text{`Air'} \tag{6}$$

$$C_v = c_v\,(Fluid\$,\ T = T_{ave}) \quad \textbf{Specific heat at constant volume} \tag{7}$$

$$C_p = c_p\,(Fluid\$,\ T = T_{ave}) \quad \textbf{Specific heat at constant pressure} \tag{8}$$

$$C_w = c_p\,(\text{Water},\ T = T_{ave},\ P = P_1) \quad \textbf{Specific heat} \tag{9}$$

$$T_{ave} = Average(T_{a1},\ T_2) \quad \textbf{Average temperature} \tag{10}$$

$$R = C_p - C_v \quad \textbf{Gas constant} \tag{11}$$

ANALYSIS

$$P_1 \cdot V_{room} = (m_a \cdot R \cdot T_{a1}) \quad \textbf{Equation of state} \tag{12}$$

$$0 = m_w \cdot C_w \cdot (T_2 - T_{w1}) + m_a \cdot C_v \cdot (T_2 - T_{a1}) \quad \textbf{Energy balance} \tag{13}$$

$$Q = m_a \cdot C_v \cdot (T_2 - T_{a1}) \quad \textbf{Heat transfered to the air} \tag{14}$$

$$\Delta S_w = m_w \cdot C_w \cdot \ln\,(T_2/T_{w1}) \quad \textbf{Water entropy change} \tag{15}$$

$$\Delta S_a = m_a \cdot (C_p \cdot \ln\,(T_2/T_{a1}) - R \cdot \ln\,(P_2/P_1)) \quad \textbf{Air entropy change} \tag{16}$$

$$P_2 \cdot V_{room} = (m_a \cdot R \cdot T_2) \tag{17}$$

$$S_{gen} = \Delta S_w + \Delta S_a \quad \textbf{Entropy generation} \tag{18}$$

Solution

$C_p = 1.007$ [kJ/kg-K]

$C_v = 0.7198$ [kJ/kg-K]

$C_w = 4.182$ [kJ/kg-C]

$\Delta S_a = 14.89$ [kJ/K]

$\Delta S_w = -13.12$ [kJ/K]

$Fluid\$ = $ 'Air'

$m_a = 111.4$ [kg]

$m_w = 45$ [kg]

$P_1 = 101.3$ [kPa]

$P_2 = 122$ [kPa]

$\boxed{Q = 4667 \text{ [kJ]}}$

$R = 0.287$ [kJ/kg-K]

$\boxed{S_{gen} = 1.77 \text{ [kJ/K]}}$

$\boxed{T_2 = 343.4 \text{ [K]}}$

$T_{a1} = 285.1$ [K]

$T_{ave} = 314.3$ [K]

$T_{w1} = 368.2$ [C]

$V_{room} = 90$ $[\text{m}^3]$

EXAMPLE 6-4   Entropy generation during expansion of R-134a

Refrigerant-134a is throttled from 900 kPa and 35°C to 200 kPa. Heat is lost from the refrigerant in the amount of 0.8 kJ/kg to the surroundings at 25°C. Determine the exit temperature of the refrigerant and the entropy generation during this process.

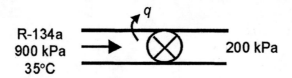

Equations

GIVEN

$$P_1 = 900 \ [\text{kPa}] \tag{1}$$

$$T_1 = 35 \ [\text{C}] \tag{2}$$

$$P_2 = 200 \ [\text{kPa}] \tag{3}$$

$$q_{out} = 0.8 \ [\text{kJ/kg}] \tag{4}$$

$$T_0 = ConvertTemp \ (C, \ K, \ 25) \tag{5}$$

ANALYSIS

$$Fluid\$ = \text{'R134a'} \tag{6}$$

$$h_1 = h \ (Fluid\$, \ P = P_1, \ T = T_1) \quad \textbf{Specific enthalpy at inlet} \tag{7}$$

$$s_1 = s \ (Fluid\$, \ P = P_1, \ T = T_1) \quad \textbf{Specific entropy at inlet} \tag{8}$$

$$h_1 = h_2 + q_{out} \quad \textbf{Energy balance} \tag{9}$$

$$s_{gen} = \Delta s_{Ref} + \Delta s_{surr} \quad \textbf{Entropy generation} \tag{10}$$

$$\Delta s_{Ref} = s_2 - s_1 \quad \textbf{R134a entropy change} \tag{11}$$

$$\Delta s_{surr} = q_{out}/T_0 \quad \textbf{Surroundings entropy change} \tag{12}$$

$$s_2 = s \ (Fluid\$, \ P = P_2, \ h = h_2) \quad \textbf{Specific entropy at exit} \tag{13}$$

$$T_2 = T \ (Fluid\$, \ P = P_2, \ h = h_2) \quad \textbf{Specific enthalpy at exit} \tag{14}$$

Solution

$\Delta s_{Ref} = 0.01749$ [kJ/kg-K]
$\Delta s_{surr} = 0.002683$ [kJ/kg-K]
$Fluid\$ = $ 'R134a'
$h_1 = 100.9$ [kJ/kg]
$h_2 = 100.1$ [kJ/kg]
$P_1 = 900$ [kPa]
$P_2 = 200$ [kPa]
$q_{out} = 0.8$ [kJ/kg]
$s_1 = 0.3714$ [kJ/kg-K]
$s_2 = 0.3888$ [kJ/kg-K]
$\boxed{s_{gen} = 0.02017 \text{ [kJ/kg-K]}}$
$T_0 = 298.1$ [K]
$T_1 = 35$ [C]
$\boxed{T_2 = -10.09 \text{ [C]}}$

EXAMPLE 6-5   Entropy generation in a steam turbine

Steam enters an adiabatic turbine steadily at 7 MPa, 500°C, and 45 m/s and leaves at 100 kPa and 75 m/s. If the power output of the turbine is 5 MW and the isentropic efficiency is 77 percent, determine (a) the mass flow rate of the steam flowing through the turbine, (b) the temperature of the steam at the turbine exit, and (c) the entropy generation during this process.

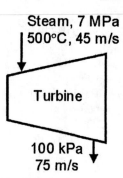

Steam, 7 MPa
500°C, 45 m/s

Turbine

100 kPa
75 m/s

Equations

GIVEN

$$P_1 = 7 \ [\text{MPa}] \cdot \left| 1000 \ \frac{kPa}{\text{MPa}} \right| \tag{1}$$

$$T_1 = 500 \ [\text{C}] \tag{2}$$

$$Vel_1 = 45 \ [\text{m/s}] \tag{3}$$

$$P_2 = 100 \ [\text{kPa}] \tag{4}$$

$$Vel_2 = 75 \ [\text{m/s}] \tag{5}$$

$$\dot{W}_{actual} = 5 \ [\text{MW}] \cdot \left| 1000 \ \frac{kW}{\text{MW}} \right| \tag{6}$$

$$\eta_T = 0.77 \tag{7}$$

ANALYSIS

$Fluid\$ = \text{'Steam\_iapws'}$ (8)

$h_1 = h\,(Fluid\$, \ P = P_1, \ T = T_1)$ **Specific enthalpy at inlet** (9)

$s_1 = s\,(Fluid\$, \ P = P_1, \ T = T_1)$ **Specific entropy at inlet** (10)

$h_{2s} = h\,(Fluid\$, \ P = P_2, \ s = s_1)$ **Isentropic, specific enthalpy at exit** (11)

Energy balance for actual process

$$\dot{m} \cdot \left(h_1 + \frac{Vel_1^2}{2} \cdot \left| 0.001 \ \frac{kJ/kg}{m^2/s^2} \right| \right) = \dot{m} \cdot \left(h_2 + Vel_2^2/2 \cdot \left| 0.001 \ \frac{kJ/kg}{m^2/s^2} \right| \right) + \dot{W}_{actual} \tag{12}$$

Energy balance for isentropic process

$$\dot{m} \cdot \left(h_1 + \frac{Vel_1^2}{2} \cdot \left| 0.001 \ \frac{kJ/kg}{m^2/s^2} \right| \right) = \dot{m} \cdot \left(h_{2s} + Vel_2^2/2 \cdot \left| 0.001 \ \frac{kJ/kg}{m^2/s^2} \right| \right) + \dot{W}_{isentropic} \tag{13}$$

$\eta_T = \dot{W}_{actual}/\dot{W}_{isentropic}$ **Thermal efficiency** (14)

$T_2 = T\,(Fluid\$, \ P = P_2, \ h = h_2)$ **Actual exit temperature** (15)

$s_2 = s\,(Fluid\$, \ P = P_2, \ h = h_2)$ **Actual entropy at exit** (16)

$\dot{S}_{gen} = \dot{m} \cdot (s_2 - s_1)$ **Entropy generation** (17)

Solution

$\eta_T = 0.77$
$Fluid\$ = $ 'Steam_iapws'
$h_1 = 3411$ [kJ/kg]
$h_2 = 2684$ [kJ/kg]
$h_{2s} = 2467$ [kJ/kg]
$\boxed{\dot{m} = 6.886 \text{ [kg/s]}}$
$P_1 = 7000$ [kPa]
$P_2 = 100$ [kPa]
$s_1 = 6.8$ [kJ/kg-K]
$s_2 = 7.382$ [kJ/kg-K]
$\boxed{\dot{S}_{gen} = 4.006 \text{ [kW/K]}}$
$T_1 = 500$ [C]
$\boxed{T_2 = 103.7 \text{ [C]}}$
$Vel_1 = 45$ [m/s]
$Vel_2 = 75$ [m/s]
$\dot{W}_{actual} = 5000$ [kW]
$\dot{W}_{isentropic} = 6494$ [kW]

EXAMPLE 6-6   Entropy analysis of a compressor with air

Air enters a compressor steadily at the ambient conditions of 100 kPa and 22°C and leaves at 800 kPa. Heat is lost from the compressor in the amount of 120 kJ/kg and the air experiences an entropy decrease of 0.40 kJ/kg-K. Using constant specific heats, determine (a) the exit temperature of the air, (b) the work input to the compressor, and (c) the entropy generation during this process.

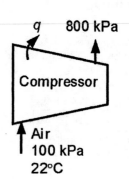

Equations

GIVEN

$$P_1 = 100 \ [\text{kPa}] \tag{1}$$

$$T_1 = ConvertTemp \ (C, \ K, \ 22) \tag{2}$$

$$P_2 = 800 \ [\text{kPa}] \tag{3}$$

$$q_{out} = 120 \ [\text{kJ/kg}] \tag{4}$$

$$\Delta s_{air} = -0.40 \ [\text{kJ/kg·K}] \tag{5}$$

PROPERTIES

$$Fluid\$ = \text{'Air'} \tag{6}$$

$$C_p = c_p \ (Fluid\$, \ T = T_{ave}) \quad \textbf{Specific heat at constant pressure} \tag{7}$$

$$T_{ave} = \text{Average}(T_1, \ T_2) \quad \textbf{Average temperature} \tag{8}$$

$$R = R_u/MM \quad \textbf{Gas constant} \tag{9}$$

$$R_u = 8.314 \ [\text{kJ/kmol·K}] \quad \textbf{Universal gas constant} \tag{10}$$

$$MM = \text{MW} \ (Fluid\$) \tag{11}$$

ANALYSIS

$$\Delta s_{air} = C_p \cdot \ln (T_2/T_1) - R \cdot \ln (P_2/P_1) \quad \textbf{Air specific entropy change} \tag{12}$$

$$C_p \cdot T_1 + w_{in} = C_p \cdot T_2 + q_{out} \quad \textbf{Energy balance} \tag{13}$$

$$\Delta s_{surr} = q_{out}/T_1 \quad \textbf{Entropy change of surroundings} \tag{14}$$

$$s_{gen} = \Delta s_{air} + \Delta s_{surr} \quad \textbf{Entropy generation} \tag{15}$$

Solution

$C_p = 1.007$ [kJ/kg-K]
$\Delta s_{air} = -0.4$ [kJ/kg-K]
$\Delta s_{surr} = 0.4066$ [kJ/kg-K]
$Fluid\$ =$ 'Air'
$MM = 28.97$ [kg/kmol]
$P_1 = 100$ [kPa]
$P_2 = 800$ [kPa]
$q_{out} = 120$ [kJ/kg]
$R = 0.287$ [kJ/kg-K]
$R_u = 8.314$ [kJ/kmol-K]
$\boxed{s_{gen} = 0.006573 \text{ [kJ/kg-K]}}$
$T_1 = 295.2$ [C]
$\boxed{T_2 = 358.9 \text{ [K]}}$
$T_{ave} = 327$ [K]
$\boxed{w_{in} = 184.2 \text{ [kJ/kg]}}$

EXAMPLE 6-7   Entropy generation during discharging of water from a tank

A rigid tank contains 7.5 kg of saturated water mixture at 400 kPa. A valve at the bottom of the tank is now opened, and liquid is withdrawn from the tank. Heat is transferred to the steam such that the pressure inside the tank remains constant. The valve is closed when no liquid is left in the tank. If it is estimated that a total of 5 kJ of heat is transferred to the tank, determine (a) the quality of steam in the tank at the initial state, (b) the amount of mass that has escaped, and (c) the entropy generation during this process if heat is supplied to the tank from a source at 500°C.

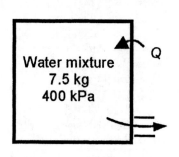

Equations

GIVEN

$$m_1 = 7.5 \ [\text{kg}] \tag{1}$$

$$P_1 = 400 \ [\text{kPa}] \tag{2}$$

$$x_2 = 1 \tag{3}$$

$$P_2 = P_1 \tag{4}$$

$$P_e = P_1 \tag{5}$$

$$x_e = 0 \tag{6}$$

$$Q_{in} = 5 \ [\text{kJ}] \tag{7}$$

$$T_s = 500 \ [\text{C}] \tag{8}$$

PROPERTIES

$$Fluid\$ = \text{'Steam\_iapws'} \tag{9}$$

$v_2 = \text{v} \, (Fluid\$, \ P = P_2, \ x = x_2)$ **Specific volume at the final state** (10)

$u_2 = \text{u} \, (Fluid\$, \ P = P_2, \ x = x_2)$ **Specific internal energy at the final state** (11)

$s_2 = \text{s} \, (Fluid\$, \ P = P_2, \ x = x_2)$ **Specific entropy at the final state** (12)

$h_e = \text{h} \, (Fluid\$, \ P = P_e, \ x = x_e)$ **Specific enthalpy at exit** (13)

$s_e = \text{s} \, (Fluid\$, \ P = P_e, \ x = x_e)$ **Specific entropy at exit** (14)

ANALYSIS

$v_1 = \text{v} \, (Fluid\$, \ P = P_1, \ u = u_1)$ **Specific volume at the initial state** (15)

$$v_1 = Vol/m_1 \tag{16}$$

$$v_2 = Vol/m_2 \tag{17}$$

$m_e = m_1 - m_2$ **Mass balance**   (18)

$Q_{in} - m_e \cdot h_e = m_2 \cdot u_2 - m_1 \cdot u_1$ **Energy balance**   (19)

$x_1 = \mathrm{x}\,(\text{Fluid\$},\ P = P_1,\ u = u_1)$ (20)

$s_1 = \mathrm{s}\,(\text{Fluid\$},\ P = P_1,\ u = u_1)$ **Specific entropy at the initial state**   (21)

$$\frac{Q_{in}}{T_s + 273} - m_e \cdot s_e + S_{gen} = m_2 \cdot s_2 - m_1 \cdot s_1$$ **Entropy balance**   (22)

Solution

$Fluid\$ = \text{'Steam\_iapws'}$
$h_e = 604.7\ [\text{kJ/kg}]$
$m_1 = 7.5\ [\text{kg}]$
$m_2 = 6.502\ [\text{kg}]$
$\boxed{m_e = 0.9978\ [\text{kg}]}$
$P_1 = 400\ [\text{kPa}]$
$P_2 = 400\ [\text{kPa}]$
$P_e = 400\ [\text{kPa}]$
$Q_{in} = 5\ [\text{kJ}]$
$s_1 = 6.213\ [\text{kJ/kg-K}]$
$s_2 = 6.896\ [\text{kJ/kg-K}]$
$s_e = 1.776\ [\text{kJ/kg-K}]$
$\boxed{S_{gen} = 0.005529\ [\text{kJ/K}]}$
$T_s = 500\ [\text{C}]$
$u_1 = 2293\ [\text{kJ/kg}]$
$u_2 = 2553\ [\text{kJ/kg}]$
$Vol = 3.007\ [\text{m}^3]$
$v_1 = 0.4009\ [\text{m}^3/\text{kg}]$
$v_2 = 0.4624\ [\text{m}^3/\text{kg}]$
$\boxed{x_1 = 0.8666}$
$x_2 = 1$
$x_e = 0$

Supplement 6.1 A reversible cycle in a closed system with steam

A piston-cylinder device contains steam that undergoes a reversible thermodynamic cycle. Initially the steam is at 400 kPa and 350°C with a volume of 0.3 m³. The steam is first expanded isothermally to 150 kPa, then compressed adiabatically to the initial pressure, and finally compressed at the constant pressure to the initial state. Determine the net work and heat transfer for the cycle after you calculate the work and heat interaction for each process. *Answer*: 14.2 kJ work in, 14.2 kJ heat out

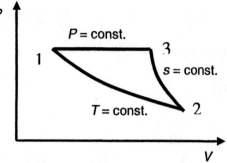

Supplement 6.2 Work input and entropy generation in a pump and a compressor

Determine the work input and entropy generation during the compression of steam from 100 kPa to 1 MPa in (a) an adiabatic pump and (b) an adiabatic compressor if the inlet state is saturated liquid in the pump and saturated vapor in the compressor and the isentropic efficiency is 85 percent for both devices. *Answers*: (a) 1.104 kJ/kg, 0.000444 kJ/kg-K, (b) 610 kJ/kg, 0.1384 kJ/kg-K

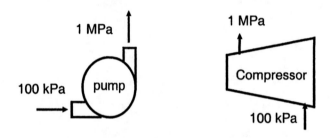

Supplement 6.3 An alternative expression of reversible work in a turbine

Consider the reversible expansion of steam in an adiabatic turbine. Steam enters the turbine at 1 MPa and 500°C. Someone proposes to express the work output by a suitable value of specific volume and the pressure values at the inlet and exit of the turbine as done for the pump, $v(P_1.P_2)$. Determine the ratio of this specific volume to the average of inlet and exit specific volumes if the exit pressure is (a) 100 kPa, (b) 300 kPa, (c) 500 kPa, and (d) 900 kPa. Discuss if you support this proposal. *Answers*: (a) 0.578, (b) 0.851, (c) 0.947, (d) 0.999

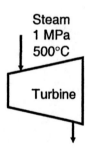

Supplement 6.4 A constant-entropy process for water

A rigid tank contains 1.5 kg of water at 120°C and 500 kPa. Now 22 kJ of paddle wheel work is done on the system and the final temperature in the tank is 95°C. If the entropy change of water is zero and the surroundings are at 15°C, determine (a) the final pressure in the tank, (b) the amount of heat transfer between the tank and the surroundings, and (c) the entropy generation during this process. *Answers*: (a) 84.6 kPa, (b) 38.4 kJ, (c) 0.1335 kJ/K

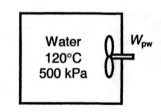

Supplement 6.5 A cylinder with two compartments containing N_2 and He

A horizontal cylinder is separated into two compartments by an adiabatic, frictionless piston. One side contains 0.2 m^3 of nitrogen and the other side contains 0.1 kg of helium, both initially at 20°C and 95 kPa. The sides of the cylinder and the helium end are insulated. Now heat is added to the nitrogen side from a reservoir at 500°C until the pressure of the helium rises to 120 kPa. Determine (a) the final temperature of the helium, (b) the final volume of the nitrogen, (c) the heat transferred to the nitrogen, and (d) the entropy generation during this process. Answers: (a) 322 K, (b) 0.284 m^3, (c) 46.7 kJ, (d) 0.0572 kJ/K

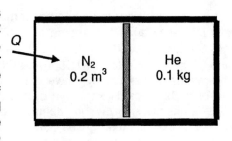

Supplement 6.6 Entropy generation during electrical heating of CO_2

A 0.8.m^3 rigid tank contains carbon dioxide (CO_2) gas at 250 K and 100 kPa. An electric resistance heater with a power rating of 500 W placed in the tank is now turned on and kept on for 40 minutes after which the pressure of CO_2 is measured to be 175 kPa. Assuming the surroundings to be at 300 and using constant specific heats, determine (a) the final temperature of CO_2, (b) the net amount of heat transfer from the tank, and (c) the entropy generation during this process. Answers: (a) 438 K, (b) 978 kJ, (c) 3.923 kJ/K

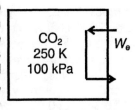

Supplement 6.7 Entropy generation during expansion of helium

Helium gas is steadily throttled from 500 kPa and 70°C. Heat is lost from the helium in the amount of 2.5 kJ/kg to the surroundings at 25°C and 100 kPa. If the entropy of the helium increases by 0.25 kJ/kg-K in the valve, determine (a) the exit pressure and temperature and (b) the entropy generation during this process. Answers: (a) 442 kPa, 69.5°C, (b) 0.258 kJ/kg-K

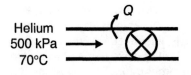

Supplement 6.8 Entropy analysis of a compressor with R.134a

Refrigerant.134a enters a compressor as a saturated vapor at 200 kPa at a rate of 0.03 m^3/s and leaves at 700 kPa. The power input to the compressor is 10 kW. If the surroundings at 20°C experiences an entropy increase of 0.008 kW/K, determine (a) the rate of heat loss from the compressor, (b) the exit temperature of the R.134a, and (c) the rate of entropy generation. Answers: (a) 2.34 kW, (b) 31.5°C, (c) 0.00754 kW/K

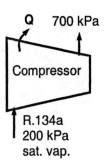

Supplement 6.9 Isentropic efficiency and entropy generation in a nozzle

Air at 500 kPa and 400 K enters an adiabatic nozzle at a velocity of 30 m/s and leaves at 300 kPa and 350 K. Using variable specific heats, determine (a) the isentropic efficiency, (b) the exit velocity, and (c) the entropy generation. Answers: (a) 0.925, (b) 319 m/s, (c) 0.0118 kJ/kg-K

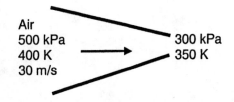

Supplement 6.10 Turbocharger of an internal combustion engine

Consider the turbocharger of an internal combustion engine. The exhaust gases enter the turbine at 450°C at a rate of 0.02 kg/s and leaves at 400°C. Air enters the compressor at 70°C and 95 kPa at a rate of 0.018 kg/s and leaves at 135 kPa. The mechanical efficiency between the turbine and the compressor is 95 percent (5 percent of turbine work is lost during its transmission to the compressor). Using air properties for the exhaust gases, determine (a) the air temperature at the compressor exit and (b) the isentropic efficiency of the compressor. *Answers*: (*a*) 126.2°C, (*b*) 0.642

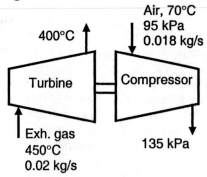

Supplement 6.11 Isothermal efficiency and entropy generation during compression of air

Air is compressed steadily by a compressor from 100 kPa and 20°C to 1200 kPa and 300°C at a rate of 0.4 kg/s. The compressor is intentionally cooled by utilizing fins on the surface of the compressor and heat is lost from the compressor at a rate of 15 kW to the surroundings at 20°C. Using constant specific heats, determine (a) the work input, (b) the isothermal efficiency, and (c) the entropy generation during this process. *Answers*: (a) 129 kW, (b) 0.649, (c) 0.0385 kW/K

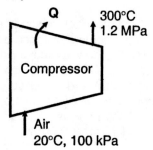

Supplement 6.12 Entropy generation during charging of air into a cylinder

A 0.25.m³ insulated piston-cylinder device initially contains 0.7 kg of air at 20°C. At this state, the piston is free to move. Now air at 500 kPa and 70°C is allowed to enter the cylinder from a supply line until the volume increases by 50 percent. Using constant specific heats at room temperature, determine (a) the final temperature, (b) the amount of mass that has entered, (c) the work done, and (d) the entropy generation. *Answers*: (a) 308 K, (b) 0.3 kg, (c) 29.4 kJ, (d) 0.0673 kJ/K

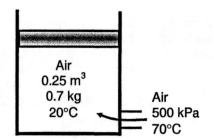

Chapter 7 Educational Objectives and Glossary

The Educational Objectives of Chapter 7 are to:

- Examine the performance of engineering devices in light of the second law of thermodynamics.
- Define *exergy* (also called availability), which is the maximum useful work that could be obtained from the system at a given state in a specified environment.
- Define reversible work, which is the maximum useful work that can be obtained as a system undergoes a process between two specified states.
- Define irreversibility (also called the exergy destruction or lost work), which is the wasted work potential during a process as a result of irreversibilities.
- Define the term second-law efficiency.
- Develop the exergy balance relation.
- Apply exergy balance to closed systems and control volumes.

Chapter 7 Glossary

Dead state is a state a system is said to be in when it is in thermodynamic equilibrium with its environment.

Decrease of exergy principle can be expressed as the exergy of an isolated system during a process always decreases or, in the limiting case of a reversible process, remains constant. In other words, it never increases and exergy is destroyed during an actual process. For an isolated system, the decrease in exergy equals exergy destroyed.

Environment refers to the region beyond the immediate surroundings whose properties are not affected by the process at any point.

Exergy (availability or available energy) is property used to determine the useful work potential of a given amount of energy at some specified state. It is important to realize that exergy does not represent the amount of work that a work-producing device will actually deliver upon installation. Rather, it represents the upper limit on the amount of work a device can deliver without violating any thermodynamic laws.

Exergy balance can be stated as the exergy change of a system during a process is equal to the difference between the net exergy transfer through the system boundary and the exergy destroyed within the system boundaries as a result of irreversibilities (or entropy generation).

Exergy balance for a control volume is stated as the rate of exergy change within the control volume during a process is equal to the rate of net exergy transfer through the control volume boundary by heat, work, and mass flow minus the rate of exergy destruction within the boundaries of the control volume as a result of irreversibilities.

Exergy destroyed is proportional to the entropy generated and is expressed as $X_{destroyed} = T_0 S_{gen} \geq 0$. Irreversibilities such as friction, mixing, chemical reactions, heat transfer through a finite temperature difference, unrestrained expansion, non-quasi-equilibrium compression, or expansion always generate entropy, and anything that generates entropy always destroys exergy.

Exergy of a closed system (or nonflow system) of mass m is $X = (U - U_0) + P_0(V - V_0) - T_0(S - S_0) + m\vec{V}^2/2 + mgz$. On a unit mass basis, the exergy of a closed system is expressed as $\phi = (u - u_0) + P_0(v - v_0) - T_0(s - s_0) + \vec{V}^2/2 + gz$ where u_0, v_0, and s_0 are the properties of the system evaluated at the dead state. Note that the exergy of a system is zero at the dead state since $u = u_0$, $v = v_0$, and $s = s_0$ at that state. The exergy change of a closed system during a process is simply the difference between the final and initial exergies of the system.

Exergy of the kinetic energy (work potential) of a system is equal to the kinetic energy itself regardless of the temperature and pressure of the environment.

Exergy of the potential energy (work potential) of a system is equal to the potential energy itself regardless of the temperature and pressure of the environment.

Exergy transfer by heat X_{heat} is the exergy as the result of heat transfer Q at a location at absolute temperature T in the amount of $X_{heat} = (1-T_0/T)Q$.

Exergy transfer by work is the useful work potential expressed as $X_{work} = W - W_{surr}$ for closed systems experiencing boundary work where $W_{surr} = P_0(v_2 - v_1)$ and P_0 is atmospheric pressure, and V_1 and V_2 are the initial and final volumes of the system, and $X_{work} = W$ for other forms of work.

Exergy transport by mass results from mass in the amount of m entering or leaving a system and carries exergy in the amount of $m\psi$, where $\psi = (h - h_0) - T_0(s - s_0) + \vec{V}^2/2 + gz$, accompanies it. Therefore, the exergy of a system increases by $m\psi$ when mass in the amount of m enters, and decreases by the same amount when the same amount of mass at the same state leaves the system.

Immediate surroundings refer to the portion of the surroundings that is affected by the process.

Irreversibility I is any difference between the reversible work W_{rev} and the useful work W_u due to the irreversibilities present during the process. Irreversibility can be viewed as the wasted work potential or the lost opportunity to do work.

Reversible work W_{rev} is defined as the maximum amount of useful work that can be produced (or the minimum work that needs to be supplied) as a system undergoes a process between the specified initial and final states. Reversible work is determined from the exergy balance relations by setting the exergy destroyed equal to zero. The work W in that case becomes the reversible work.

Second-law efficiency η_{II} is the ratio of the actual thermal efficiency to the maximum possible (reversible) thermal efficiency under the same conditions. The second-law efficiency of various steady-flow devices can be determined from its general definition, $\eta_{II} = $ (exergy recovered)/(exergy supplied).

Surroundings work is the work done by or against the surroundings during a process.

Useful work W_u is the difference between the actual work W and the surroundings work W_{surr}.

Useful work potential is the maximum possible work that a system will deliver as it undergoes a reversible process from the specified initial state to the state of its environment, that is, the dead state.

EXAMPLE 7-1   Exergy destroyed during heat exchange between water and air

A 0.04-m³ tank initially contains air at ambient conditions of 100 kPa and 22°C. Now, a 15-liter tank containing liquid water at 85°C is placed into the tank during which no air escapes. After some heat transfer from the water to the air and the surroundings, both the air and water are measured to be at 44°C. Determine (a) the amount of heat lost to the surroundings and (b) the exergy destruction during this process.

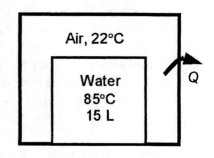

Equations

GIVEN

$$V_{air,1} = 0.04 \ [\text{m}^3] \tag{1}$$

$$P_{air,1} = 100 \ [\text{kPa}] \tag{2}$$

$$T_{air,1} = 22 \ [\text{C}] \tag{3}$$

$$V_w = 0.015 \ [\text{m}^3] \tag{4}$$

$$T_{w,1} = 85 \ [\text{C}] \tag{5}$$

$$T_2 = 44 \ [\text{C}] \tag{6}$$

$$T_0 = ConvertTemp \, (C, \ K, \ 22) \tag{7}$$

PROPERTIES

$$\rho_w = \rho \, (\text{Water}, \ T = T_{w,1}, \ x = 0) \tag{8}$$

$$R_{air} = R_u / MM \quad \textbf{Gas constant} \tag{9}$$

$$R_u = 8.314 \ [\text{kJ/kmol·K}] \quad \textbf{Universal gas constant} \tag{10}$$

$$MM = \text{MW} \, (\text{Air}) \tag{11}$$

$$u_{air,1} = \text{u} \, (\text{Air}, \ T = T_{air,1}) \quad \textbf{Initial specific internal energy for air} \tag{12}$$

$$s_{air,1} = \text{s} \, (\text{Air}, \ T = T_{air,1}, \ P = P_{air,1}) \quad \textbf{Initial specific entropy for air} \tag{13}$$

$$u_{air,2} = \text{u} \, (\text{Air}, \ T = T_2) \quad \textbf{Final specific heat at constant volume for air} \tag{14}$$

$$s_{air,2} = \text{s} \, (\text{Air}, \ T = T_2, \ P = P_{air,2}) \quad \textbf{Final specific entropy for air} \tag{15}$$

$$u_{w,1} = \text{u} \, (\text{Water}, \ T = T_{w,1}, \ x = 0) \quad \textbf{Initial specific heat at constant volume for water} \tag{16}$$

$$s_{w,1} = \text{s} \, (\text{Water}, \ T = T_{w,1}, \ x = 0) \quad \textbf{Initial specific entropy for water} \tag{17}$$

$u_{w,2} = $ u (Water, $T = T_2$, $x = 0$)   **Final specific heat at constant volume for water**   (18)

$s_{w,2} = $ s (Water, $T = T_2$, $x = 0$)   **Final specific entropy for water**   (19)

ANALYSIS

$V_{air,2} = V_{air,1} - V_w$ (20)

$P_{air,1} \cdot V_{air,1} = m_{air} \cdot R_{air} \cdot ConvertTemp\,(C,\ K,\ T_{air,1})$ **Equation of state**   (21)

$P_{air,2} \cdot V_{air,2} = m_{air} \cdot R_{air} \cdot ConvertTemp\,(C,\ K,\ T_2)$ (22)

$m_w = \rho_w \cdot V_w$ (23)

$-Q_{out} = m_w \cdot (u_{w,2} - u_{w,1}) + m_{air} \cdot (u_{air,2} - u_{air,1})$,   **Energy balance**   (24)

$EX_{destoyed} = \Delta EX_w + \Delta EX_{air}$ **Exergy balance on the extended system (system + immediate surroundings)** (25)

$\Delta EX_w = m_w \cdot (u_{w,1} - u_{w,2} - T_0 \cdot (s_{w,1} - s_{w,2}))$ (26)

$\Delta EX_{air} = m_{air} \cdot (u_{air,1} - u_{air,2} - T_0 \cdot (s_{air,1} - s_{air,2}))$ (27)

Solution

$\Delta EX_{air} = -1.907\ [\text{kJ}]$
$\Delta EX_w = 311.3\ [\text{kJ}]$
$\boxed{EX_{destoyed} = 309.4\ [\text{kJ}]}$
$MM = 28.97\ [\text{kg/kmol}]$
$m_{air} = 0.04722\ [\text{kg}]$
$m_w = 14.53\ [\text{kg}]$
$\boxed{Q_{out} = 2493\ [\text{kJ}]}$
$\rho_w = 968.6\ [\text{kg/m}^3]$
$R_{air} = 0.287\ [\text{kJ/kg-K}]$
$R_u = 8.314\ [\text{kJ/kmol-K}]$
$T_0 = 295.2\ [\text{K}]$
$T_2 = 44\ [\text{C}]$
$T_{air,1} = 22\ [\text{C}]$
$T_{w,1} = 85\ [\text{C}]$
$V_{air,1} = 0.04\ [\text{m}^3]$
$V_{air,2} = 0.025\ [\text{m}^3]$
$V_w = 0.015\ [\text{m}^3]$

Arrays

Row	$P_{air,i}$ [kPa]	$s_{air,i}$ [kJ/kg-K]	$s_{w,i}$ [kJ/kg-K]	$u_{air,i}$ [kJ/kg]	$u_{w,i}$ [kJ/kg]
1	100	5.689	1.134	210.8	355.9
2	171.9	5.606	0.6254	226.7	184.2

EXAMPLE 7-2   Exergy analysis of a steam turbine

Steam enters a turbine at 12 MPa, 550°C, and 60 m/s and leaves at 20 kPa and 130 m/s with a moisture content of 5 percent. The turbine is not well insulated and it estimated that heat is lost from the turbine at a rate of 150 kW. The power output of the turbine is 2.5 MW. Assuming the surroundings to be at 25°C, determine (a) the reversible power output of the turbine, (b) the exergy destroyed in the turbine, and (c) the second-law efficiency of the turbine. (d) Also, estimate the possible increase in the power output of the turbine if the turbine is to be well insulated.

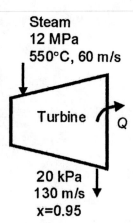

Equations

GIVEN

$$P_1 = 12 \ [\text{MPa}] \cdot \left| 1000 \ \frac{\text{kPa}}{\text{MPa}} \right| \tag{1}$$

$$T_1 = 550 \ [\text{C}] \tag{2}$$

$$Vel_1 = 60 \ [\text{m/s}] \tag{3}$$

$$P_2 = 20 \ [\text{kPa}] \tag{4}$$

$$Vel_2 = 130 \ [\text{m/s}] \tag{5}$$

$$x_2 = 0.95 \tag{6}$$

$$\dot{Q}_{out} = 150 \ [\text{kW}] \tag{7}$$

$$\dot{W}_{actual} = 2.5 \ [\text{MW}] \cdot \left| 1000 \ \frac{\text{kW}}{\text{MW}} \right| \tag{8}$$

$$T_0 = 25 \ [\text{C}] \tag{9}$$

PROPERTIES

$$Fluid\$ = \text{'Steam\_iapws'} \tag{10}$$

$h_0 = \text{h} \, (Fluid\$, \ T = T_0, \ x = 0)$ **Specific enthalpy at surroundings conditions** (11)

$h_1 = \text{h} \, (Fluid\$, \ P = P_1, \ T = T_1)$ **Specific enthalpy at inlet** (12)

$s_1 = \text{s} \, (Fluid\$, \ P = P_1, \ T = T_1)$ **Specific entropy at inlet** (13)

$h_2 = \text{h} \, (Fluid\$, \ P = P_2, \ x = x_2)$ **Specific enthalpy at exit** (14)

$s_2 = s\,(\text{Fluid\$},\ P = P_2,\ x = x_2)$ **Specific entropy at exit**   (15)

Analysis

$$\dot{m} \cdot h_1 + \dot{m} \cdot \frac{Vel_1^2}{2} \cdot \left| 0.001\, \frac{kJ/kg}{m^2/s^2} \right| = \dot{m} \cdot h_2 + \dot{m} \cdot Vel_1^2/2 \cdot \left| 0.001\, \frac{kJ/kg}{m^2/s^2} \right| + \dot{Q}_{out} + \dot{W}_{actual} \quad \textbf{Energy balance} \quad (16)$$

$$\dot{W}_{rev} = \dot{m} \cdot \left(h_1 - h_2 - (T_0 + 273) \cdot (s_1 - s_2) + \frac{Vel_1^2 - Vel_2^2}{2} \cdot \left| 0.001\, \frac{kJ/kg}{m^2/s^2} \right| \right) \quad \textbf{Reversible power} \quad (17)$$

$EX_{destroyed} = \dot{W}_{rev} - \dot{W}_{actual}$ **Exergy destroyed**   (18)

$\eta_{II} = \dot{W}_{actual}/\dot{W}_{rev}$ **Second-law efficiency**   (19)

$\dot{Q}_{max} = \dot{m} \cdot (h_1 - h_0)$ **Energy of steam at the turbine inlet in the given environment**   (20)

$f = \dfrac{\dot{W}_{actual}}{\dot{Q}_{max}}$ **Fraction of steam energy converted to power**   (21)

$\dot{W}_{increase} = f \cdot \dot{Q}_{out}$ **Estimated possible increase of turbine power**   (22)

Solution

$\boxed{\eta_{II} = 0.7467}$

$\boxed{EX_{destroyed} = 848.2\ [\text{kW}]}$

$f = 0.2767$

$Fluid\$ = \text{'Steam\_iapws'}$

$\dot{m} = 2.675\ [\text{kg/s}]$

$\dot{Q}_{max} = 9034\ [\text{kW}]$

$\dot{Q}_{out} = 150\ [\text{kW}]$

$\dot{W}_{actual} = 2500\ [\text{kW}]$

$\boxed{\dot{W}_{increase} = 41.51\ [\text{kW}]}$

$\boxed{\dot{W}_{rev} = 3348\ [\text{kW}]}$

$x_2 = 0.95$

Arrays

Row	h_i [kJ/kg]	s_i [kJ/kg-K]	T_i [C]	P_i [kPa]	Vel_i [m/s]
0	104.8		25		
1	3482	6.655	550	12000	60
2	2491	7.553		20	130

EXAMPLE 7-3   Exergy analysis of an air compressor

Air enters a compressor at ambient conditions of 100 kPa and 20°C at a rate of 4.5 m³/s with a low velocity and exits at 900 kPa, 60°C, and 80 m/s. The compressor is cooled by cooling water that experiences a temperature rise of 10°C. The isothermal efficiency of the compressor is 70 percent. Determine (a) the actual and reversible power inputs, (b) the second-law efficiency, and (c) the mass flow rate of the cooling water.

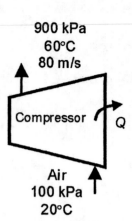

Equations

GIVEN

$$P_1 = 100 \ [\text{kPa}] \tag{1}$$

$$T_1 = ConvertTemp\,(C,\ K,\ 20) \tag{2}$$

$$Vel_1 = 0 \ [\text{m/s}] \tag{3}$$

$$\dot{V} = 4.5 \ [\text{m}^3/\text{s}] \tag{4}$$

$$P_2 = 900 \ [\text{kPa}] \tag{5}$$

$$T_2 = ConvertTemp\,(C,\ K,\ 60) \tag{6}$$

$$Vel_2 = 80 \ [\text{m/s}] \tag{7}$$

$$\Delta T_w = 10 \ [\text{C}] \tag{8}$$

$$\eta_t = 0.70 \tag{9}$$

PROPERTIES

$$Fluid\$ = \text{'Air'} \tag{10}$$

$R = R_u/MM$ **Gas constant** $\tag{11}$

$R_u = 8.314 \ [\text{kJ/kmol·K}]$ **Universal gas constant** $\tag{12}$

$MM = \text{MW}\,(Fluid\$) \tag{13}$

$C_w = c_p\,(\text{Water},\ T = T_1,\ P = P_1)$ **Specific heat of Water** $\tag{14}$

$h_1 = \text{h}\,(Fluid\$,\ T = T_1)$ **Air specific enthalpy at inlet** $\tag{15}$

$h_2 = \text{h}\,(Fluid\$,\ T = T_2)$ **Air specific enthalpy at exit** $\tag{16}$

ANALYSIS

$$\rho = \frac{P_1}{(R \cdot T_1)} \qquad \text{Density of air at inlet} \tag{17}$$

$$\dot{m} = \rho \cdot \dot{V} \tag{18}$$

$$\dot{W}_{rev} = \dot{m} \cdot R \cdot T_1 \cdot \ln{(P_2/P_1)} \qquad \text{Reversible isothermal power} \tag{19}$$

$$\dot{W}_{actual} = \frac{\dot{W}_{rev}}{\eta_t} \qquad \text{Actual power} \tag{20}$$

$$\eta_{II} = \frac{\dot{W}_{rev}}{\dot{W}_{actual}} \qquad \text{Second-law efficiency} \tag{21}$$

$$\dot{m} \cdot h_1 + \dot{m} \cdot \frac{Vel_1^2}{2} \cdot \left| 0.001 \, \frac{kJ/kg}{m^2/s^2} \right| + \dot{W}_{actual} = \dot{m} \cdot h_2 + \dot{m} \cdot Vel_1^2/2 \cdot \left| 0.001 \, \frac{kJ/kg}{m^2/s^2} \right| + \dot{Q}_{out} \qquad \text{Energy balance} \tag{22}$$

$$\dot{Q}_{out} = \dot{m}_w \cdot (C_w \cdot \Delta T_w) \qquad \text{Rate of energy transfer to the cooling water} \tag{23}$$

Solution

$C_w = 4.183 \, [\text{kJ/kg-K}]$
$\Delta T_w = 10 \, [\text{C}]$
$\boxed{\eta_{II} = 0.7}$
$\eta_t = 0.7$
$Fluid\$ = \text{`Air'}$
$h_1 = 293.5 \, [\text{kJ/kg}]$
$h_2 = 333.8 \, [\text{kJ/kg}]$
$MM = 28.97 \, [\text{kg/kmol}]$
$\dot{m} = 5.348 \, [\text{kg/s}]$
$\boxed{\dot{m}_w = 28.62 \, [\text{kg/s}]}$
$P_1 = 100 \, [\text{kPa}]$
$P_2 = 900 \, [\text{kPa}]$
$\dot{Q}_{out} = 1197 \, [\text{kW}]$
$R = 0.287 \, [\text{kJ/kg-K}]$
$\rho = 1.189 \, [\text{kg/m}^3]$
$R_u = 8.314 \, [\text{kJ/kmol-K}]$
$T_1 = 293.2 \, [\text{K}]$
$T_2 = 333.2 \, [\text{K}]$
$Vel_1 = 0 \, [\text{m/s}]$
$Vel_2 = 80 \, [\text{m/s}]$
$\dot{V} = 4.5 \, [\text{m}^3/\text{s}]$
$\boxed{\dot{W}_{actual} = 1413 \, [\text{kW}]}$
$\boxed{\dot{W}_{rev} = 988.8 \, [\text{kW}]}$

EXAMPLE 7-4   Exergy analysis of an expansion valve

Refrigerant-134a is expanded adiabatically in an expansion valve from 1.2 MPa and 40°C to 180 kPa. If the ambient state is 100 kPa and 20°C, determine (a) the work potential of R-134a at the inlet, (b) the exergy destruction during the process, and (c) the second-law efficiency.

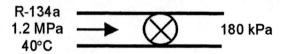

Equations

GIVEN

$$P_1 = 1200 \ [\text{kPa}] \tag{1}$$

$$T_1 = ConvertTemp\,(C, \ K, \ 40) \tag{2}$$

$$P_2 = 180 \ [\text{kPa}] \tag{3}$$

$$T_0 = ConvertTemp\,(C, \ K, \ 20) \tag{4}$$

$$P_0 = 100 \ [\text{kPa}] \tag{5}$$

ANALYSIS

$$Fluid\$ = \text{'R134a'} \tag{6}$$

$h_0 = \text{h}\,(Fluid\$, \ P = P_0, \ T = T_0)$ **Specific enthalpy at surroundings conditions**   (7)

$s_0 = \text{s}\,(Fluid\$, \ P = P_0, \ T = T_0)$ **Specific entropy at surroundings conditions**   (8)

$h_1 = \text{h}\,(Fluid\$, \ P = P_1, \ T = T_1)$ **Specific enthalpy at inlet**   (9)

$s_1 = \text{s}\,(Fluid\$, \ P = P_1, \ T = T_1)$ **Specific entropy at inlet**   (10)

$h_1 = h_2$ **Energy balance**   (11)

$s_2 = \text{s}\,(Fluid\$, \ P = P_2, \ h = h_2)$ **Specific entropy at exit**   (12)

$ex_1 = h_1 - h_0 - T_0 \cdot (s_1 - s_0)$ **Exergy at the inlet**   (13)

$ex_2 = h_2 - h_0 - T_0 \cdot (s_2 - s_0)$ **Exergy at the exit**   (14)

$s_{gen} = s_2 - s_1$ **Entropy generation**   (15)

$ex_{dest} = T_0 \cdot s_{gen}$ **Exergy destruction**   (16)

$\eta_{II} = \dfrac{ex_2}{ex_1}$ **Second-law efficiency**   (17)

Solution

$\boxed{\eta_{II} = 0.7942}$

$\boxed{ex_1 = 40.55 \,[\text{kJ/kg}]}$

$ex_2 = 32.2 \,[\text{kJ/kg}]$

$\boxed{ex_{dest} = 8.344 \,[\text{kJ/kg}]}$

$Fluid\$ = \text{'R134a'}$

$h_0 = 272.2 \,[\text{kJ/kg}]$

$h_1 = 108.2 \,[\text{kJ/kg}]$

$h_2 = 108.2 \,[\text{kJ/kg}]$

$P_0 = 100 \,[\text{kPa}]$

$P_1 = 1200 \,[\text{kPa}]$

$P_2 = 180 \,[\text{kPa}]$

$s_0 = 1.092 \,[\text{kJ/kg-K}]$

$s_1 = 0.3942 \,[\text{kJ/kg-K}]$

$s_2 = 0.4227 \,[\text{kJ/kg-K}]$

$s_{gen} = 0.02846 \,[\text{kJ/kg-K}]$

$T_0 = 293.2 \,[\text{K}]$

$T_1 = 313.2 \,[\text{K}]$

EXAMPLE 7-5   Exergy analysis of a steam nozzle

Steam enters an adiabatic nozzle at 3.5 MPa and 300°C with a low velocity and leaves at 1.6 MPa and 250°C at a rate of 0.4 kg/s. If the ambient state is 100 kPa and 18°C, determine (a) the exit velocity, (b) the rate of exergy destruction, and (c) the second-law efficiency.

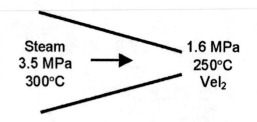

Equations

GIVEN

$$P_1 = 3.5 \ [\text{MPa}] \cdot \left| 1000 \ \frac{kPa}{\text{MPa}} \right| \tag{1}$$

$$T_1 = 300 \ [\text{C}] \tag{2}$$

$$Vel_1 = 0 \ [\text{m/s}] \tag{3}$$

$$P_2 = 1.6 \ [\text{MPa}] \cdot \left| 1000 \ \frac{kPa}{\text{MPa}} \right| \tag{4}$$

$$T_2 = 250 \ [\text{C}] \tag{5}$$

$$\dot{m} = 0.4 \ [\text{kg/s}] \tag{6}$$

$$T_0 = 18 \ [\text{C}] \tag{7}$$

$$P_0 = 100 \ [\text{kPa}] \tag{8}$$

PROPERTIES

$$Fluid\$ = \text{'Steam\_iapws'} \tag{9}$$

$h_0 = \text{h}\,(Fluid\$, \ P = P_0, \ T = T_0)$ **Specific enthalpy at surroundings conditions** $\qquad$ (10)

$s_0 = \text{s}\,(Fluid\$, \ P = P_0, \ T = T_0)$ **Specific entropy at surroundings conditions** $\qquad$ (11)

$h_1 = \text{h}\,(Fluid\$, \ P = P_1, \ T = T_1)$ **Specific enthalpy at inlet** $\qquad$ (12)

$s_1 = \text{s}\,(Fluid\$, \ P = P_1, \ T = T_1)$ **Specific entropy at inlet** $\qquad$ (13)

$h_2 = \text{h}\,(Fluid\$, \ P = P_2, \ T = T_2)$ **Specific enthalpy at exit** $\qquad$ (14)

$s_2 = \text{s}\,(Fluid\$, \ P = P_2, \ T = T_2)$ **Specific entropy at exit** $\qquad$ (15)

ANALYSIS

$$h_1 + \frac{Vel_1^2}{2} \cdot \left| 0.001 \ \frac{kJ/kg}{m^2/s^2} \right| = h_2 + Vel_2^2/2 \cdot \left| 0.001 \ \frac{kJ/kg}{m^2/s^2} \right| \qquad \textbf{Energy balance} \tag{16}$$

$$ex_1 = h_1 - h_0 + \left(\frac{Vel_1^2}{2} \cdot \left| 0.001 \, \frac{kJ/kg}{m^2/s^2} \right| \right) - (ConvertTemp\,(C,\ K,\ T_0)) \cdot (s_1 - s_0) \tag{17}$$

$$ex_2 = h_2 - h_0 + \left(\frac{Vel_2^2}{2} \cdot \left| 0.001 \, \frac{kJ/kg}{m^2/s^2} \right| \right) - (ConvertTemp\,(C,\ K,\ T_0)) \cdot (s_2 - s_0) \tag{18}$$

$$\dot{EX}_{dest} = \dot{m} \cdot (ex_1 - ex_2) \qquad \textbf{Exergy destruction} \tag{19}$$

$$\eta_{II} = ex_2/ex_1 \qquad \textbf{Second law efficiency} \tag{20}$$

Alternative method

$$s_{gen} = s_2 - s_1 \tag{21}$$

$$\dot{EX}_{dest,b} = \dot{m} \cdot (ConvertTemp\,(C,\ K,\ T_0)) \cdot s_{gen} \tag{22}$$

$$\dot{EX}_1 = \dot{m} \cdot ex_1 \tag{23}$$

$$\eta_{II,b} = 1 - \dot{EX}_{dest}/\dot{EX}_1 \tag{24}$$

Solution

$$\boxed{\eta_{II} = 0.9401}$$
$\eta_{II,b} = 0.9401$
$ex_1 = 1103 \ [\text{kJ/kg}]$
$ex_2 = 1037 \ [\text{kJ/kg}]$
$\dot{EX}_1 = 441.3 \ [\text{kW}]$
$$\boxed{\dot{EX}_{dest} = 26.43 \ [\text{kW}]}$$
$\dot{EX}_{dest,b} = 26.43 \ [\text{kW}]$
$Fluid\$ = \text{'Steam\_iapws'}$
$h_0 = 75.64 \ [\text{kJ/kg}]$
$h_1 = 2978 \ [\text{kJ/kg}]$
$h_2 = 2920 \ [\text{kJ/kg}]$
$\dot{m} = 0.4 \ [\text{kg/s}]$
$P_0 = 100 \ [\text{kPa}]$
$P_1 = 3500 \ [\text{kPa}]$
$P_2 = 1600 \ [\text{kPa}]$
$s_0 = 0.2678 \ [\text{kJ/kg-K}]$
$s_1 = 6.448 \ [\text{kJ/kg-K}]$
$s_2 = 6.675 \ [\text{kJ/kg-K}]$
$s_{gen} = 0.2269 \ [\text{kJ/kg-K}]$
$T_0 = 18 \ [\text{C}]$
$T_1 = 300 \ [\text{C}]$
$T_2 = 250 \ [\text{C}]$
$Vel_1 = 0 \ [\text{m/s}]$
$$\boxed{Vel_2 = 342 \ [\text{m/s}]}$$

Supplement 7.1 Exergy analysis of a geothermal power plant

A geothermal power plant uses geothermal liquid water at 160°C at a rate of 440 kg/s as the heat source and produces 14 MW of net power. The waste heat is rejected to the ambient air at 25°C. If 18.5 MW of exergy entering the plant with the geothermal water is destructed within the plant, determine (a) the exergy of the geothermal water entering the plant, (b) the second-law efficiency, and (c) the exergy of the heat rejected from the plant. *Answers*: (a) 44.53 MW, (b) 31.4%, (c) 12.03 MW

Supplement 7.2 Exergy destruction during heating of R.134a in a cylinder

A piston-cylinder device initially contains 1.4 kg of refrigerant.134a at 140 kPa and 20°C. Heat is now transferred to the refrigerant, and the piston, which is resting on a set of stops, starts moving when the pressure inside reaches 180 kPa. Heat transfer continues until the temperature is 120°C. Assuming the surroundings to be at 25°C and 100 kPa, determine (a) the work done, (b) the heat transfer, (c) the exergy destroyed, and (d) the second-law efficiency for the process. *Answers*: (a) 2.57 kJ, (b) 120 kJ, (c) 13.5 kJ, (d) 0.078

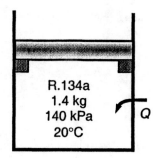

Supplement 7.3 Exergy destruction during heating of a room by an electrical radiator

A 30 liter electrical radiator containing heating oil is placed in a 50.m^3 room. Both the air in the room and the oil in the radiator are initially at 10°C. Electricity with a rating of 1.8 kW is now turned on. Heat is also lost from the room at an average rate of 0.35 kW. It is measured after a while that the room is at 20°C and the oil is at 50°C at which point the heater is turned off. Taking the density and the specific heat of oil to be 950 kg/m^3 and 2.2 kJ/kg-°C, respectively, determine (a) how long it has been since the heater was first turned on, (b) the exergy destruction, and (c) the second-law efficiency during the process. Assume the room is well sealed and the surroundings are at 10°C. *Answers*: (a) 2039 s, (b) 3500 kJ, (c) 0.046

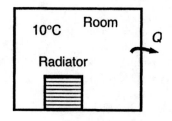

Supplement 7.4 Exergy analysis of a mixing chamber

Liquid water at 15°C is heated in a chamber by mixing it with saturated steam. Liquid water enters the chamber at the steam pressure at a rate of 4.6 kg/s and the saturated steam enters at a rate of 0.23 kg/s. The mixture leaves the mixing chamber as a liquid at 45°C. If the surroundings are at 15°C, determine (*a*) the temperature of saturated steam entering the chamber, (*b*) the exergy destruction during this mixing process, and (*c*) the second-law efficiency of the mixing chamber. *Answers*: (*a*) 114.3°C, (*b*) 114.7 kW, (*c*) 0.207

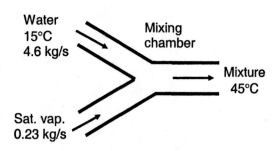

Supplement 7.5 Exergy analysis of a heat exchanger

Hot exhaust gases leaving an internal combustion engine at 400°C and 150 kPa at a rate of 0.8 kg/s is to be used to obtain saturated steam at 200°C in an insulated heat exchanger. Water enters the heat exchanger at the ambient temperature of 20°C and the exhaust gases leave the heat exchanger at 350°C. Determine (a) the rate at which the steam is obtained, (b) the rate of exergy destruction in the heat exchanger, and (c) the second-law efficiency of the heat exchanger. Answers: (a) 0.0157 kg/s, (b) 8.98 kW, (c) 0.614

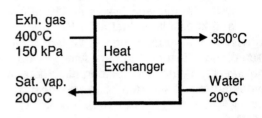

Supplement 7.6 Exergy analysis of a gas turbine

Combustion gases enter a gas turbine at 750°C and 1.2 MPa at a rate of 3.4 kg/s and leave at 630°C and 500 kPa. The turbine is not well insulated and it estimated that heat is lost from the turbine at a rate of 30 kW. Using air properties for the combustion gases and assuming the surroundings to be at 25°C and 100 kPa, determine (a) the actual and reversible power outputs of the turbine, (b) the exergy destroyed in the turbine, and (c) the second-law efficiency of the turbine. Answers: (a) 432.4 kW, 516.8 kW, (b) 84.4 kW, (c) 0.837

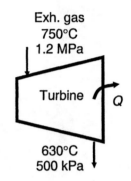

Supplement 7.7 Exergy analysis of a R.134a compressor

Refrigerant.134a enters an adiabatic compressor at 160 kPa superheated by 3°C and leaves at 1.0 MPa. If the compressor has a second-law efficiency of 80 percent, determine (a) the actual work input, (b) the isentropic efficiency, and (c) the exergy destruction. The environment temperature is 25°C. Answers: (a) 49.8 kJ/kg, (b) 0.78, (c) 9.95 kJ/kg

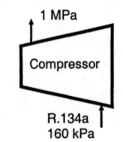

Supplement 7.8 Exergy analysis of a water pump

Water enters a pump at 100 kPa and 30°C at a rate of 1.35 kg/s and leaves at 4 MPa. If the pump has an isentropic efficiency of 70 percent, determine (a) the actual power input, (b) the rate of frictional heating, (c) the exergy destruction, and (d) the second-law efficiency. The environment temperature is 20°C. Answers: (a) 7.55 kW, (b) 2.27 kW, (c) 2.19 kW, (d) 0.71

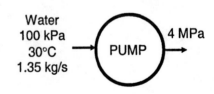

Supplement 7.9 Exergy analysis of an expansion valve

Argon gas is expanded adiabatically from 3.5 MPa and 100°C to 500 kPa. If the ambient state is 100 kPa and 25°C, determine (a) the exergy of argon at the inlet, (b) the exergy destruction during the process, and (c) the second-law efficiency. Answers: (a) 225 kJ/kg, (b) 121 kJ/kg, (c) 0.463

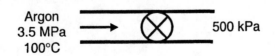

Supplement 7.10 Exergy analysis of a diffuser

Nitrogen gas enters a diffuser at 100 kPa and 150°C with a velocity of 180 m/s and leaves at 110 kPa with a velocity of 25 m/s. It is estimated that 4.5 kJ/kg of heat is lost from the diffuser to the surroundings at 100 kPa and 27°C. The exit area of the diffuser is 0.06 m². Accounting for the variation of the specific heats with temperature, determine (a) the exit temperature, (b) the rate of exergy destruction, and (c) the second-law efficiency. *Answers:* (a) 161°C, (b) 5.11 kW, (c) 0.892

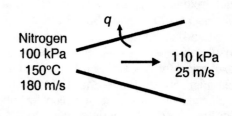

Chapter 8 Educational Objectives and Glossary

The Educational Objectives of Chapter 8 are to:

- Evaluate the performance of gas power cycles for which the working fluid remains a gas throughout the entire cycle.
- Develop simplifying assumptions applicable to gas power cycles.
- Review the operation of reciprocating engines.
- Analyze both closed and open gas power cycles.
- Solve problems based on the Otto, Diesel, Stirling, and Ericsson cycles.
- Solve problems based on the Brayton cycle, the Brayton cycle with regeneration, and the Brayton cycle with intercooling, reheating, and regeneration.
- Analyze jet-propulsion cycles.
- Identify simplifying assumptions for second-law analysis of gas power cycles.
- Perform second-law analysis of gas power cycles.

Chapter 8 Glossary

Afterburner is a section added between the turbine and the nozzle of an aircraft turbine engine where additional fuel is injected into the oxygen-rich combustion gases leaving the turbine. As a result of this added energy, the exhaust gases leave at a higher velocity, providing extra thrust for short takeoffs or combat conditions.

Air-standard assumptions reduce the analysis of gas power cycles to a manageable level by utilizing the following approximations:
1. The working fluid is air, which continuously circulates in a closed loop and always behaves as an ideal gas.
2. All the processes that make up the cycle are internally reversible.
3. The combustion process is replaced by a heat-addition process from an external source.
4. The exhaust process is replaced by a heat rejection process that restores the working fluid to its initial state.

Air-standard cycle is a cycle for which the air-standard assumptions are applicable.

Autoignition is the premature ignition of the fuel produces an audible noise, which is called engine knock

Back work ratio is the ratio of the compressor work to the turbine work in gas-turbine power plants.

Bore is the diameter of a piston.

Bottom dead center (BDC) is the position of the piston when it forms the largest volume in the cylinder.

Brayton cycle was first proposed by George Brayton around 1870. It is used for gas turbines, which operate on an open cycle, where both the compression and expansion processes take place in rotating machinery. The open gas-turbine cycle can be modeled as a closed cycle by utilizing the air-standard assumptions. The combustion process is replaced by a constant-pressure heat-addition process from an external source, and the exhaust process is replaced by a constant-pressure heat-rejection process to the ambient air. The ideal Brayton cycle is made up of four internally reversible processes:
    1-2 Isentropic compression (in a compressor)
    2-3 Constant pressure heat addition
    3-4 Isentropic expansion (in a turbine)
    4-1 Constant pressure heat rejection ·

Brayton cycle with regeneration is the Brayton cycle modified with a regenerator, a counterflow heat exchanger, to allow the transfer of heat to the high pressure air leaving the compressor from the high-temperature exhaust gas leaving the turbine.

Clearance volume is the minimum volume formed in the cylinder when the piston is at top dead center.

Cold-air-standard assumption combines the air-standard assumptions with the assumption that the air has constant specific heats whose values are determined at room temperature (25°C, or 77°F).

Compression-ignition (CI) **engines** are reciprocating engines in which the combustion of the air–fuel mixture is self-ignited as a result of compressing the mixture above its self-ignition temperature.

Compression ratio r of an engine is the ratio of the maximum volume formed in the cylinder to the minimum (clearance) volume. Notice that the compression ratio is a *volume ratio* and should not be confused with the pressure ratio.

Cutoff ratio r_c is the ratio of the cylinder volumes after and before the combustion process in the Diesel cycle.

Diesel cycle is the ideal cycle for compress-ignition reciprocating engines, and was first proposed by Rudolf Diesel in the 1890s. Using the air-standard assumptions, the cycle consists of four internally reversible processes:
    1-2 Isentropic compression
    2-3 Constant pressure heat addition
    3-4 Isentropic expansion
    4-1 Constant volume heat rejection

Displacement volume is the volume displaced by the piston as it moves between top dead center and bottom dead center.

Dual cycle is the ideal cycle which models the combustion process in both gasoline and diesel engines as a combination of two heat-transfer processes, one at constant volume and the other at constant pressure.

Gas power cycles are cycles where the working fluid remains a gas throughout the entire cycle. Spark-ignition automobile engines, diesel engines, and conventional gas turbines are familiar examples of devices that operate on gas cycles.

Ericsson cycle is made up of four totally reversible processes:
    1-2 T = constant expansion (heat addition from the external source)
    2-3 P = constant regeneration (internal heat transfer from the working fluid to the regenerator)
    3-4 T = constant compression (heat rejection to the external sink)
    4-1 P = constant regeneration (internal heat transfer from the regenerator back to the working fluid)

Exhaust valve is the exit through which the combustion products are expelled from the cylinder.

External combustion engines are engines in which the fuel is burned outside the system boundary.

Four-stroke internal combustion engines are engines in which the piston executes four complete strokes (two mechanical cycles) within the cylinder, and the crankshaft completes two revolutions for each thermodynamic cycle.

Heat engines are devices designed for the purpose of converting other forms of energy (usually in the form of heat) to work.

Ideal cycle is an actual cycle stripped of all the internal irreversibilities and complexities. The ideal cycle resembles the actual cycle closely but is made up totally of internally reversible processes.

Intake valve is an inlet through which the air or air–fuel mixture is drawn into the cylinder.

Internal combustion engines are engines where the energy is provided by burning a fuel within the system boundaries.

Jet-propulsion cycle is the cycle used in aircraft gas turbines. The ideal jet-propulsion cycle differs from the simple ideal Brayton cycle in that the gases are not expanded to the ambient pressure in the turbine. Instead, they are expanded to a pressure such that the power produced by the turbine is just sufficient to drive the compressor and the auxiliary equipment. The gases that exit the turbine at a relatively high pressure are subsequently accelerated in a nozzle to provide the thrust to propel the aircraft.

Knock, or engine knock, is the audible noise occurring in the engine because of autoignition, the premature ignition of the fuel.

Mean effective pressure (MEP) is a fictitious pressure that, if it acted on the piston during the entire power stroke, would produce the same amount of net work as that produced during the actual cycle. The mean effective pressure can be used as a parameter to compare the performances of reciprocating engines of equal size. The engine with a larger value of MEP will deliver more net work per cycle and thus will perform better.

Multistage compression with intercooling requires the compression process in a compressor to be carried out in stages and to cool the gas in between each stage such that the work required to compress a gas between two specified pressures can be decreased.

Multistage expansion with reheating requires the expansion process in a turbine be carried out in stages and reheating the gas between the stages such that the work output of a turbine operating between two pressure levels can be increased.

Octane rating of a fuel is a measure of the engine knock resistance of a fuel.

Otto cycle is the ideal cycle for spark-ignition reciprocating engines. It is named after Nikolaus A. Otto, who built a successful four-stroke engine in 1876 in Germany using the cycle proposed by Frenchman Beau de Rochas in 1862. The ideal Otto cycle, which closely resembles the actual operating conditions, utilizes the air-standard assumptions. It consists of four internally reversible processes:
    1-2 Isentropic compression
    2-3 Constant volume heat addition
    3-4 Isentropic expansion
    4-1 Constant volume heat rejection

Pressure ratio is the ratio of final to initial pressures during a compression process.

Propulsive efficiency of an aircraft turbojet engine is the ratio of the power produced to propel the aircraft and the thermal energy of the fuel released during the combustion process.

Propulsive power is the power developed from the thrust of the aircraft gas turbines and is the propulsive force (thrust) times the distance this force acts on the aircraft per unit time, that is, the thrust times the aircraft velocity.

Ramjet engine is a properly shaped duct with no compressor or turbine, and is sometimes used for high-speed propulsion of missiles and aircraft. The pressure rise in the engine is provided by the ram effect of the incoming high-speed air being rammed against a barrier. Therefore, a ramjet engine needs to be brought to a sufficiently high speed by an external source before it can be fired.

Regeneration is a process during which heat is transferred to a thermal energy storage device (called a regenerator) during one part of the cycle and is transferred back to the working fluid during another part of the cycle.

Regenerator effectiveness is the extent to which a regenerator approaches an ideal regenerator and is defined as the ratio of the heat transfer to the compressor exit gas to the maximum possible heat transfer to the compressor exit gas.

Rocket is a device where a solid or liquid fuel and an oxidizer react in the combustion chamber. The high-pressure combustion gases are then expanded in a nozzle. The gases leave the rocket at very high velocities, producing the thrust to propel the rocket.

Scramjet engine is essentially a ramjet in which air flows through at supersonic speeds (above the speed of sound).

Spark-ignition (SI) engines are reciprocating engines in which the combustion of the air–fuel mixture is initiated by a spark plug.

Stirling cycle is made up of four totally reversible processes:
> 1-2 *T constant* expansion (heat addition from the external source)
> 2-3 *v constant* regeneration (internal heat transfer from the working fluid to the regenerator)
> 3-4 *T constant* compression (heat rejection to the external sink)
> 4-1 *v constant* regeneration (internal heat transfer from the regenerator back to the working fluid)

Stroke is the distance between the top dead center and the bottom dead center is the largest distance that the piston can travel in one direction within a cylinder.

Thermal efficiency η_{th} is the ratio of the net work produced by a heat engine to the total heat input, $\eta_{th} = W_{net}/Q_{in}$.

Thrust is the unbalanced force developed in a turbojet engine that is caused by the difference in the momentum of the low-velocity air entering the engine and the high-velocity exhaust gases leaving the engine, and it is determined from Newton's second law.

Top dead center (TDC) is the position of the piston when it forms the smallest volume in the cylinder.

Turbofan (or *fan-jet*) engine is the most widely used engine in aircraft propulsion. In this engine a large fan driven by the turbine forces a considerable amount of air through a duct (cowl) surrounding the engine. The fan exhaust leaves the duct at a higher velocity, enhancing the total thrust of the engine significantly. A turbofan engine is based on the principle that for the same power, a large volume of slower-moving air will produce more thrust than a small volume of fast-moving air. The first commercial turbofan engine was successfully tested in 1955.

Turboprop engine uses propellers powered by the aircraft turbine to produce the aircraft propulsive power.

Two-stroke engines execute the entire cycle in just two strokes: the power stroke and the compression stroke.

EXAMPLE 8-1   Carnot heat engine in a closed system

A Carnot heat engine with air as the working fluid operates between the temperature limits of 180°C and 30°C and the maximum and minimum pressures in the cycle are 2.5 MPa and 100 kPa, respectively. The cycle is executed in a piston-cylinder device. The volume of the air changes from 0.25 m³ to 0.4 m³ during the isothermal expansion process and it changes from 0.50 m³ to 0.35 m³ during the isothermal compression process. Using constant specific heats at room temperature, determine (a) the thermal efficiency, (b) the amount of heat input to the cycle, and (c) the net work output.

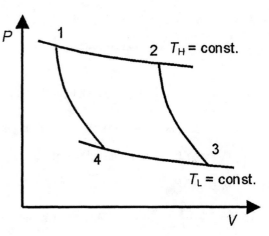

Equations

GIVEN

$$T_1 = ConvertTemp\,(C,\ K,\ 180) \tag{1}$$

$$T_2 = T_1 \tag{2}$$

$$T_3 = ConvertTemp\,(C,\ K,\ 30) \tag{3}$$

$$T_4 = T_3 \tag{4}$$

$$P_1 = 2.5\ [\text{MPa}] \cdot \left| 1000\ \frac{kPa}{\text{MPa}} \right| \tag{5}$$

$$P_3 = 100\ [\text{kPa}] \tag{6}$$

$$V_1 = 0.25\ [\text{m}^3] \tag{7}$$

$$V_2 = 0.40\ [\text{m}^3] \tag{8}$$

$$V_3 = 0.50\ [\text{m}^3] \tag{9}$$

$$V_4 = 0.35\ [\text{m}^3] \tag{10}$$

PROPERTIES

$$Fluid\$ = \text{'Air'} \tag{11}$$

$$C_p = c_p\,(Fluid\$,\ T = T_3) \qquad \textbf{Specific heat at constant pressure} \tag{12}$$

$$C_v = c_v\,(Fluid\$,\ T = T_3) \qquad \textbf{Specific heat at constant volume} \tag{13}$$

$$k = C_p / C_v \tag{14}$$

$$R = C_p - C_v \quad \textbf{Gas constant} \tag{15}$$

ANALYSIS

$$\eta_{th} = 1 - \frac{T_3}{T_1} \quad \textbf{Thermal efficiency} \tag{16}$$

$$W_{12} = P_1 \cdot V_1 \cdot \ln\left(\frac{V_2}{V_1}\right) \quad \textbf{Work of isothermal expansion, process 1-2} \tag{17}$$

$$Q_{12} = W_{12} \quad \textbf{Isothermal process of an ideal gas, internal energy change is zero} \tag{18}$$

$$P_1 \cdot V_1 = m \cdot R \cdot T_1 \quad \textbf{Equation of state} \tag{19}$$

$$P_2 \cdot V_2 = m \cdot R \cdot T_2 \tag{20}$$

$$W_{23} = \frac{P_3 \cdot V_3 - P_2 \cdot V_2}{1 - k} \quad \textbf{Work of isentropic expansion, process 2-3} \tag{21}$$

$$W_{34} = P_3 \cdot V_3 \cdot \ln\left(\frac{V_4}{V_3}\right) \quad \textbf{Work of isothermal compression, process 3-4} \tag{22}$$

$$P_4 \cdot V_4 = m \cdot R \cdot T_4 \tag{23}$$

$$W_{41} = \frac{P_1 \cdot V_1 - P_4 \cdot V_4}{1 - k} \quad \textbf{Work of isentropic compression, process 4-1} \tag{24}$$

$$W_{net} = W_{12} + W_{23} + W_{34} + W_{41} \quad \textbf{Network, compression works are negative} \tag{25}$$

Solution

$C_p = 1.007$ [kJ/kg-K] $C_v = 0.7197$ [kJ/kg-K]

$\boxed{\eta_{th} = 0.331}$ $Fluid\$ = $ 'Air'

$k = 1.399$ $m = 4.805$ [kg]

$\boxed{Q_{12} = 293.8 \text{ [kJ]}}$ $R = 0.287$ [kJ/kg-K]

$W_{12} = 293.8$ [kJ] $W_{23} = 1442$ [kJ]

$W_{34} = -17.83$ [kJ] $W_{41} = -518.7$ [kJ]

$\boxed{W_{net} = 1199 \text{ [kJ]}}$

Arrays

Row	P_i [kPa]	T_i [K]	V_i [m^3]
1	2500	453.1	0.25
2	1562	453.1	0.4
3	100	303.2	0.5
4	1195	303.2	0.35

EXAMPLE 8-2   Otto cycle with constant specific heats

A four-cylinder, four-stroke, 2.2-liter gasoline engine operates on the Otto cycle with a compression ratio of 10. The air is at 100 kPa and 60°C at the beginning of the compression process. The maximum pressure in the cycle is 8 MPa. The compression and expansion processes may be modeled as polytropic with a polytropic constant of 1.3. Using constant specific heats at 850 K, determine (a) the temperature at the end of the expansion process, (b) the net work output and the thermal efficiency, (c) the mean effective pressure, (d) the engine speed for a net power output of 70 kW, and (e) the specific fuel consumption, in g/kWh, defined as the ratio of the mass of the fuel consumed to the work produced. The air-fuel ratio, defined as the amount of air divided by the amount of fuel to the engine, is 16.

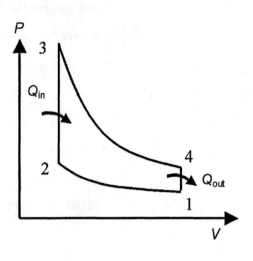

Equations

GIVEN

$$Vol_d = 0.0022 \; [\text{m}^3] \quad \text{Total engine displacement volume} \tag{1}$$

$$r = 10 \quad r = v_1 / v_2 = v_4 / v_3 \tag{2}$$

$$P_1 = 100 \; [\text{kPa}] \tag{3}$$

$$T_1 = ConvertTemp\,(C, \; K, \; 60) \tag{4}$$

$$P_3 = 8 \; [\text{MPa}] \cdot \left| 1000 \, \frac{\text{kPa}}{\text{MPa}} \right| \tag{5}$$

$$n = 1.3 \quad \text{Polytropic constant} \tag{6}$$

$$\dot{W}_{net} = 70 \; [\text{kW}] \tag{7}$$

$$AF = 16 \quad AF = m_{air} / m_{fuel} \tag{8}$$

PROPERTIES

$$Fluid\$ = \text{'Air'} \tag{9}$$

$$C_p = c_p\,(Fluid\$, \; T = 850) \quad \text{Specific heat at constant pressure} \tag{10}$$

$$C_v = c_v\,(Fluid\$, \; T = 850) \quad \text{Specific heat at constant volume} \tag{11}$$

$$R_{air} = C_p - C_v \quad \text{Gas constant} \tag{12}$$

ANALYSIS

$$T_2 / T_1 = r^{n-1} \quad \text{Process 1-2: polytropic compression} \tag{13}$$

$$P_2/P_1 = r^n \tag{14}$$

$$T_3/T_2 = (P_3/P_2) \qquad \text{Process 2-3: constant volume heat addition} \tag{15}$$

$$q_{in} = C_v \cdot (T_3 - T_2) \qquad \text{Process 2-3: constant volume heat addition} \tag{16}$$

$$T_4/T_3 = (1/r)^{n-1} \qquad \text{Process 3-4: polytropic expansion} \tag{17}$$

$$P_4/P_3 = (1/r)^n \tag{18}$$

$$q_{out} = C_v \cdot (T_4 - T_1) \qquad \text{Process 4-1: constant volume heat rejection} \tag{19}$$

$$w_{net} = q_{in} - q_{out} \qquad \text{Net output work} \tag{20}$$

$$\eta_{th} = w_{net}/q_{in} \qquad \text{Thermal efficeincy} \tag{21}$$

$$P_1 \cdot v_1 = (R_{air} \cdot T_1) \qquad \text{Equation of state per mass basis} \tag{22}$$

$$r = v_1/v_2 \tag{23}$$

$$MEP = \frac{w_{net}}{v_1 - v_2} \tag{24}$$

$$r = \frac{Vol_c + Vol_d}{Vol_c} \qquad \text{Vol}_c \text{ is the total engine clearence volume} \tag{25}$$

$$Vol_1 = Vol_d + Vol_c \tag{26}$$

$$m_t = \frac{P_1 \cdot Vol_1}{R_{air} \cdot T_1} \qquad \text{Total air+fuel mass in engine} \tag{27}$$

$$\dot{W}_{net} = \left(\frac{\dot{n} \cdot \left| 0.016667 \, \frac{rps}{rpm} \right|}{n_{rev}} \cdot m_t \right) \cdot w_{net} \tag{28}$$

$$n_{rev} = 2 \qquad \text{For four-stroke cycle, there are two revolutions per cycle} \tag{29}$$

$$m_t = m_{air} + m_{fuel} \tag{30}$$

$$AF = m_{air}/m_{fuel} \tag{31}$$

$$sfc = \frac{m_{fuel}}{m_t \cdot w_{net}} \cdot \left| 3.6 \times 10^6 \, \frac{g/kWh}{kg/kJ} \right| \qquad \text{Specific fuel consumption} \tag{32}$$

Solution

$AF = 16$ $C_p = 1.11$ [kJ/kg-K] $C_v = 0.8229$ [kJ/kg-K] $\boxed{\eta_{th} = 0.4988}$

$Fluid\$ = \text{'Air'}$ $\boxed{MEP = 954.1 \text{ [kPa]}}$ $m_{air} = 0.002406$ [kg] $m_{fuel} = 0.0001504$ [kg]

$m_t = 0.002556$ [kg] $n = 1.3$ $\boxed{\dot{n} = 4002 \text{ [rpm]}}$ $n_{rev} = 2$ [rev/cycle]

$P_1 = 100$ [kPa] $P_2 = 1995$ [kPa] $P_3 = 8000$ [kPa] $P_4 = 400.9$ [kPa]

$q_{in} = 1646$ [kJ/kg] $q_{out} = 825$ [kJ/kg] $r = 10$ $R_{air} = 0.287$ [kJ/kg-K]

$\boxed{sfc = 257.9 \text{ [g/kWh]}}$ $T_1 = 333.2$ [K] $T_2 = 664.7$ [K] $T_3 = 2665$ [K]

$\boxed{T_4 = 1336 \text{ [K]}}$ $Vol_1 = 0.002444 \left[\text{m}^3\right]$ $Vol_c = 0.0002444 \left[\text{m}^3\right]$ $Vol_d = 0.0022 \left[\text{m}^3\right]$

$v_1 = 0.9562 \left[\text{m}^3/\text{kg}\right]$ $v_2 = 0.09562 \left[\text{m}^3/\text{kg}\right]$ $\dot{W}_{net} = 70$ [kW] $\boxed{w_{net} = 821.1 \text{ [kJ/kg]}}$

EXAMPLE 8-3   A diesel-fuel burning gas-turbine cycle

A gas-turbine plant operates on the simple Brayton cycle between the pressure limits of 100 and 700 kPa. The air enters the compressor at 30°C at a rate of 12.6 kg/s and leaves at 260°C. A diesel fuel with a heating value of 42,000 kJ/kg is burned in the combustion chamber with an air-fuel ratio of 60 and a combustion efficiency of 97 percent. The combustion gases leave the combustion chamber and enter an 85 percent efficient turbine. Using the properties of the air for the combustion gases and using constant specific heats at 500°C, determine (a) the isentropic efficiency of the compressor, (b) the net power output and the back work ratio, (c) the thermal efficiency, and (d) the second-law efficiency.

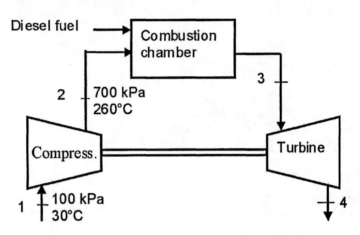

Equations

GIVEN

$$P_1 = 100 \ [\text{kPa}] \tag{1}$$

$$P_2 = 700 \ [\text{kPa}] \tag{2}$$

$$T_1 = ConvertTemp \, (C, \ K, \ 30) \tag{3}$$

$$T_2 = ConvertTemp \, (C, \ K, \ 260) \tag{4}$$

$$\dot{m}_a = 12.6 \ [\text{kg/s}] \tag{5}$$

$$HV = 42000 \ [\text{kJ/kg}] \tag{6}$$

$$AF = 60 \tag{7}$$

$$\eta_{comb} = 0.97 \tag{8}$$

$$\eta_T = 0.85 \tag{9}$$

PROPERTIES

$$Fluid\$ = \text{‘Air’} \tag{10}$$

$$C_p = c_p \,(\text{Fluid\$},\ T = T) \qquad \textbf{Specific heat at constant pressure} \tag{11}$$

$$C_v = c_v \,(\text{Fluid\$},\ T = T) \qquad \textbf{Specific heat at constant volume} \tag{12}$$

$$T = ConvertTemp\,(C,\ K,\ 500) \tag{13}$$

$$k = C_p/C_v \tag{14}$$

ANALYSIS

$$T_{2s}/T_1 = (P_2/P_1)^{\frac{k-1}{k}} \tag{15}$$

$$\eta_C = \frac{T_{2s} - T_1}{T_2 - T_1} \qquad \textbf{Isentropic efficiency} \tag{16}$$

$$AF = \dot{m}_a/\dot{m}_f \tag{17}$$

$$\dot{m} = \dot{m}_a + \dot{m}_f \tag{18}$$

$$\dot{Q}_{in} = \dot{m}_f \cdot HV \cdot \eta_{comb} \tag{19}$$

$$\dot{Q}_{in} = (\dot{m} \cdot C_p) \cdot (T_3 - T_2) \tag{20}$$

$$T_{4s}/T_3 = (P_1/P_2)^{\frac{k-1}{k}} \tag{21}$$

$$\eta_T = \frac{T_4 - T_3}{(T_3 - T_{4s})} \qquad \textbf{Turbine efficiency} \tag{22}$$

$$\dot{W}_{C,in} = \dot{m}_a \cdot C_p \cdot (T_2 - T_1) \qquad \textbf{Compression power} \tag{23}$$

$$\dot{W}_{T,out} = \dot{m} \cdot C_p \cdot (T_3 - T_4) \qquad \textbf{Turbine output power} \tag{24}$$

$$\dot{W}_{net} = \dot{W}_{T,out} - \dot{W}_{C,in} \qquad \textbf{Net power} \tag{25}$$

$$r_{bw} = \dot{W}_{C,in}/\dot{W}_{T,out} \qquad \textbf{Back-work ratio} \tag{26}$$

$$\eta_{th} = \dot{W}_{net}/\dot{Q}_{in} \qquad \textbf{Thermal efficiency} \tag{27}$$

$$\eta_{th,max} = 1 - T_1/T_3 \qquad \textbf{Carnot efficiency} \tag{28}$$

$$\eta_{II} = \eta_{th}/\eta_{th,max} \qquad \textbf{Second-law efficiency} \tag{29}$$

Solution

$AF = 60$ $C_p = 1.093$ [kJ/kg-K] $C_v = 0.8055$ [kJ/kg-K] $\boxed{\eta_C = 0.8796}$

$\eta_{comb} = 0.97$ $\boxed{\eta_{II} = -1.37}$ $\eta_T = 0.85$ $\boxed{\eta_{th} = -1.007}$

$\eta_{th,max} = 0.7351$ $Fluid\$ = \text{'Air'}$ $HV = 42000$ [kJ/kg] $k = 1.356$

$\dot{m} = 12.81$ [kg/s] $\dot{m}_a = 12.6$ [kg/s] $\dot{m}_f = 0.21$ [kg/s] $P_1 = 100$ [kPa]

$P_2 = 700$ [kPa] $\dot{Q}_{in} = 8555$ [kW] $\boxed{r_{bw} = -0.581}$ $T = 773.2$

$T_1 = 303.2$ [K] $T_2 = 533.2$ [K] $T_{2s} = 505.5$ [K] $T_3 = 1144$ [K]

$T_4 = 1534$ [K] $T_{4s} = 686.4$ [K] $\dot{W}_{C,in} = 3166$ [kW] $\boxed{\dot{W}_{net} = -8615 \text{ [kW]}}$

$\dot{W}_{T,out} = -5449$ [kW]

Supplement 8.1 Otto cycle with variable specific heats

A four-cylinder, four-stroke spark-ignition engine operates on the ideal Otto cycle with a compression ratio of 11 and a total displacement volume of 1.8 liter. The air is at 90 kPa and 50°C at the beginning of the compression process. The heat input is 1.5 kJ per cycle per cylinder. Accounting for the variation of specific heats of air with temperature, determine (a) the maximum temperature and pressure that occur during the cycle, (b) the net work per cycle per cylinder and the thermal efficiency, (c) the mean effective pressure, and (d) the power output for an engine speed of 3000 rpm. *Answers*: (a) 4037 K, 12,375 kPa, (b) 0.792 kJ, 0.528, (c) 1761 kPa, (d) 79.2 kW

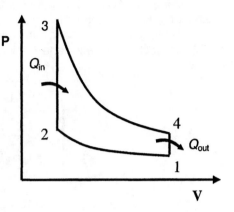

Supplement 8.2 Power output and fuel consumption of a diesel engine

A six-cylinder, four-stroke, 4.5 liter compression-ignition engine operates on the ideal diesel cycle with a compression ratio of 17. The air is at 95 kPa and 55°C at the beginning of the compression process and the engine speed is 2000 rpm. The engine uses light diesel fuel with a heating value of 42,500 kJ/kg, an air-fuel ratio of 24, and a combustion efficiency of 98 percent. Using constant specific heats at 850 K, determine (a) the maximum temperature in the cycle and the cutoff ratio (b) the net work output per cycle and the thermal efficiency, (c) the mean effective pressure, (d) the net power output, and (e) the specific fuel consumption, in g/kWh, defined as the ratio of the mass of the fuel consumed to the work produced. *Answers*: (a) 2382 K, 2.7 (b) 4.36 kJ, 0.542, (c) 969 kPa, (d) 72.7 kW, (e) 159 g/kWh

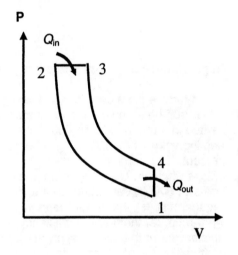

Supplement 8.3 Energy and exergy analyses of a dual cycle

A four-cylinder, four-stroke, 2.8 liter modern, high-speed compression-ignition engine operates on the ideal dual cycle with a compression ratio of 14. The air is at 95 kPa and 55°C at the beginning of the compression process and the engine speed is 3500 rpm. Half of the fuel can be considered burned at constant volume, and half at constant pressure. Due to structural limitations, maximum allowable pressure in the cycle will be 9 MPa. Using constant specific heats at 850 K, determine (a) the maximum temperature in the cycle, (b) the net work output and the thermal efficiency, (c) the mean effective pressure, and (d) the net power output. Also, determine (e) the second law efficiency of the cycle and the rate of exergy of the exhaust gases when they are purged. *Answers*: (a) 3255 K, (b) 1348 kJ/kg, 0.587, (c) 1465 kPa, (d) 120 kW, (e) 0.646, 50.8 kW

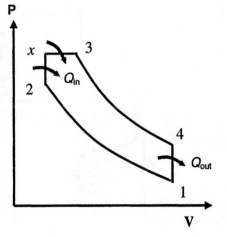

Supplement 8.4 An actual gas-turbine cycle

A gas-turbine plant operates on the simple Brayton cycle between the pressure limits of 100 and 1200 kPa. The working fluid is air. The air enters the compressor at 30°C at a rate of 150 m³/min and leaves the turbine at 500°C. Assuming a compressor isentropic efficiency of 82 percent and a turbine isentropic efficiency of 88 percent, and using variable specific heats, determine (a) the net power output, (b) the back work ratio, and (c) the thermal efficiency. *Answers*: (a) 659 kW, (b) 0.625, (c) 0.319

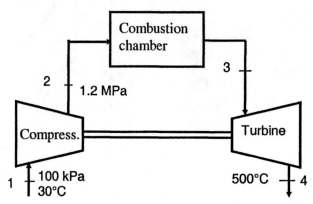

Supplement 8.5 Energy and exergy analyses of a regenerative gas-turbine cycle

A gas-turbine plant operates on the regenerative Brayton cycle between the pressure limits of 100 and 700 kPa. The air enters the compressor at 30°C at a rate of 12.6 kg/s and leaves at 260°C. Then, it is heated in a regenerator to 400°C by the hot combustion gases leaving the turbine. A diesel fuel with a heating value of 42,000 kJ/kg is burned in the combustion chamber with a combustion efficiency of 97 percent. The combustion gases leave the combustion chamber at 871°C and enter an 85 percent efficient turbine. Using the properties of the air for the combustion gases and using constant specific heats at 500°C, determine (a) the isentropic efficiency of the compressor, (b) the effectiveness of the regenerator, (c) the air-fuel ratio in the combustion chamber, (d) the net power output and the back work ratio, (e) the thermal efficiency, and (f) the second law efficiency. Also, determine (g) the exergy efficiencies of the compressor, the turbine, and the regenerator, and (h) the rate of the exergy of the combustion gases at the regenerator exit. *Answers*: (a) 0.879, (b) 0.631, (c) 78.2, (d) 2260 kW, 0.584, (e) 0.344, (f) 0.468, (g) 0.930, 0.931, 0.890, (h) 1353 kW

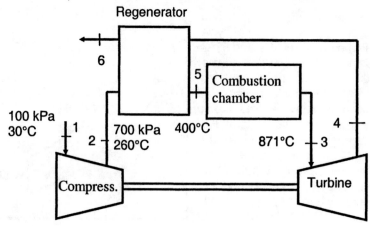

Supplement 8.6 A regenerative gas-turbine cycle with reheating and intercooling

A gas-turbine plant operates on the regenerative Brayton cycle with two stages of reheating and two-stages of intercooling between the pressure limits of 100 and 1200 kPa. The working fluid is air. The air enters the first and the second stages of the compressor at 300 K and 350 K, respectively and the first and the second stages of the turbine at 1400 K and 1300 K, respectively. Assuming both the compressor and the turbine have an isentropic efficiency of 80 percent and the regenerator has an effectiveness of 75 percent, and using variable specific heats, determine (a) the back work ratio and the net work output (b) the thermal efficiency, and (c) the second-law efficiency. Also, determine (d) the exergies at the exits of the combustion chamber (state 6) and the regenerator (state 10) (See Figure 8.43 in the text). *Answers*: (a) 0.523, 317 kJ/kg, (b) 0.553, (c) 0.704, (d) 931 kJ/kg, 129 kJ/kg

Supplement 8.7 A gas-turbine cogeneration plant

The electricity and the process heat requirements of a manufacturing facility are to be met by a cogeneration plant consisting of a gas-turbine and a heat exchanger for steam production. The plant operates on the simple Brayton cycle between the pressure limits of 100 and 1200 kPa with air as the working fluid. The air enters the compressor at 30°C and the combustion gases leave the turbine at 500°C before entering the heat exchanger. The combustion gases leave the heat exchanger at 350°C while the liquid water enters the heat exchanger at 25°C and leaves at 200°C as a saturated vapor. The net power produced by the gas-turbine cycle is 800 kW. Assuming a compressor isentropic efficiency of 82 percent and a turbine isentropic efficiency of 88 percent, and using variable specific heats, determine (a) the mass flow rate of the air in the cycle, (b) the back work ratio and the thermal efficiency, and (c) the rate at which steam is produced in the heat exchanger. Also, determine (d) the utilization efficiency of the cogeneration plant defined as the total useful energy output divided by the heat input to the plant. *Answers*: (a) 3.49 kg/s, (b) 0.625, 0.319, (c) 0.209 kg/s, (d) 0.544

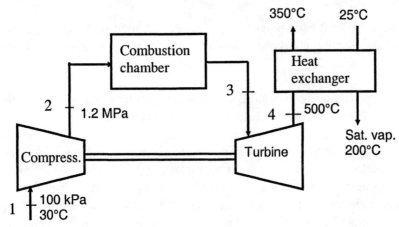

Supplement 8.8 An actual jet propulsion cycle

A turbojet aircraft flies with a velocity of 900 km/h at an altitude where the air is .35°C and 40 kPa. The air leaves the diffuser at 50 kPa with a velocity of 15 m/s. The gases are at 450 kPa and 950°C at the turbine inlet. The power consumed by the compressor and that produced by the turbine is same, and it is equal to 500 kW. Assuming an isentropic efficiency of 83 percent for all the compressor, turbine, and nozzle, and using variable specific heats, determine (a) the pressure of the gases at the turbine exit, (b) the mass flow rate of the air through the compressor, (c) the velocity of the gases at the nozzle exit, and (d) the propulsive power and the propulsive efficiency of the cycle. See Figure 8.48 in the text. *Answers*: (a) 147 kPa, (b) 1.76 kg/s, (c) 719 m/s, (d) 206 kW, 0.156

Chapter 9 Educational Objectives and Glossary

The Educational Objectives of Chapter 9 are to:

- Analyze vapor power cycles in which the working fluid is alternately vaporized and condensed.
- Analyze power generation coupled with process heating called cogeneration.
- Investigate ways to modify the basic Rankine vapor power cycle to increase the cycle thermal efficiency.
- Analyze the reheat and regenerative vapor power cycles.
- Analyze power cycles that consist of two separate cycles known as combined cycles
- Introduce the concepts of binary cycles.

Chapter 9 Glossary

Binary vapor cycle is a vapor cycle in which the condenser of the high-temperature cycle (also called the topping cycle) serves as the boiler of the low-temperature cycle (also called the bottoming cycle). That is, the heat output of the high-temperature cycle is used as the heat input to the low-temperature one.

Boiler is basically a large heat exchanger where the heat originating from combustion gases, nuclear reactors, or other sources is transferred to the water essentially at constant pressure.

Bottoming cycle is a power cycle operating at low average temperatures that receives heat from a power cycle operating at higher average temperatures.

Closed feedwater heater is a feedwater heater in which heat is transferred from the extracted steam to the feedwater without any mixing taking place. The two streams are typically not at the same pressures, since they do not mix. In an ideal closed feedwater heater, the feedwater is heated to the exit temperature of the extracted steam, which ideally leaves the heater as a saturated liquid at the extraction pressure. In actual power plants, the feedwater leaves the heater below the exit temperature of the extracted steam because a temperature difference of at least a few degrees is required for any effective heat transfer to take place.

Cogeneration is the production of more than one useful form of energy (such as process heat and electric power) from the same energy source.

Combined gas–vapor cycle, or just the **combined cycle** is the gas-turbine (Brayton) cycle topping a steam-turbine (Rankine) cycle, which has a higher thermal efficiency than either of the cycles executed individually.

Condenser is a heat exchanger in which a vapor, such as steam, condenses to the saturated liquid state as the result of heat transfer from the vapor to a cooling medium such as a lake, a river, or the atmosphere.

Feedwater heater is the device where the feedwater is heated by regeneration. This technique is used to raise the temperature of the liquid leaving the pump (called the feedwater) before it enters the boiler. A practical regeneration process in steam power plants is accomplished by extracting, or "bleeding," steam from the turbine at various points. This steam, which could have produced more work by expanding further in the turbine, is used to heat the feedwater instead.

Heat rate is the expression of the conversion efficiency of power plants in the United States and is the amount of heat supplied, in Btu's, to generate 1 kWh of electricity. The smaller the heat rate, the greater the efficiency.

Open (or **direct-contact) feedwater heater** is basically a mixing chamber, where the steam extracted from the turbine mixes with the feedwater exiting the pump. Ideally, the mixture leaves the heater as a saturated liquid at the heater pressure.

Process heat is required energy input in the form of heat for many industrial processes. The process heat is often obtained as heat transfer from high-pressure, high-temperature steam. Some industries that rely heavily on process heat are chemical, pulp and paper, oil production and refining, steel making, food processing, and textile industries.

Pump is a steady flow device used to increase the pressure of a liquid.

Rankine cycle is the ideal cycle for vapor power plants. The ideal Rankine cycle does not involve any internal irreversibilities and consists of the following four processes:
    1-2 Isentropic compression in a pump
    2-3 Constant pressure heat addition in a boiler
    3-4 Isentropic expansion in a turbine
    4-1 Constant pressure heat rejection in a condenser

Rankine cycle with reheat is a modification of the Rankine cycle in which the steam is expanded in the turbine in two stages and reheated in between. Reheating is a practical solution to the excessive moisture problem in the lower-pressure stages of turbines, and it is used frequently in modern steam power plants.

Steam generator is the combination of a boiler and a heat exchanger section (the superheater), where steam is superheated.

Topping cycle is a power cycle operating at high average temperatures that rejects heat to a power cycle operating at lower average temperatures.

Trap is a device that allows condensed steam to be routed to another heater or to the condenser. A trap allows the liquid to be throttled to a lower-pressure region but traps the vapor. The enthalpy of steam remains constant during this throttling process.

Utilization factor is a measure of the energy transferred to the steam in the boiler of a steam power plant that is utilized as either process heat or electric power. Thus the utilization factor is defined for a cogeneration plant as the ratio of the sum of the net work output and the process heat to the total heat input.

EXAMPLE 9-1   Comparison of Carnot and Rankine cycles

Calculate and compare the net work output and the thermal efficiency for a Carnot cycle and a simple ideal Rankine cycle with steam as the working fluid. In both cycles, the steam enters the turbine at 10 MPa as a saturated vapor and the condenser pressure is 20 kPa. In Rankine cycle, the condenser exit state is saturated liquid and in Carnot cycle, the boiler inlet state is saturated liquid.

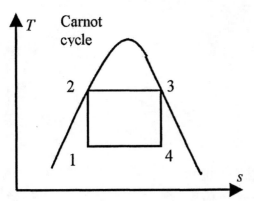
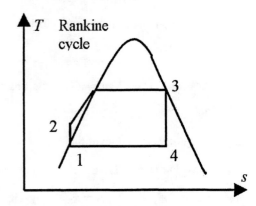

Equations

GIVEN

$$P_3 = 10 \ [\text{MPa}] \cdot \left| 1000 \ \frac{\text{kPa}}{\text{MPa}} \right| \tag{1}$$

$$x_3 = 1 \tag{2}$$

$$P_4 = 20 \ [\text{kPa}] \tag{3}$$

ANALYSIS

$$Fluid\$ = \text{'Steam\_iapws'} \tag{4}$$

Rankine cycle

$P_1 = P_4$ **Condenser pressure** $\qquad\qquad$ (5)

$P_2 = P_3$ **Boiler pressure** $\qquad\qquad$ (6)

$h_1 = \text{h}\,(\text{Fluid\$}, \ P = P_1, \ x = 0)$ **Specific enthalpy at condenser exit** $\qquad$ (7)

$v_1 = \text{v}\,(\text{Fluid\$}, \ P = P_1, \ x = 0)$ **Specific volume at condenser exit** $\qquad$ (8)

$s_1 = \text{s}\,(\text{Fluid\$}, \ P = P_1, \ x = 0)$ **Specific entropy at condenser exit** $\qquad$ (9)

$w_{pump} = v_1 \cdot (P_2 - P_1)$ **Pumping work** $\qquad\qquad$ (10)

$w_{pump} = h_2 - h_1$ $\qquad\qquad$ (11)

$h_3 = \text{h}\,(\text{Fluid\$}, \ P = P_3, \ x = x_3)$ **Specific enthalpy at turbine inlet** $\qquad$ (12)

$s_3 = \text{s}\,(\text{Fluid\$}, \; P = P_3, \; x = x_3)$ **Specific entropy at turbine inlet**   (13)

$h_4 = \text{h}\,(\text{Fluid\$}, \; P = P_4, \; s = s_3)$ **Specific enthalpy at condenser inlet**   (14)

$q_{in,R} = h_3 - h_2$ **Heat added in the boiler**   (15)

$q_{out} = h_4 - h_1$ **Heat rejected in the condesner**   (16)

$w_{net,R} = q_{in,R} - q_{out}$ **Net output work**   (17)

$\eta_{th,R} = 1 - q_{out}/q_{in,R}$ **Thermal efficiency**   (18)

Carnot cycle

$T_3 = \text{T}\,(\text{Fluid\$}, \; P = P_3, \; x = x_3)$ **Boiling temperature**   (19)

$T_2 = T_3$ (20)

$x_2 = 0$ **Saturated liquid at boiler inlet**   (21)

$h_{2,C} = \text{h}\,(\text{Fluid\$}, \; T = T_2, \; x = x_2)$ **Specific enthalpy at boiler inlet**   (22)

$s_{2,C} = \text{s}\,(\text{Fluid\$}, \; T = T_2, \; x = x_2)$ **Specific entropy at boiler inlet**   (23)

$h_{1,C} = \text{h}\,(\text{Fluid\$}, \; P = P_1, \; s = s_{2,C})$ **Specific enthalpy at condenser exit**   (24)

$q_{in,C} = h_3 - h_{2,C}$ (25)

$q_{out,C} = h_4 - h_{1,C}$ (26)

$w_{net,C} = q_{in,C} - q_{out,C}$ (27)

$\eta_{th,C} = 1 - q_{out,C}/q_{in,C}$ (28)

Solution

$\boxed{\eta_{th,C} = 0.4296}$ $\boxed{\eta_{th,R} = 0.353}$ $Fluid\$ = \text{'Steam\_iapws'}$ $h_{1,C} = 1094 \,[\text{kJ/kg}]$

$h_{2,C} = 1408 \,[\text{kJ/kg}]$ $q_{in,C} = 1318 \,[\text{kJ/kg}]$ $q_{in,R} = 2464 \,[\text{kJ/kg}]$ $q_{out} = 1594 \,[\text{kJ/kg}]$

$q_{out,C} = 751.6 \,[\text{kJ/kg}]$ $s_{2,C} = 3.36 \,[\text{kJ/kg-K}]$ $T_2 = 311 \,[\text{C}]$ $T_3 = 311 \,[\text{C}]$

$\boxed{w_{net,C} = 566 \,[\text{kJ/kg}]}$ $\boxed{w_{net,R} = 869.9 \,[\text{kJ/kg}]}$ $w_{pump} = 10.15 \,[\text{kJ/kg}]$ $x_2 = 0$

$x_3 = 1$

Arrays

Row	h_i [kJ/kg]	P_i [kPa]	s_i [kJ/kg-K]	v_i [m³/kg]
1	251.4	20	0.832	0.001017
2	261.6	10000		
3	2725	10000	5.616	
4	1845	20		

EXAMPLE 9-2   A binary geothermal power plant

A binary geothermal power plant uses geothermal hot water at 160°C as the heat source. The cycle operates on the simple Rankine cycle with isobutane as the working fluid. Heat is supplied to the cycle with a heat exchanger in which geothermal liquid water enters at 160°C at a rate of 555.9 kg/s and leaves at 90°C. Isobutane enters the turbine at 3.25 MPa and 147°C at a rate of 305.6 kg/s and leaves at 79.5°C and 410 kPa. Isobutane is condensed in air-cooled condenser and pumped to the heat exchanger pressure. Assuming the pump to have an isentropic efficiency of 90 percent, determine (a) the isentropic efficiency of the turbine, (b) the net power output from the cycle, and (c) the thermal efficiency of the cycle.

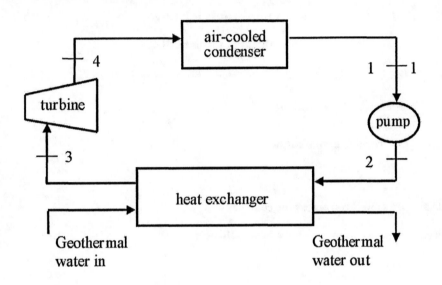

Equations

GIVEN

$$T_{geo,in} = 160 \ [C] \tag{1}$$

$$T_{geo,out} = 90 \ [C] \tag{2}$$

$$\dot{m}_{geo} = 555.9 \ [kg/s] \tag{3}$$

$$T_3 = 147 \ [C] \tag{4}$$

$$P_3 = 3.250 \ [MPa] \cdot \left| 1000 \ \frac{kPa}{MPa} \right| \tag{5}$$

$$T_4 = 79.5 \ [C] \tag{6}$$

$$P_4 = 410 \ [kPa] \tag{7}$$

$$\dot{m}_{iso} = 305.6 \ [\text{kg/s}] \tag{8}$$

$$\eta_P = 0.90 \tag{9}$$

ANALYSIS

$$Fluid\$ = \text{`Isobutane'} \tag{10}$$

Turbine

$$h_3 = \text{h}\,(Fluid\$,\ T = T_3,\ P = P_3) \qquad \textbf{Specific enthalpy at turbine inlet} \tag{11}$$

$$s_3 = \text{s}\,(Fluid\$,\ T = T_3,\ P = P_3) \qquad \textbf{Specific entropy at turbine inlet} \tag{12}$$

$$h_4 = \text{h}\,(Fluid\$,\ T = T_4,\ P = P_4) \qquad \textbf{Specific enthalpy at turbine exit} \tag{13}$$

$$h_{4s} = \text{h}\,(Fluid\$,\ P = P_4,\ s = s_3) \qquad \textbf{Isentropic specific enthalpy at turbine exit} \tag{14}$$

$$\eta_T = \frac{h_3 - h_4}{(h_3 - h_{4s})} \qquad \textbf{Turbine isentropic efficiency} \tag{15}$$

$$\dot{W}_T = \dot{m}_{iso} \cdot (h_3 - h_4) \qquad \textbf{Turbine power output} \tag{16}$$

Pump

$$P_1 = P_4 \qquad \textbf{Neglecting pressure drop across the condenser} \tag{17}$$

$$P_2 = P_3 \qquad \textbf{Neglecting pressure drop across the heat exchanger} \tag{18}$$

$$x_1 = 0 \qquad \textbf{Saturated liquid at pump inlet} \tag{19}$$

$$h_1 = \text{h}\,(Fluid\$,\ P = P_1,\ x = x_1) \qquad \textbf{Specific enthalpy at condenser exit} \tag{20}$$

$$v_1 = \text{v}\,(Fluid\$,\ P = P_1,\ x = x_1) \qquad \textbf{Specific volume at condenser exit} \tag{21}$$

$$\eta_P = \frac{v_1 \cdot (P_2 - P_1)}{h_2 - h_1} \tag{22}$$

$$\dot{W}_P = \dot{m}_{iso} \cdot (h_2 - h_1) \qquad \textbf{Pump power input} \tag{23}$$

$$\dot{W}_{net} = \dot{W}_T - \dot{W}_P \qquad \textbf{Net power} \tag{24}$$

Heat exchanger

$$\dot{Q}_{in} = \dot{m}_{geo} \cdot C_{geo} \cdot (T_{geo,in} - T_{geo,out}) \qquad \textbf{Heat input to the plant} \tag{25}$$

$$C_{geo} = \text{c}_\text{p}\,(\text{water},\ T = T_{geo,ave},\ x = 0) \qquad \textbf{Specific heat of geo. water} \tag{26}$$

$$T_{geo,ave} = \text{Average}(T_{geo,in},\ T_{geo,out}) \qquad \textbf{Average geo. water temperature} \tag{27}$$

$$\eta_{th} = \dot{W}_{net}/\dot{Q}_{in} \qquad \textbf{Thermal efficiency} \tag{28}$$

Solution

$C_{geo} = 4.258$ [kJ/kg-K]

$\eta_P = 0.9$

$\boxed{\eta_T = 0.7878}$

$\boxed{\eta_{th} = 0.1217}$

$Fluid\$ = $ 'Isobutane'

$h_{4s} = 670.4$ [kJ/kg]

$\dot{m}_{geo} = 555.9$ [kg/s]

$\dot{m}_{iso} = 305.6$ [kg/s]

$\dot{Q}_{in} = 165680$ [kW]

$s_3 = 2.546$ [kJ/kg-K]

$T_{geo,ave} = 125$ [C]

$T_{geo,in} = 160$ [C]

$T_{geo,out} = 90$ [C]

$v_1 = 0.001842$ $\left[\text{m}^3/\text{kg}\right]$

$\boxed{\dot{W}_{net} = 20165 \text{ [kW]}}$

$\dot{W}_P = 1777$ [kW]

$\dot{W}_T = 21941$ [kW]

$x_1 = 0$

Arrays

Row	h_i [kJ/kg]	P_i [kPa]	T_i [C]
1	273	410	
2	278.8	3250	
3	761.5	3250	147
4	689.7	410	79.5

EXAMPLE 9-3   A combined gas-steam power cycle

Consider a combined gas-steam power cycle. The topping cycle is a simple Brayton cycle that has a pressure ratio of 7. Air enters the compressor at 15°C at a rate of 10 kg/s and the gas turbine at 950°C. The bottoming cycle is a reheat Rankine cycle between the pressure limits of 6 MPa and 10 kPa. Steam is heated in a heat exchanger at a rate of 1.15 kg/s by the exhaust gases leaving the gas turbine and the exhaust gases leave the heat exchanger at 200°C. Steam leaves the high-pressure turbine at 1.0 MPa and is reheated to 400°C in the heat exchanger before it expands in the low-pressure turbine. Assuming 80 percent isentropic efficiency for all the work consuming or producing devices in the combined cycle, determine (a) the moisture percentage at the exit of the low-pressure turbine, (b) the steam temperature at the inlet of the high-pressure turbine, (c) the net power output from the plant, and (d) the thermal efficiency of the combined plant.

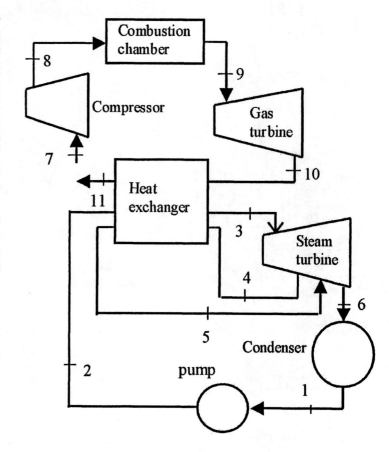

Equations

GIVEN

$P_7 = 100$ [kPa]   assumed   (1)

$r = 7$ (2)

$r = \dfrac{P_8}{P_7}$ (3)

$P_9 = P_8$ (4)

$P_{10} = P_7$ (5)

$P_{11} = P_7$ (6)

$T_7 = 15$ [C]   (7)

$T_9 = 950$ [C]   (8)

$T_{11} = 200$ [C]   (9)

$$\dot{m}_{gas} = 10 \ [\text{kg/s}] \tag{10}$$

$$\dot{m}_{steam} = 1.15 \ [\text{kg/s}] \tag{11}$$

$$P_3 = 6 \ [\text{MPa}] \cdot \left| 1000 \ \frac{\text{kPa}}{\text{MPa}} \right| \tag{12}$$

$$P_6 = 10 \ [\text{kPa}] \tag{13}$$

$$P_2 = P_3 \tag{14}$$

$$P_1 = P_6 \tag{15}$$

$$T_5 = 400 \ [\text{C}] \tag{16}$$

$$P_5 = 1 \ [\text{MPa}] \cdot \left| 1000 \ \frac{\text{kPa}}{\text{MPa}} \right| \tag{17}$$

$$P_4 = P_5 \tag{18}$$

$$\eta_C = 0.80 \tag{19}$$

$$\eta_T = 0.80 \tag{20}$$

$$\eta_P = 0.80 \tag{21}$$

PROPERTIES, gas cycle

$$GasFluid\$ = \text{'Air'} \tag{22}$$

$$h_7 = \text{h} \left(GasFluid\$, \ T = T_7 \right) \quad \textbf{Specific enthalpy at compressor inlet} \tag{23}$$

$$s_7 = \text{s} \left(GasFluid\$, \ T = T_7, \ P = P_7 \right) \quad \textbf{Specific entropy at compressor inlet} \tag{24}$$

$$h_{8s} = \text{h} \left(GasFluid\$, \ P = P_8, \ s = s_7 \right) \quad \textbf{Isentropic specific enthalpy at compressor exit} \tag{25}$$

$$\eta_C = \frac{h_{8s} - h_7}{(h_8 - h_7)} \quad \textbf{Compressor efficiency} \tag{26}$$

$$h_9 = \text{h} \left(GasFluid\$, \ T = T_9 \right) \quad \textbf{Specific enthalpy at turbine inlet} \tag{27}$$

$$s_9 = \text{s} \left(GasFluid\$, \ P = P_9, \ T = T_9 \right) \quad \textbf{Specific entropy at turbine inlet} \tag{28}$$

$$h_{10s} = \text{h} \left(GasFluid\$, \ P = P_{10}, \ s = s_9 \right) \quad \textbf{Isentropic specific enthalpy at turbine exit} \tag{29}$$

$$\eta_T = \frac{h_9 - h_{10}}{(h_9 - h_{10s})} \quad \textbf{Turbine efficiency} \tag{30}$$

$$T_{10} = \text{T} \left(GasFluid\$, \ h = h_{10} \right) \quad \textbf{Turbine exit temperature} \tag{31}$$

$$h_{11} = \text{h} \left(GasFluid\$, \ T = T_{11} \right) \quad \textbf{Specific enthalpy at heat exchanger exit} \tag{32}$$

PROPERTIES, steam cycle

$$SteamFluid\$ = \text{'Steam\_iapws'} \tag{33}$$

$h_1 = $ h (SteamFluid\$, $P = P_1$, $x = 0$)   **Specific enthalpy at condenser exit**   (34)

$v_1 = $ v (SteamFluid\$, $P = P_1$, $x = 0$)   **Specific volume at condenser exit**   (35)

$w_{pump} = \dfrac{v_1 \cdot (P_2 - P_1)}{\eta_P}$ **Pumping work**   (36)

$w_{pump} = h_2 - h_1$ (37)

$h_5 = $ h (SteamFluid\$, $P = P_5$, $T = T_5$)   **Specific enthalpy at inlet to the low pressure turbine**   (38)

$s_5 = $ s (SteamFluid\$, $P = P_5$, $T = T_5$)   **Specific entropy at inlet to the low pressure turbine**   (39)

$h_{6s} = $ h (SteamFluid\$, $P = P_6$, $s = s_5$)   **Isentropic specific enthalpy at low pressure turbine exit**   (40)

$\eta_T = \dfrac{h_5 - h_6}{(h_5 - h_{6s})}$ **Low pressure turbine efficiency**   (41)

$h_3 = $ h (SteamFluid\$, $P = P_3$, $T = T_3$)   **Specific enthalpy at inlet to the high pressure turbine**   (42)

$s_3 = $ s (SteamFluid\$, $P = P_3$, $T = T_3$)   **Specific entropy at inlet to the high pressure turbine**   (43)

$h_{4s} = $ h (SteamFluid\$, $P = P_4$, $s = s_3$)   **Isentropic specific enthalpy at high pressure turbine exit**   (44)

$\eta_T = \dfrac{h_3 - h_4}{(h_3 - h_{4s})}$ **High pressure turbine efficiency**   (45)

ANALYSIS

$\dot{m}_{gas} \cdot (h_{10} - h_{11}) = \dot{m}_{steam} \cdot (h_3 - h_2) + \dot{m}_{steam} \cdot (h_5 - h_4)$ **Energy balance on heat exchanger**   (46)

$T_3 = T_3$ **Temperature of steam at the turbine inlet**   (47)

$x_6 = $ x (SteamFluid\$, $P = P_6$, $h = h_6$)   (48)

MoisturePercentage $= (1 - x_6) \cdot |100\,\%|$ **Moisture percentage at the turbine exit**   (49)

$\dot{W}_{T,gas} = \dot{m}_{gas} \cdot (h_9 - h_{10})$ **Gas turbine output power**   (50)

$\dot{W}_{C,gas} = \dot{m}_{gas} \cdot (h_8 - h_7)$ **Compressor input power**   (51)

$\dot{W}_{net,gas} = \dot{W}_{T,gas} - \dot{W}_{C,gas}$ **Net power output from the gas cycle**   (52)

$\dot{W}_{T,steam} = \dot{m}_{steam} \cdot (h_3 - h_4 + h_5 - h_6)$ **Steam turbine output power**   (53)

$\dot{W}_{P,steam} = \dot{m}_{steam} \cdot w_{pump}$ **Pumping power**   (54)

$\dot{W}_{net,steam} = \dot{W}_{T,steam} - \dot{W}_{P,steam}$ **Net power output from the steam cycle**   (55)

$\dot{W}_{net,plant} = \dot{W}_{net,gas} + \dot{W}_{net,steam}$ **Net power output from the plant**   (56)

$\dot{Q}_{in} = \dot{m}_{gas} \cdot (h_9 - h_8)$ **Heat input**   (57)

$\eta_{th} = \dot{W}_{net,plant} / \dot{Q}_{in}$ **Thermal efficiency**   (58)

Solution

$\eta_C = 0.8$

$\eta_P = 0.8$

$\eta_T = 0.8$

$\boxed{\eta_{th} = 0.3875}$

$GasFluid\$ = \text{'Air'}$

$h_{10s} = 763.8 \ [\text{kJ/kg}]$

$h_{4s} = 2870 \ [\text{kJ/kg}]$

$h_{6s} = 2366 \ [\text{kJ/kg}]$

$h_{8s} = 503.5 \ [\text{kJ/kg}]$

$\boxed{MoisturePercentage = 1.583 \ [\%]}$

$\dot{m}_{gas} = 10 \ [\text{kg/s}]$

$\dot{m}_{steam} = 1.15 \ [\text{kg/s}]$

$\dot{Q}_{in} = 7476 \ [\text{kW}]$

$r = 7$

$SteamFluid\$ = \text{'Steam\_iapws'}$

$\boxed{T_3 = 468 \ [\text{C}]}$

$v_1 = 0.00101 \ [\text{m}^3/\text{kg}]$

$\dot{W}_{C,gas} = 2687 \ [\text{kW}]$

$\dot{W}_{net,gas} = 1641 \ [\text{kW}]$

$\boxed{\dot{W}_{net,plant} = 2897 \ [\text{kW}]}$

$\dot{W}_{net,steam} = 1256 \ [\text{kW}]$

$\dot{W}_{P,steam} = 8.699 \ [\text{kW}]$

$\dot{W}_{T,gas} = 4328 \ [\text{kW}]$

$\dot{W}_{T,steam} = 1265 \ [\text{kW}]$

$w_{pump} = 7.564 \ [\text{kJ/kg}]$

$x_6 = 0.9842$

Arrays

Row	h_i [kJ/kg]	s_i [kJ/kg-K]	T_i [C]	P_i [kPa]
1	191.8			10
2	199.4			6000
3	3347	6.781	468	6000
4	2965			1000
5	3264	7.467	400	1000
6	2546			10
7	288.5	5.665	15	100
8	557.2			700
9	1305	6.646	950	700
10	872		572.1	100
11	475.6		200	100

Supplement 9.1 A single-flash geothermal power plant

The schematic of a single-flash geothermal power plant with state numbers is given in the figure. Geothermal water is found saturated liquid at 230°C in the production well. The geothermal liquid is withdrawn from the well at a rate of 230 kg/s and it is flashed to a pressure of 500 kPa by an essentially isenthalpic flashing process where the resulting vapor is separated from the liquid in a separator, and directed to a steam turbine. The steam leaves the turbine at 10 kPa with a moisture content of 10 percent. The steam is then condensed and sent to a reinjection well along with the liquid coming off the separator. Determine (a) the mass flow rate of steam through the turbine, (b) the isentropic efficiency of the turbine, (c) the power output from the turbine, and (d) the thermal efficiency of the plant (turbine work output divided by the energy of the geothermal fluid in the reservoir with respect to standard ambient conditions). *Answers*: (*a*) 38.2 kg/s, (*b*) 0.686, (*c*) 15,410 kW, (*d*) 0.0757

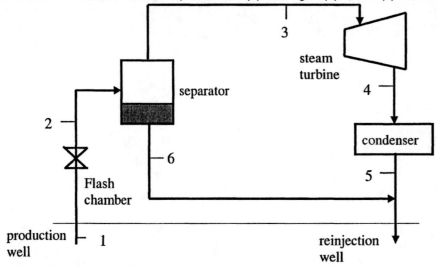

Supplement 9.2 A double-flash geothermal power plant

Reconsider Problem 9.1. Now, it is proposed that the liquid water coming out of the separator is sent through another flash chamber maintained at 150 kPa. The resulting steam is directed to a lower stage of the same turbine and both the primary and this secondary steam leave the turbine at the same state of 10 kPa and 90 percent quality. Determine (a) the temperature of the steam at the exit of the second flash chamber, (b) the power produced from the second turbine, and (c) the thermal efficiency of the plant. *Answers*: (a) 111°C, (b) 5190 kW, (c) 0.101

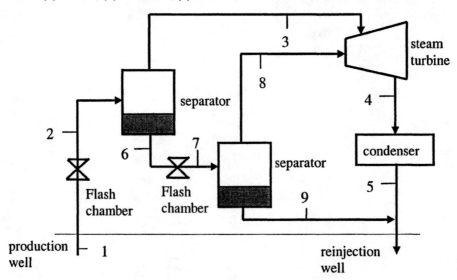

Supplement 9.3 A combined flash-binary geothermal power plant

Reconsider Problem 9.1. Now, it is proposed that the liquid water coming out of the separator is used as the heat source in a binary cycle with isobutane as the working fluid. Geothermal liquid water leaves the heat exchanger at 90°C while isobutane enters the turbine at 3.25 MPa and 145°C and leaves at 80°C and 400 kPa. Isobutane is condensed in air.cooled condenser and pumped to the heat exchanger pressure. Assuming an isentropic efficiency of 90 percent for the pump, determine (a) the mass flow rate of isobutane in the binary cycle, (b) the net power outputs from the steam turbine and the binary cycle, and (c) the thermal efficiencies for the binary cycle and the combined plant. *Answers*: (a) 105 kg/s, (b) 15,410 kW, 6220 kW, (c) 0.123, 0.106

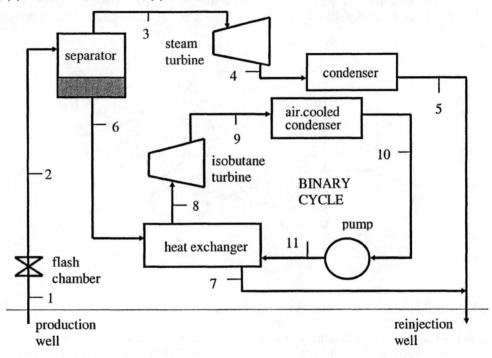

Supplement 9.4 An actual reheat Rankine cycle

A steam power plant operates on the reheat Rankine cycle. Steam enters the high-pressure stage of turbine at 12.5 MPa and 550°C at a rate of 7.7 kg/s and leaves at 2 MPa. Steam is reheated at constant pressure to 450°C before it expands in the low-pressure stage of the turbine. The isentropic efficiency of the turbine is 85 percent and that of the pump is 90 percent. Steam leaves the condenser as a saturated liquid. If the moisture content of the steam at the exit of the turbine is not to exceed 5 percent, determine (a) the condenser pressure, (b) the net power output, and (c) the thermal efficiency. *Answers*: (a) 9.73 kPa, (b) 10,240 kW, (c) 0.369

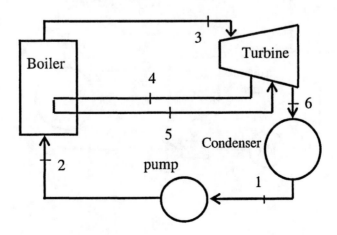

Supplement 9.5 A Rankine cycle with reheating and regeneration

A steam power plant operates on the reheat-regenerative Rankine cycle with a closed feedwater heater. Steam enters the turbine at 12.5 MPa and 550°C at a rate of 24 kg/s and is condensed in the condenser at a pressure of 20 kPa. Steam is reheated at 5 MPa to 550°C. Some steam is extracted from the low-pressure turbine at 1.0 MPa for the closed feedwater heater. The extracted steam is completely condensed in the heater and is pumped to 12.5 MPa before it mixes with the feedwater at the same pressure. Assuming an isentropic efficiency of 88 percent for both the turbine and the pump, determine (a) the temperature of the steam at the inlet of the closed feedwater heater, (b) the mass flow rate of the steam extracted from the turbine for the closed feedwater heater, (c) the net power output, and (d) the thermal efficiency. *Answers*: (a) 328°C, (b) 4.29 kg/s, (c) 28,550 kW, (d) 0.393

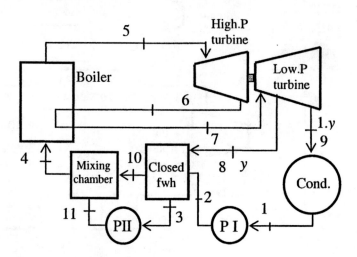

Supplement 9.6 A cogeneration plant

A textile plant requires 4 kg/s of saturated steam at 2 MPa, which is extracted from the turbine of a cogeneration plant. Steam enters the turbine at 8 MPa and 500°C at a rate of 11 kg/s and steam leaves the process heater as a saturated liquid. The remaining steam continues to expand to 20 kPa. The steam leaves the process heater as a saturated liquid and mixes with feedwater at constant pressure and the mixture is pumped to the boiler pressure. Assuming an isentropic efficiency of 88 percent for both the turbine and the pump, determine (a) the rate of process heat, (b) the net power output, and (c) the utilization factor of the plant. *Answers*: (a) 8560 kW, (b) 8600 kW, (c) 0.538

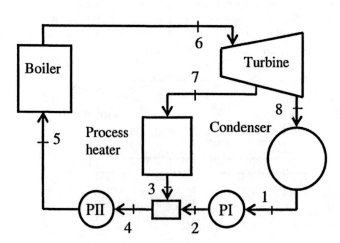

Supplement 9.7 Exergy analysis of a single-flash geothermal power plant

The schematic of a single-flash geothermal power plant with state numbers is given in the figure. Geothermal water is found saturated liquid at 230°C in the production well. The geothermal liquid is withdrawn from the well at a rate of 230 kg/s and it is flashed to a pressure of 500 kPa by an essentially isenthalpic flashing process where the resulting vapor is separated from the liquid in a separator, and directed to a steam turbine. The steam leaves the turbine at 10 kPa with a moisture content of 5 percent. The steam is then condensed and sent to a reinjection well along with the liquid coming off the separator. Using the standard atmospheric conditions for the dead state, determine (a) the power output from the turbine and the thermal efficiency of the plant, (b) the exergy of the geothermal liquid at the exit of the flash chamber, and the exergy destructions and exergy efficiencies for (c) the flash chamber, (d) the turbine, and (e) the entire plant. *Answers*: (a) 10,840 kW, 0.053, (b) 95,490 kW, (c) 426 kW, 0.998, (d) 910 kW, 0.923, (e) 179,860 kW, 0.0569

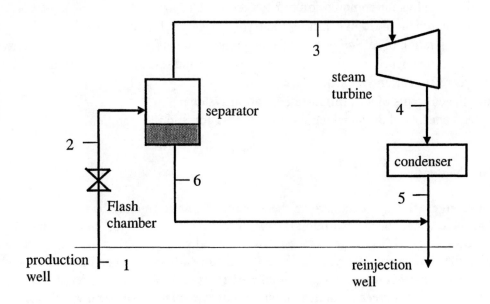

Chapter 10 Educational Objectives and Glossary

The Educational Objectives of Chapter 10 are to:

- Introduce the concepts of refrigerators and heat pumps and the measure of their performance.
- Evaluate the maximum possible coefficient of performance for refrigerators and heat pumps based on the reversed Carnot cycle.
- Analyze the ideal vapor-compression refrigeration cycle.
- Analyze the actual vapor-compression refrigeration cycle.
- Review the factors involved in selecting the right refrigerant for an application.
- Discuss the operation of refrigeration and heat pump systems.
- Evaluate the performance of innovative vapor-compression refrigeration systems.
- Analyze gas refrigeration systems.
- Introduce the concepts of absorption-refrigeration systems.
- Review the concepts of thermoelectric power generation and refrigeration.

Chapter 10 Glossary

Absorption refrigeration systems involve the absorption of a refrigerant by a transport medium. The most widely used absorption refrigeration system is the ammonia–water system, where ammonia (NH_3) serves as the refrigerant and water (H_2O) as the transport medium. Absorption refrigeration systems are economically attractive when there is a source of inexpensive heat energy at a temperature of 100 to 200°C. Some examples of inexpensive heat energy sources include geothermal energy, solar energy, and waste heat from cogeneration or process steam plants, and even natural gas when it is available at a relatively low price.

Carnot heat pump is a heat pump that operates on the reversed Carnot cycle.

Carnot refrigerator is a refrigerator that operates on the reversed Carnot cycle.

Cascade refrigeration cycles perform the refrigeration process in stages, that is, to have two or more refrigeration cycles that operate in series.

Coefficient of performance (COP) is the measure of performance of refrigerators and heat pumps. It is expressed in terms of the desired result for each device (heat absorbed from the refrigerated space for the refrigerator or heat added to the hot space by the heat pump) divided by the input, the energy expended to accomplish the energy transfer (usually work input).

Cooling capacity is the rate of heat removal from the refrigerated space by a refrigeration system.

Gas refrigeration cycle is based on the reversed Brayton cycle where the compressor exit gases are cooled and then expanded in a turbine to further reduce the temperature of the working fluid. The lower-temperature fluid is used to produce the refrigeration effect.

Heat-driven systems are refrigeration systems whose energy input is based on heat transfer from an external source. Absorption refrigeration systems are often classified as heat-driven systems.

Heat pump is a cyclic device which causes the transfer of heat from a low-temperature region to a high-temperature region. The objective of a heat pump is to maintain the heated space at a high temperature by supplying heat to it.

Ideal vapor-compression refrigeration cycle completely vaporizes the refrigerant before it is compressed and expands the refrigerant with a throttling device, such as an expansion valve or capillary tube. The vapor-compression refrigeration cycle is the most widely used cycle for refrigerators, air-conditioning systems, and heat pumps. It consists of four processes:
    1-2 Isentropic compression in a compressor
    2-3 Constant-pressure heat rejection in a condenser
    3-4 Throttling in an expansion device
    4-1 Constant-pressure heat absorption in an evaporator

Multistage compression refrigeration system is a cascade refrigeration system where the fluid used throughout the cascade refrigeration system is the same, and the heat exchanger between the stages is replaced by a device that has better heat-transfer characteristics, a mixing chamber (called a flash chamber).

Peltier effect is the cooling effect that occurs when a small current passes through the junction of two dissimilar wires. This effect forms the basis for thermoelectric refrigeration and is named in honor of Jean Charles Athanase Peltier, who discovered this phenomenon in 1834.

Refrigerants are the working fluids used in the refrigeration cycles.

Refrigerator is a cyclic device which causes the transfer of heat from a low-temperature region to a high-temperature region. The objective of a refrigerator is to maintain the refrigerated space at a low temperature by removing heat from it.

Reversed Carnot cycle is a reversible cycle in which all four processes that comprise the Carnot cycle are reversed during operation. Reversing the cycle will also reverse the directions of any heat and work interactions. The result is a cycle that operates in the counterclockwise direction.

Seebeck effect results when two wires made from different metals are joined at both ends (junctions), form a closed circuit, and one of the ends is heated. As a result of the applied heat a current flows continuously in the circuit. The Seebeck effect is named in honor of Thomas Seebeck, who made its discovery in 1821.

Thermoelectric refrigerator is a refrigerator using electric energy to directly produce cooling without involving any refrigerants and moving parts.

Ton of refrigeration is the capacity of a refrigeration system equivalent to the energy that can freeze 1 ton (2000 lbm) of liquid water at 0°C (32°F) into ice at 0°C in 24 h. One ton of refrigeration is equivalent to 211 kJ/min or 200 Btu/min. The cooling load of a typical 200-m^2 (2153-ft^2) residence is in the 3-ton (10-kW) range.

EXAMPLE 10-1 Actual vs. ideal cycle operation for a heat pump with R22

Refrigerant-22 enters the condenser of a residential heat pump at 800 kPa and 55°C at a rate of 0.018 kg/s and leaves at 750 kPa subcooled by 3°C. The refrigerant enters the compressor at 200 kPa superheated by 4°C. Determine (a) the isentropic efficiency of the compressor, (b) the rate of heat supplied to the heated room, and (c) the COP of the heat pump. Also, determine (d) the COP and the rate of heat supplied to the heated room if this heat pump operated on the ideal vapor-compression cycle between the pressure limits of 200 and 800 kPa.

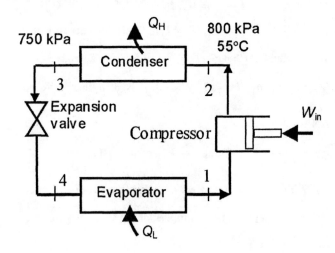

Equations

GIVEN

$$P_2 = 800 \ [\text{kPa}] \tag{1}$$

$$T_2 = 55 \ [\text{C}] \tag{2}$$

$$\dot{m} = 0.018 \ [\text{kg/s}] \tag{3}$$

$$P_3 = 750 \ [\text{kPa}] \tag{4}$$

$$\Delta T_{subcool} = 3 \ [\text{C}] \tag{5}$$

$$P_1 = 200 \ [\text{kPa}] \tag{6}$$

$$\Delta T_{superheat} = 4 \ [\text{C}] \tag{7}$$

PROPERTIES

$$Fluid\$ = \text{`R22'} \tag{8}$$

$h_2 = \text{h (Fluid\$, } P = P_2, \ T = T_2)$ **Specific enthalpy at condenser inlet** (9)

$T_{sat,3} = \text{T (Fluid\$, } P = P_3, \ x = 0)$ **Condensation temperature** (10)

$T_3 = T_{sat,3} - \Delta T_{subcool}$ **Condenser exit temperature** (11)

$h_3 = \text{h (Fluid\$, } P = P_3, \ T = T_3)$ **Specific enthalpy at condenser exit** (12)

$h_4 = h_3$ **Isoenthalpic expansion is assumed** (13)

$$T_{sat,1} = \text{T}(\text{Fluid\$}, \; P = P_1, \; x = 1) \qquad \textbf{Evaporation temperature} \tag{14}$$

$$T_1 = T_{sat,1} + \Delta T_{superheat} \qquad \textbf{Evaporator exit temperature} \tag{15}$$

$$h_1 = \text{h}(\text{Fluid\$}, \; P = P_1, \; T = T_1) \qquad \textbf{Specific enthalpy at evaporator exit} \tag{16}$$

$$s_1 = \text{s}(\text{Fluid\$}, \; P = P_1, \; T = T_1) \qquad \textbf{Specific entropy at evaporator exit} \tag{17}$$

$$h_{2s} = \text{h}(\text{Fluid\$}, \; P = P_2, \; s = s_1) \qquad \textbf{Isentropic, specific enthalpy at compressor exit} \tag{18}$$

ANALYSIS

$$\eta_C = \frac{h_{2s} - h_1}{h_2 - h_1} \qquad \textbf{Compressor isentropic efficiency} \tag{19}$$

$$\dot{Q}_H = \dot{m} \cdot (h_2 - h_3) \qquad \textbf{Heat supplied to the room} \tag{20}$$

$$\dot{W}_{in} = \dot{m} \cdot (h_2 - h_1) \qquad \textbf{Compressor power} \tag{21}$$

$$COP = \dot{Q}_H / \dot{W}_{in} \tag{22}$$

Ideal vapor-compression cycle analysis

$$h_{1,ideal} = \text{h}(\text{Fluid\$}, \; P = P_1, \; x = 1) \tag{23}$$

$$s_{1,ideal} = \text{s}(\text{Fluid\$}, \; P = P_1, \; x = 1) \tag{24}$$

$$h_{2,ideal} = \text{h}(\text{Fluid\$}, \; P = P_2, \; s = s_{1,ideal}) \tag{25}$$

$$h_{3,ideal} = \text{h}(\text{Fluid\$}, \; P = P_2, \; x = 0) \tag{26}$$

$$h_{4,ideal} = h_{3,ideal} \tag{27}$$

$$COP_{ideal} = \frac{h_{2,ideal} - h_{3,ideal}}{h_{2,ideal} - h_{1,ideal}} \tag{28}$$

$$\dot{Q}_{H,ideal} = \dot{m} \cdot (h_{2,ideal} - h_{3,ideal}) \tag{29}$$

Solution

$\boxed{COP = 5.221}$	$\boxed{COP_{ideal} = 6.147}$	$\Delta T_{subcool} = 3 \; [\text{C}]$	$\Delta T_{superheat} = 4 \; [\text{C}]$
$\boxed{\eta_C = 0.7959}$	$Fluid\$ = \text{`R22'}$	$h_1 = 397.3 \; [\text{kJ/kg}]$	$h_{1,ideal} = 394.7 \; [\text{kJ/kg}]$
$h_2 = 441.2 \; [\text{kJ/kg}]$	$h_{2s} = 432.2 \; [\text{kJ/kg}]$	$h_{2,ideal} = 428.9 \; [\text{kJ/kg}]$	$h_3 = 212.2 \; [\text{kJ/kg}]$
$h_{3,ideal} = 218.6 \; [\text{kJ/kg}]$	$h_4 = 212.2 \; [\text{kJ/kg}]$	$h_{4,ideal} = 218.6 \; [\text{kJ/kg}]$	$\dot{m} = 0.018 \; [\text{kg/s}]$
$P_1 = 200 \; [\text{kPa}]$	$P_2 = 800 \; [\text{kPa}]$	$P_3 = 750 \; [\text{kPa}]$	$\boxed{\dot{Q}_H = 4.121 \; [\text{kW}]}$
$\boxed{\dot{Q}_{H,ideal} = 3.786 \; [\text{kW}]}$	$s_1 = 1.802 \; [\text{kJ/kg-K}]$	$s_{1,ideal} = 1.792 \; [\text{kJ/kg-K}]$	$T_1 = -21.18 \; [\text{C}]$
$T_2 = 55 \; [\text{C}]$	$T_3 = 10.24 \; [\text{C}]$	$T_{sat,1} = -25.18 \; [\text{C}]$	$T_{sat,3} = 13.24 \; [\text{C}]$
$\dot{W}_{in} = 0.7892 \; [\text{kW}]$			

EXAMPLE 10-2   Analysis of a commercial refrigerator with heat rejection to water

A commercial refrigerator with refrigerant-134a as the working fluid is used to keep the refrigerated space at -30°C by rejecting its waste heat to cooling water that enters the condenser at 18°C at a rate of 0.25 kg/s and leaves at 26°C. The refrigerant enters the condenser at 1.2 MPa and 65°C and leaves at 42°C. The inlet state of the compressor is 60 kPa and -34°C and the compressor is estimated to gain a net heat of 450 W from the surroundings. Determine (a) the quality of the refrigerant at the evaporator inlet, (b) the refrigeration load, (c) the COP of the refrigerator, and (d) the theoretical maximum refrigeration load for the same power input to the compressor.

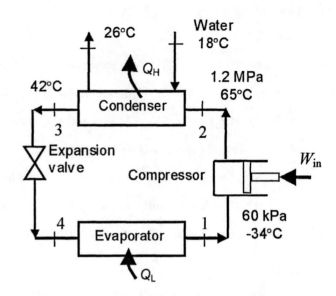

Equations

GIVEN

$$T_L = -30 \ [\text{C}] \tag{1}$$

$$T_H = 18 \ [\text{C}] \tag{2}$$

$$T_{w1} = 18 \ [\text{C}] \tag{3}$$

$$\dot{m}_w = 0.25 \ [\text{kg/s}] \tag{4}$$

$$T_{w2} = 26 \ [\text{C}] \tag{5}$$

$$P_2 = 1.2 \ [\text{MPa}] \cdot \left| 1000 \ \frac{\text{kPa}}{\text{MPa}} \right| \tag{6}$$

$$T_2 = 65 \ [\text{C}] \tag{7}$$

$$P_3 = P_2 \tag{8}$$
$$T_3 = 42 \ [\text{C}] \tag{9}$$

$$P_1 = 60 \ [\text{kPa}] \tag{10}$$

$$T_1 = -34 \ [\text{C}] \tag{11}$$

$$\dot{Q}_{in} = 0.45 \ [\text{kW}] \tag{12}$$

PROPERTIES

$Fluid\$ = $ 'R134a' $\tag{13}$

$h_1 = \text{h}\,(Fluid\$,\ P = P_1,\ T = T_1)$ **Specific enthalpy at evaporator exit** $\tag{14}$

$h_2 = \text{h}\,(Fluid\$,\ P = P_2,\ T = T_2)$ **Specific enthalpy at condenser inlet** $\tag{15}$

$h_3 = \text{h}\,(Fluid\$,\ P = P_3,\ T = T_3)$ **Specific enthalpy at condenser exit** $\tag{16}$

$h_4 = h_3$ **Isenthalpic expansion is assumed** $\tag{17}$

$x_4 = \text{x}\,(Fluid\$,\ P = P_1,\ h = h_4)$ **Quality of refrigerant at evaporator inlet** $\tag{18}$

$h_{w1} = \text{h}\,(\text{Water},\ T = T_{w1},\ x = 0)$ **Specific enthalpy of cooling water at inlet** $\tag{19}$

$h_{w2} = \text{h}\,(\text{Water},\ T = T_{w2},\ x = 0)$ **Specific enthalpy of cooling water at exit** $\tag{20}$

ANALYSIS

$\dot{Q}_H = \dot{m}_w \cdot (h_{w2} - h_{w1})$ **Waste heat transferred to cooling water** $\tag{21}$

$\dot{Q}_H = \dot{m}_R \cdot (h_2 - h_3)$ **Waste heat transferred from the refrigerant** $\tag{22}$

$\dot{W}_{in} = \dot{m}_R \cdot (h_2 - h_1) - \dot{Q}_{in}$ **Compressor energy balance** $\tag{23}$

$\dot{Q}_L = \dot{Q}_H - \dot{W}_{in}$ **Refrigeration load** $\tag{24}$

$COP = \dot{Q}_L / \dot{W}_{in}$ **Actual COP** $\tag{25}$

$$COP_{max} = \frac{1}{(ConvertTemp\,(C,\ K,\ T_H))\,/\,(ConvertTemp\,(C,\ K,\ T_L)) - 1} \quad \textbf{Maximum COP} \tag{26}$$

$\dot{Q}_{L,max} = COP_{max} \cdot \dot{W}_{in}$ **Maximum refrigeration load** $\tag{27}$

Solution

$\boxed{COP = 2.33}$	$COP_{max} = 5.066$	$Fluid\$ = $ 'R134a'	$h_1 = 230 \ [\text{kJ/kg}]$
$h_2 = 295.2 \ [\text{kJ/kg}]$	$h_3 = 111.2 \ [\text{kJ/kg}]$	$h_4 = 111.2 \ [\text{kJ/kg}]$	$h_{w1} = 75.47 \ [\text{kJ/kg}]$
$h_{w2} = 108.9 \ [\text{kJ/kg}]$	$\dot{m}_R = 0.04549 \ [\text{kg/s}]$	$\dot{m}_w = 0.25 \ [\text{kg/s}]$	$P_1 = 60 \ [\text{kPa}]$
$P_2 = 1200 \ [\text{kPa}]$	$P_3 = 1200 \ [\text{kPa}]$	$\dot{Q}_H = 8.367 \ [\text{kW}]$	$\dot{Q}_{in} = 0.45 \ [\text{kW}]$
$\boxed{\dot{Q}_L = 5.854 \ [\text{kW}]}$	$\boxed{\dot{Q}_{L,max} = 12.73 \ [\text{kW}]}$	$T_1 = -34 \ [\text{C}]$	$T_2 = 65 \ [\text{C}]$
$T_3 = 42 \ [\text{C}]$	$T_H = 18 \ [\text{C}]$	$T_L = -30 \ [\text{C}]$	$T_{w1} = 18 \ [\text{C}]$
$T_{w2} = 26 \ [\text{C}]$	$\dot{W}_{in} = 2.513 \ [\text{kW}]$	$\boxed{x_4 = 0.4795}$	

EXAMPLE 10-3   Gas refrigeration cycle with regeneration, variable specific heats

A gas refrigeration system using air as the working fluid has a pressure ratio of 5. Air enters the compressor at 0°C. The high-pressure air is cooled to 35°C by rejecting heat to the surroundings. The refrigerant leaves the turbine at -80°C and then it absorbs heat from the refrigerated space before entering the regenerator. The mass flow rate of air is 0.4 kg/s. Assuming isentropic efficiencies of 80 percent for the compressor and 85 percent for the turbine and using variable specific heats, determine (a) the effectiveness of the regenerator, (b) the rate of heat removal from the refrigerated space, and (c) the COP of the cycle. Also, determine (d) the refrigeration load and the COP if this system operated on the simple gas refrigeration cycle. Use the same compressor inlet temperature as given and the same turbine inlet temperature as calculated, and the same compressor and turbine efficiencies.

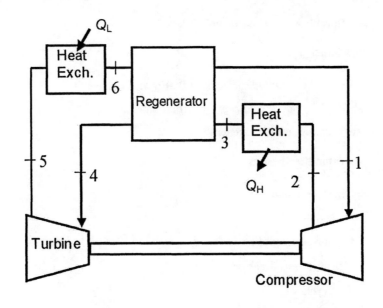

Equations

GIVEN

$r = 5$ (1)

$T_1 = ConvertTemp\,(C,\ K,\ 0)$ (2)

$T_3 = ConvertTemp\,(C,\ K,\ 35)$ (3)

$T_5 = ConvertTemp\,(C,\ K,\ -80)$ (4)

$\dot{m} = 0.4\ [\text{kg/s}]$ (5)

$\eta_C = 0.80$ (6)

$\eta_T = 0.85$ (7)

$P_1 = 100$ **Assumed** (8)

$r = P_2/P_1$ (9)

PROPERTIES

$Fluid\$ = \text{`Air'}$ (10)

$h_1 = h\,(Fluid\$, \; T = T_1)$ **Specific enthalpy at compressor inlet** (11)

$s_1 = s\,(Fluid\$, \; T = T_1, \; P = P_1)$ **Specific entropy at compressor inlet** (12)

$h_3 = h\,(Fluid\$, \; T = T_3)$ **Specific enthalpy at regenerator inlet** (13)

$h_5 = h\,(Fluid\$, \; T = T_5)$ **Specific enthalpy at turbine exit** (14)

ANALYSIS

$h_{2s} = h\,(Fluid\$, \; P = P_2, \; s = s_1)$ **Isentropic specific enthalpy at compressor exit** (15)

$\eta_C = \dfrac{h_{2s} - h_1}{(h_2 - h_1)}$ **Compressor efficiency** (16)

$h_4 = h\,(Fluid\$, \; T = T_4)$ **Specific enthalpy at turbine inlet** (17)

$\eta_T = \dfrac{h_4 - h_5}{(h_4 - h_{5s})}$ **Turbine efficiency** (18)

$h_{5s} = h\,(Fluid\$, \; P = P_1, \; s = s_4)$ **Isentropic specific enthalpy at turbine exit** (19)

$s_4 = s\,(Fluid\$, \; T = T_4, \; P = P_2)$ **Specific entropy at turbine inlet** (20)

$h_6 = h_1 - h_3 + h_4$ **Energy balance on the regenerator** (21)

$\epsilon_{regen} = \dfrac{h_3 - h_4}{h_3 - h_6}$ **Regenerator effectiveness** (22)

$\dot{Q}_L = \dot{m} \cdot (h_6 - h_5)$ **Refrigeration load** (23)

$\dot{W}_{net,in} = \dot{W}_{C,in} - \dot{W}_{T,out}$ **Net power** (24)

$\dot{W}_{C,in} = \dot{m} \cdot (h_2 - h_1)$ **Compressor input power** (25)

$\dot{W}_{T,out} = \dot{m} \cdot (h_4 - h_5)$ **Turbine output power** (26)

$COP = \dot{Q}_L / \dot{W}_{net,in}$ **COP of cycle** (27)

Simple gas refrigeration cycle analysis, the subscript 'a' is used

$h_{a,1} = h_1$ (28)

$h_{a,2} = h_2$ (29)

$h_{a,3} = h_3$ (30)

$s_{3,a} = s\,(Fluid\$, \; h = h_{a,3}, \; P = P_2)$ (31)

$h_{4s,a} = h\,(Fluid\$, \; P = P_1, \; s = s_{3,a})$ (32)

$\eta_T = \dfrac{h_{a,3} - h_{a,4}}{h_{a,3} - h_{4s,a}}$ (33)

$\dot{Q}_{L,a} = \dot{m} \cdot (h_{a,1} - h_{a,4})$ (34)

$\dot{W}_{in,net,a} = \dot{m} \cdot (h_{a,2} - h_{a,1}) - \dot{m} \cdot (h_{a,3} - h_{a,4})$ (35)

$COP_a = \dot{Q}_{L,a} / \dot{W}_{net,in}$ (36)

Solution

$COP = 0.479$

$COP_a = 0.554$

$\epsilon_{regen} = 0.4298$

$\eta_C = 0.8$

$\eta_T = 0.85$

$Fluid\$ = \text{`Air'}$

$h_{2s} = 433.5 \ [\text{kJ/kg}]$

$h_{4s,a} = 194.5 \ [\text{kJ/kg}]$

$h_{5s} = 177.8 \ [\text{kJ/kg}]$

$\dot{m} = 0.4 \ [\text{kg/s}]$

$P_1 = 100 \ [\text{kPa}]$

$P_2 = 500 \ [\text{kPa}]$

$\dot{Q}_L = 21.36 \ [\text{kW}]$

$\dot{Q}_{L,a} = 24.71 \ [\text{kW}]$

$r = 5$

$s_1 = 5.611 \ [\text{kJ/kg-K}]$

$s_{3,a} = 5.27 \ [\text{kJ/kg-K}]$

$s_4 = 5.18 \ [\text{kJ/kg-K}]$

$\dot{W}_{C,in} = 80.05 \ [\text{kW}]$

$\dot{W}_{in,net,a} = 41.25 \ [\text{kW}]$

$\dot{W}_{net,in} = 44.59 \ [\text{kW}]$

$\dot{W}_{T,out} = 35.45 \ [\text{kW}]$

Arrays

Row	h_i [kJ/kg]	T_i [K]	$h_{a,i}$ [kJ/kg]
1	273.4	273.1	273.4
2	473.5		473.5
3	308.6	308.2	308.6
4	282.1	281.8	211.6
5	193.4	193.2	
6	246.8		

Supplement 10.1 The ideal vapor-compression refrigeration cycle

A refrigerator uses refrigerant.134a as the working fluid and operates on the ideal vapor-compression refrigeration cycle. The refrigerant enters the evaporator at 120 kPa with a quality of 30 percent and leaves the compressor at 60°C. If the compressor consumes 450 W of power, determine (a) the mass flow rate of the refrigerant, (b) the condenser pressure, and (c) the COP of the refrigerator. *Answers*: (a) 0.00727 kg/s, (b) 672 kPa, (c) 2.43

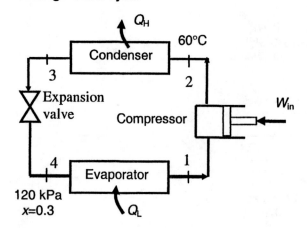

Supplement 10.2 Analysis of an air-conditioner

An air-conditioner with refrigerant.134a as the refrigerant is used to keep a room at 26°C by rejecting the waste heat to the outside air at 34°C. The room is gaining heat through the walls and the windows at a rate of 250 kJ/min while the heat generated by the computer, TV, and lights amounts to 900 W. Unknown amount of heat is also generated by the people in the room. The condenser and evaporator pressures are 1200 kPa and 500 kPa, respectively. The refrigerant is saturated liquid at the condenser exit and saturated vapor at the compressor inlet. If the refrigerant enters the compressor at a rate of 100 L/min and the isentropic efficiency of the compressor is 75 percent, determine (a) the temperature of the refrigerant at the compressor exit, (b) the rate of heat generated by the people in the room, (c) the COP of the air-conditioner, and (d) the minimum volume flow rate of the refrigerant at the compressor inlet for the same compressor inlet and exit conditions. *Answers*: (a) 54.5°C, (b) 670 W, (c) 5.87, (d) 15.7 L/min

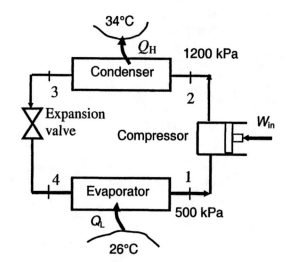

Supplement 10.3 Analysis of a geothermal heat pump

A heat pump with refrigerant.134a as the working fluid is used to keep a space at 25°C by absorbing heat from geothermal water that enters the evaporator at 50°C at a rate of 0.065 kg/s and leaves at 40°C. The refrigerant enters the evaporator at 20°C with a quality of 23 percent and leaves at the inlet pressure as a saturated vapor. The refrigerant loses 300 W of heat to the surroundings as it flows through the compressor and the refrigerant leaves the compressor at 1.4 MPa at the same entropy as the inlet. Determine (a) the degrees of subcooling done on the refrigerant in the condenser, (b) the mass flow rate of the refrigerant, (c) the heating load and the COP of the heat pump, and (d) the theoretical minimum power input to the compressor for the same heating load. *Answers*: (a) 3.8C, (b) 0.0194 kg/s, (c) 3.375 kW, 5.14, (d) 0.261 kW

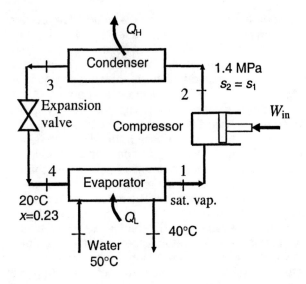

Supplement 10.4 A two-stage cascade refrigeration cycle

Consider a two-stage cascade refrigeration system operating between the pressure limits of 1.2 MPa and 200 kPa with refrigerant.134a as the working fluid. Heat rejection from the lower cycle to the upper cycle takes place in an adiabatic counterflow heat exchanger where the pressure in the upper and lower cycles are 0.4 MPa and 0.5 MPa, respectively. In both cycles, the refrigerant is a saturated liquid at the condenser exit and a saturated vapor at the compressor inlet, and the isentropic efficiency of the compressor is 80 percent. If the mass flow rate of the refrigerant through the lower cycle is 0.15 kg/s, determine (a) the mass flow rate of the refrigerant through the upper cycle, (b) the rate of heat removal from the refrigerated space, and (c) the COP of this refrigerator. *Answers*: (a) 0.212 kg/s, (b) 26.67 kW, (c) 2.68

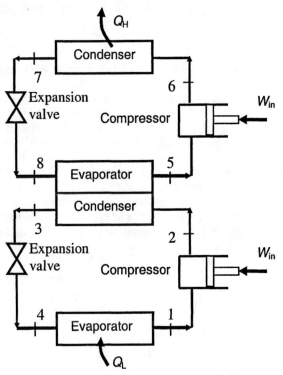

Supplement 10.5 A two-stage refrigeration cycle with a flash chamber

Consider a two-stage cascade refrigeration system operating between the pressure limits of 1.2 MPa and 200 kPa with refrigerant.134a as the working fluid. The refrigerant leaves the condenser as a saturated liquid and is throttled to a flash chamber operating at 0.45 MPa. Part of the refrigerant evaporates during this flashing process, and this vapor is mixed with the refrigerant leaving the low-pressure compressor. The mixture is then compressed to the condenser pressure by the high-pressure compressor. The liquid in the flash chamber is throttled to the evaporator pressure and cools the refrigerated space as it vaporizes in the evaporator. The mass flow rate of the refrigerant through the low-pressure compressor is 0.15 kg/s. Assuming the refrigerant leaves the evaporator as a saturated vapor and the isentropic efficiency is 80 percent for both compressors, determine (a) the mass flow rate of the refrigerant through the high-pressure compressor, (b) the rate of heat removal from the refrigerated space, and (c) the COP of this refrigerator. Also, determine (d) the rate of heat removal and the COP if this refrigerator operated on a single-stage cycle between the same pressure limits with the same compressor efficiency and the same flow rate as in part (a). *Answers*: (a) 0.2025 kg/s, (b) 26.35 kW, (c) 3.12, (d) 25.66 kW, 2.71

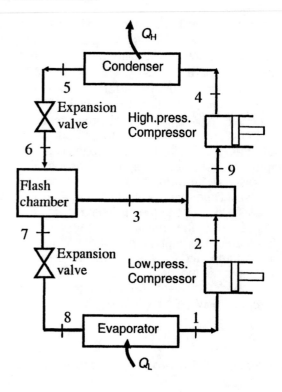

Supplement 10.6 Gas refrigeration cycle with regeneration, constant specific heats

A gas refrigeration system using air as the working fluid has a pressure ratio of 5. Air enters the compressor at 0°C. The high-pressure air is cooled to 35°C by rejecting heat to the surroundings. The refrigerant leaves the turbine at .80°C and then it absorbs heat from the refrigerated space before entering the regenerator. The mass flow rate of air is 0.4 kg/s. Assuming isentropic efficiencies of 80 percent for the compressor and 85 percent for the turbine and using constant specific heats at room temperature, determine (a) the effectiveness of the regenerator, (b) the rate of heat removal from the refrigerated space, and (c) the COP of the cycle. Also, determine (d) the refrigeration load and the COP if this system operated on the simple gas refrigeration cycle. Use the same compressor inlet temperature as given and the same turbine inlet temperature as calculated, and the same compressor and turbine efficiencies. *Answers*: (a) 0.437, (b) 21.28 kW, (c) 0.477, (d) 24.7 kW, 0.553

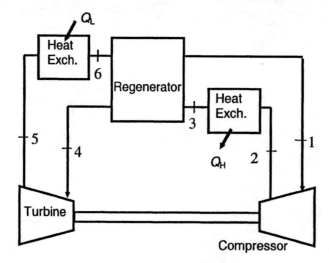

Supplement 10.7 A reversible absorption refrigeration cycle

A reversible absorption refrigerator consists of a reversible heat engine and a reversible refrigerator. The system removes heat from a cooled space at .10°C at a rate of 22 kW. The refrigerator operates in an environment at 25°C. If the heat is supplied to the cycle by condensing saturated steam at 200°C, determine (a) the rate at which the steam condenses and (b) the power input to the reversible refrigerator. If the COP of an actual absorption chiller at the same temperature limits has a COP of 0.7, determine (c) the second law efficiency of this chiller. *Answers*: (a) 0.00408 kg/s, (b) 2.93 kW, (c) 0.252

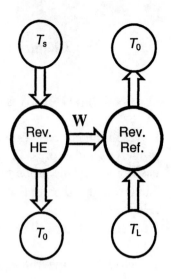

Chapter 11 Educational Objectives and Glossary

The Educational Objectives of Chapter 11 are to:

- Develop fundamental relations between commonly encountered thermodynamic properties and express the properties that cannot be measured directly in terms of easily measurable properties.
- Review and use partial derivatives in the development of thermodynamic property relations.
- Develop the Maxwell relations, which form the basis for many thermodynamic relations.
- Develop the Clapeyron equation and determine the enthalpy of vaporization from P, v, and T measurements alone.
- Develop general relations for C_v, C_p, du, dh, and ds that are valid for all pure substances under all conditions.
- Discuss the Joule-Thomson coefficient.
- Develop a method of evaluating the Δh, Δu, and Δs of real gases through the use of generalized enthalpy and entropy departure charts.

Chapter 11 Glossary

Clapeyron equation, after the French engineer and physicist E. Clapeyron (1799–1864), relates the enthalpy change associated with a phase change (such as the enthalpy of vaporization h_{fg}) from knowledge of P, v, and T data alone.

Clapeyron–Clausius equation is used to determine the variation of saturation pressure with temperature.

Cyclic relation of partial derivatives shows that the derivatives of a function of two variables are related in a cyclic manner.

$$\left(\frac{\partial x}{\partial y}\right)_z \left(\frac{\partial y}{\partial z}\right)_x \left(\frac{\partial z}{\partial x}\right)_y = -1$$

Derivative of a function $f(x)$ with respect to x represents the rate of change of f with x. The derivative is equivalent to steepness of a curve at a point as measured by the slope of a line tangent to the curve at that point.

$$\frac{df}{dx} = \lim_{\Delta x \to 0} \frac{\Delta f}{\Delta x} = \lim_{\Delta x \to 0} \frac{f(x+\Delta x) - f(x)}{\Delta x}$$

Enthalpy departure is the difference between the enthalpy of a real gas and the enthalpy of the gas at an ideal gas state and it represents the variation of the enthalpy of a gas with pressure at a fixed temperature.

Enthalpy departure factor is the nondimensionalized form of the enthalpy departure.

Entropy departure is the difference between the entropy of a real gas at a given P and T and the entropy of the gas at an ideal gas state at the same P and T.

Entropy departure factor is the nondimensionalized form of the entropy departure.

Generalized enthalpy departure chart is a plot of the enthalpy departure factor as a function of reduced pressure and reduced temperature. It is used to determine the deviation of the enthalpy of a gas at a given P and T from the enthalpy of an ideal gas at the same T.

Generalized entropy departure chart is a plot of the entropy departure factor as a function of reduced pressure and reduced temperature. It is used to determine the deviation of the entropy of a gas at a given P and T from the entropy of an ideal gas at the same P and T.

Gibbs function g is defined as $g = h - Ts$.

Helmholtz function a is defined as $a = u - Ts$

Inversion line is the line that passes through the points of zero slope of constant-enthalpy lines or zero Joule-Thomson coefficient on the T-P diagram. The slopes of the $h =$ constant lines are negative ($\mu_{JT} < 0$) at states to the right of the inversion line and positive ($\mu_{JT} > 0$) to the left of the inversion line.

Inversion temperature is the temperature at a point where a constant-enthalpy line intersects the inversion line.

Isothermal compressibility relates how volume changes when pressure changes when temperature is held constant.

Joule-Thomson coefficient μ_{JT} is a measure of the change in temperature with pressure during a constant-enthalpy process.

Maximum inversion temperature is the temperature at the intersection of the $P = 0$ line (ordinate) on the T-P diagram and the upper part of the inversion line.

Maxwell relations are equations that relate the partial derivatives of properties P, v, T, and s of a simple compressible system to each other.

Mayer relation, named in honor of the German physician and physicist J. R. Mayer (1814–1878, shows how the difference between the constant-pressure specific heat and constant-volume specific heat is related to the specific volume, temperature, isothermal compressibility, and volume expansivity.

Partial derivative is the change in a function that depends on two (or more) variables, such as $z = z(x, y)$, when allowing one variable to change while holding the others constant and observing the change in the function as another variable is held constant. The variation of $z(x, y)$ with x when y is held constant is called the partial derivative of z with respect to x.

$$\left(\frac{\partial z}{\partial x}\right)_y = \lim_{\Delta x \to 0}\left(\frac{\Delta z}{\Delta x}\right)_y = \lim_{\Delta x \to 0}\frac{z(x + \Delta x, y) - z(x, y)}{\Delta x}$$

Reciprocity relation shows that the inverse of a partial derivative is equal to its reciprocal.

$$\left(\frac{\partial x}{\partial z}\right)_y = \frac{1}{(\partial z / \partial x)_y}$$

Total differential of a dependent variable in terms of its partial derivatives with respect to the independent variables is expressed as, for $z = z(x, y)$,

$$dz = \left(\frac{\partial z}{\partial x}\right)_y dx + \left(\frac{\partial z}{\partial y}\right)_x dy$$

Volume expansivity (also called the coefficient of volumetric expansion) relates how volume changes when temperature changes when pressure is held constant.

EXAMPLE 11-1 Enthalpy of Vaporization

Plot the enthalpy of vaporization of steam as a function of temperature over the temperature range 10 to 200°C by using the Clapeyron equation and steam data in EES.

Equations

ANALYSIS

Make a parametric table with T ranging from 10 to 240 C

$$T_{increment} = 5 \ [C] \tag{1}$$

$$T_2 = T + T_{increment} \tag{2}$$

$$T_1 = T - T_{increment} \tag{3}$$

$$P_1 = P\,(\text{Steam},\ T = T_1,\ x = 0) \tag{4}$$

$$P_2 = P\,(\text{Steam},\ T = T_2,\ x = 0) \tag{5}$$

$$\Delta P = P_2 - P_1 \tag{6}$$

$$\Delta T = T_2 - T_1 \tag{7}$$

$$v_f = v\,(\text{Steam},\ T = T,\ x = 0) \qquad \textbf{Specific volume of saturated liquid} \tag{8}$$

$$v_g = v\,(\text{Steam},\ T = T,\ x = 1) \qquad \textbf{Specific volume of saturated vapor} \tag{9}$$

$$h_f = h\,(\text{Steam},\ T = T,\ x = 0) \qquad \textbf{Specific enthalpy of saturated liquid} \tag{10}$$

$$h_g = h\,(\text{Steam},\ T = T,\ x = 1) \qquad \textbf{Specific enthalpy of saturated vapor} \tag{11}$$

$$h_{fg} = h_g - h_f \qquad \textbf{Latent heat} \tag{12}$$

$$v_{fg} = v_g - v_f \tag{13}$$

The Clapeyron equation (Eq. 11-22) provides a means to calculate the enthalpy of vaporization, h_{fg} at a given temperature by determining the slope of the saturation curve on a P-T diagram and the specific volume of the saturated liquid and satruated vapor at the temperature. 23803

$$h_{fg,Clapeyron} = (T + 273.2) \cdot v_{fg} \cdot \frac{\Delta P}{\Delta T} \cdot \left|1 \ \frac{kJ}{m^3\text{-}kPa}\right| \tag{14}$$

$$PercentError = \frac{ABS\,(h_{fg,Clapeyron} - h_{fg})}{h_{fg}} \cdot |100\ \%| \tag{15}$$

Table 1

Run	h_{fg} [kJ/kg]	$h_{fg,Clapeyron}$ [kJ/kg]	*PercentError* [%]	T [C]
1	2476.90	2508.08	1.259	10
2	2429.67	2451.15	0.8844	30
3	2381.86	2396.92	0.6322	50
4	2333.09	2343.81	0.4594	70
5	2282.70	2290.44	0.3392	90
6	2229.93	2235.61	0.2546	110
7	2174.00	2178.23	0.1943	130
8	2114.06	2117.26	0.151	150
9	2014.54	2016.69	0.1069	180
10	1900.04	1901.54	0.07891	210
11	1765.72	1766.80	0.06107	240

Plot 1

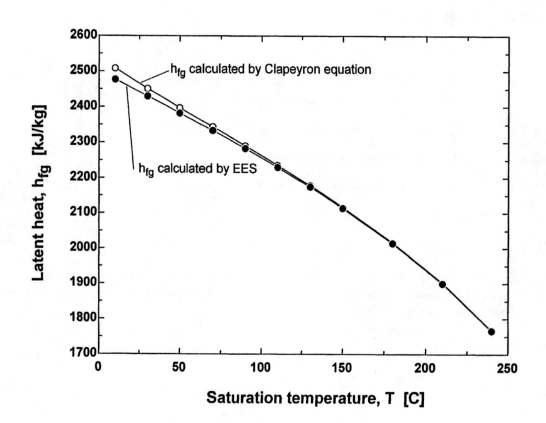

EXAMPLE 11-2 Generalized Chart Solution

Carbon dioxide is contained in a constant volume tank and is heated from 100°C and 1 MPa to 8 MPa. Determine the heat transfer and entropy change per unit mass of the carbon dioxide using the ideal gas assumption, the generalized charts and real fluid (EES) data.

Equations

The generalized charts in EES are incorporated in three external functions: Compress, EnthDep and EntrDep.

GIVEN

$$T_1 = ConvertTemp\,(C,\ K,\ 100) \tag{1}$$

$$P_1 = 1\ [\text{MPa}] \cdot \left| 1000\ \frac{\text{kPa}}{\text{MPa}} \right| \tag{2}$$

$$P_2 = 8\ [\text{MPa}] \cdot \left| 1000\ \frac{\text{kPa}}{\text{MPa}} \right| \tag{3}$$

PROPERTIES

$$T_{critical} = \text{T}_{\text{crit}}\,(\text{CO2}\,) \tag{4}$$

$$P_{critical} = \text{P}_{\text{crit}}\,(\text{CO2}\,) \tag{5}$$

$$R = R_u/MM \quad \textbf{Gas constant} \tag{6}$$

$$R_u = 8.314 \quad \textbf{Universal gas constant} \tag{7}$$

$$MM = \text{MW}\,(\text{CO2}\,) \tag{8}$$

$$h_{ideal,1} = \text{h}\,(\text{CO2},\ T = T_1) \quad \textbf{State-1 specific enthalpy of ideal gas} \tag{9}$$

$$s_{ideal,1} = \text{s}\,(\text{CO2},\ T = T_1,\ P = P_1) \quad \textbf{State-1 specific entropy of ideal gas} \tag{10}$$

$$h_{ideal,2} = \text{h}\,(\text{CO2},\ T = T_2) \quad \textbf{State-2 specific enthalpy of ideal gas} \tag{11}$$

$$s_{ideal,2} = \text{s}\,(\text{CO2},\ T = T_2,\ P = P_2) \quad \textbf{State-2 specific entropy of ideal gas} \tag{12}$$

ANALYSIS

$$v_1 = 3\,\frac{[\text{m}^3]}{2\,[\text{kg}]} \quad \textbf{Specific volume} \tag{13}$$

$$v_2 = v_1 \tag{14}$$

a-Ideal gas solution

$$u_{ideal,1} = h_{ideal,1} - R \cdot T_1 \quad \textbf{State-1 specific internal energy of ideal gas} \tag{15}$$

$$\frac{T_2}{T_1} = P_2/P_1 \quad \textbf{Constant volume process, ideal gas} \tag{16}$$

$$u_{ideal,2} = h_{ideal,2} - R \cdot T_2 \qquad \textbf{State-2 specific internal energy of ideal gas} \tag{17}$$

$$W_{ideal} = 0 \qquad \textbf{Constant volume process} \tag{18}$$

$$q_{ideal} - w_{ideal} = u_{ideal,2} - u_{ideal,1} \qquad \textbf{Energy balance on the tank} \tag{19}$$

$$\Delta s_{ideal} = s_{ideal,2} - s_{ideal,1} \qquad \textbf{Entropy change} \tag{20}$$

b-Compressability chart solution

$$Tr_1 = \frac{T_1}{T_{critical}} \qquad \textbf{State-1 reduced temperature} \tag{21}$$

$$pr_1 = \frac{p_1}{p_{critical}} \qquad \textbf{State-1 reduced pressure} \tag{22}$$

$$Z_1 = \text{Compress}(Tr_1, \ Pr_1) \tag{23}$$

$$\Delta h_1 = \text{Enthdep}(Tr_1, \ Pr_1) \cdot R \cdot T_{critical} \qquad \textbf{State-1 enthalpy departure} \tag{24}$$

$$hideal_{chart,1} = h\,(CO2, \ T = T_1) \tag{25}$$

$$h_1 = h_{ideal,1} - \Delta h_1 \qquad \textbf{State-1 sepecific enthalpy of real gas using charts} \tag{26}$$

$$u_1 = h_1 - Z_1 \cdot R \cdot T_1 \qquad \textbf{State-1 specific internal energy of gas using charts} \tag{27}$$

$$\Delta s_1 = \text{Entrdep}(Tr_1, \ Pr_1) \cdot R \qquad \textbf{State-1 entropy departure} \tag{28}$$

$$s_1 = s_{ideal,1} - \Delta s_1 \qquad \textbf{State-1 specific entropy of real gas using charts} \tag{29}$$

$$T_{chart,2} = \frac{P_2}{P_1} \cdot Z_1 \cdot T_1 / (Z_2) \qquad \textbf{Constant volume process} \tag{30}$$

$$Tr_2 = \frac{T_{chart,2}}{T_{critical}} \qquad \textbf{State-2 reduced temperature} \tag{31}$$

$$Pr_2 = \frac{p_2}{P_{critical}} \qquad \textbf{State-2 reduced pressure} \tag{32}$$

$$Z_2 = \text{Compress}(Tr_2, \ Pr_2) \tag{33}$$

$$\Delta h_2 = \text{Enthdep}(Tr_2, \ Pr_2) \cdot R \cdot T_{critical} \qquad \textbf{State-2 enthalpy departure} \tag{34}$$

$$\Delta s_2 = \text{Entrdep}(Tr_2, \ Pr_2) \cdot R \qquad \textbf{State-2 entropy departure} \tag{35}$$

$$hideal_{chart,2} = h\,(CO2, \ T = T_{chart,2}) \tag{36}$$

$$h_2 = hideal_{chart,2} - \Delta h_2 \qquad \textbf{State-2 enthalpy of real gas using charts} \tag{37}$$

$$sideal_{chart,2} = s\,(CO2, \ T = T_{chart,2}, \ P = P_2) \tag{38}$$

$$s_2 = sideal_{chart,2} - \Delta s_2 \qquad \textbf{State-2 specific entropy of real gas using charts} \tag{39}$$

$$u_2 = h_2 - Z_2 \cdot R \cdot T_{chart,2} \qquad \textbf{State-2 internal energy of gas using charts} \tag{40}$$

$$w_{chart} = 0 \qquad \textbf{Constant volume process} \tag{41}$$

$$q_{chart} - w_{chart} = u_2 - u_1 \qquad \textbf{Energy balance on the tank} \tag{42}$$

$$\Delta s_{chart} = s_2 - s_1 \qquad \textbf{Entropy Change} \tag{43}$$

c-Solution using EES built-in property data

$$v_{EES,1} = v\,(\text{CarbonDioxide},\ T = T_1,\ P = P_1) \quad \textbf{State-1 specific volume} \tag{44}$$

$$v_{EES,2} = v_{EES,1} \tag{45}$$

$$u_{EES,1} = u\,(\text{CarbonDioxide},\ T = T_1,\ p = p_1) \quad \textbf{State-1 specific internal energy} \tag{46}$$

$$s_{EES,1} = s\,(\text{CarbonDioxide},\ T = T_1,\ p = p_1) \quad \textbf{State-1 specific entropy} \tag{47}$$

$$T_{EES,2} = T\,(\text{CarbonDioxide},\ v = v_{EES,2},\ P = P_2) \tag{48}$$

$$u_{EES,2} = u\,(\text{CarbonDioxide},\ v = v_{EES,2},\ p = p_2) \quad \textbf{State-2 specific internal energy} \tag{49}$$

$$s_{EES,2} = s\,(\text{CarbonDioxide},\ v = v_{EES,2},\ p = p_2) \quad \textbf{State-2 specific entropy} \tag{50}$$

$$w_{EES} = 0 \quad \textbf{Constant volume process} \tag{51}$$

$$q_{EES} - w_{EES} = u_{EES,2} - u_{EES,1} \quad \textbf{Energy balance on the tank} \tag{52}$$

$$\Delta s_{EES} = s_{EES,2} - s_{EES,1} \quad \textbf{Entropy change} \tag{53}$$

Solution

$\boxed{\Delta s_{chart} = 2.101\ [\text{kJ/kg-K}]}$ $\boxed{\Delta s_{EES} = 2.097\ [\text{kJ/kg-K}]}$ $\boxed{\Delta s_{ideal} = 2.137\ [\text{kJ/kg-K}]}$ $MM = 44.01\ [\text{kg/kmol}]$

$P_{critical} = 7377\ [\text{kpa}]$ $\boxed{q_{chart} = 2777\ [\text{kJ/kg}]}$ $\boxed{q_{EES} = 2763\ [\text{kJ/kg}]}$ $\boxed{q_{ideal} = 2891\ [\text{kJ/kg}]}$

$R = 0.1889\ [\text{kJ/kg-K}]$ $R_u = 8.314\ [\text{kJ/kmol-K}]$ $T_{critical} = 304.1\ [\text{K}]$ $\boxed{w_{chart} = 0\ [\text{kJ/kg}]}$

$w_{EES} = 0\ [\text{kJ/kg}]$ $W_{ideal} = 0\ [\text{kJ/kg}]$

Arrays

Row	$u_{EES,i}$ [kJ/kg]	Δh_i [kJ/kg]	Δs_i [kJ/kg-K]	P_i [kPa]	T_i [K]	$T_{EES,i}$ [K]	$T_{chart,i}$ [K]	Tr_i	Z_i
1	-8.614	5.906	0.01131	1000	373.1			1.227	0.976
2	2754	-6.574	-0.0005072	8000	2985	2879	2887	9.491	1.009

Row	h_i [kJ/kg]	$h_{ideal,i}$ [kJ/kg]	$hideal_{chart,i}$ [kJ/kg]	pr_i	s_i [kJ/kg-K]	$s_{EES,i}$ [kJ/kg-K]	$s_{ideal,i}$ [kJ/kg-K]	$sideal_{chart,i}$ [kJ/kg-K]	u_i [kJ/kg]
1	-8882	-8876	-8876	0.1356	4.606	-0.2464	4.617		-8950
2	-5623	-5491	-5630	1.084	6.707	1.85	6.754	6.706	-6174

Row	$u_{ideal,i}$ [kJ/kg]	v_i [m³/kg]	$v_{EES,i}$ [m³/kg]
1	-8946	1.5	0.06885
2	-6055	1.5	0.06885

Supplement 11.1 Estimate Sublimation Pressure

Using the Clapeyron-Clausius equation and the triple point data of water, estimate the sublimation pressure of water at -30°C and compare to the value in Table A-8. Answer: 0.038 kPa, 0.004 %

Supplement 11.2 Generalized Chart Solution

Refrigerant 134a undergoes an isothermal process at 60C from 3 MPa to 0.1 MPa in a closed system. Determine the work done by the refrigerant 134a by using the tabular (EES) data and the generalized charts, in kJ/kg. Answer: 95.42 kJ/kg, 98.53 kJ/kg

Supplement 11.3 Generalized Chart Solution

Methane is contained in a piston-cylinder device and is heated at constant pressure of 4 MPa from 100°C to 350°C. Determine the heat transfer, work and entropy change per unit mass of the Methane using the ideal gas assumption, the generalized charts and real fluid (EES) data. Answer: 721.2 kJ/kg, 129.6 kJ/kg, 1.46 kJ/kg-K, 742.5 kJ/kg, 136.8 kJ/kg, 1.506 kJ/kg-K, 741.3 kJ/kg, 137 kJ/kg, 1.502 kJ/kg-K.

Chapter 12 Educational Objectives and Glossary

The Educational Objectives of Chapter 12 are to:

- Develop rules for determining nonreacting gas mixture properties from knowledge of mixture composition and the properties of the individual components.
- Define the quantities used to describe the composition of a mixture, such as mass fraction, mole fraction, and volume fraction.
- Apply the rules for determining mixture properties to ideal-gas mixtures and real-gas mixtures.
- Predict the *P-v-T* behavior of gas mixtures based on Dalton's law of additive pressures and Amagat's law of additive volumes.
- Develop the concept of chemical potential and determine the separation work of mixtures.

Chapter 12 Glossary

Amagat's law of additive volumes: The volume of a gas mixture is equal to the sum of the volumes each gas would occupy if it existed alone at the mixture temperature and pressure.

Apparent (or **average**) **molar mass** of a mixture can be expressed as the sum of the products of the mole fraction and molar mass of each component in the mixture.

Average (or **apparent**) **gas constant** of a mixture is the universal gas constant divided by the apparent molar mass of the mixture.

Chemical potential is the change in the Gibbs function of the mixture in a specified phase when a unit amount of a given component of the mixture in the same phase is added as pressure and temperature and the amounts of all other components are held constant. The chemical potential of a component of an ideal gas mixture depends on the mole fraction of the components as well as the mixture temperature and pressure, and is independent of the identity of the other constituent gases.

Component pressure is the pressure a component in a gas mixture would have if it existed alone at the volume and temperature of the mixture.

Component volume is the volume a component in a gas mixture would occupy if it existed alone at the temperature and pressure of the mixture.

Dalton's law of additive pressures: The pressure of a gas mixture is equal to the sum of the pressures each gas would exert if it existed alone at the mixture temperature and volume.

Extensive properties of a nonreacting ideal-or real-gas mixture are obtained by just adding the contributions of each component of the mixture.

Gibbs–Dalton law, an extension of Dalton's law of additive pressures, states that under the ideal-gas approximation, the properties of a gas in a mixture are not influenced by the presence of other gases, and each gas component in the mixture behaves as if it exists alone at the mixture temperature and mixture volume.

Gravimetric analysis is one way to describe the composition of a mixture that is accomplished by specifying the mass of each component.

Ideal mixture or **ideal solution** is a mixture where the effect of dissimilar molecules in a mixture on each other is negligible and the chemical potential of a component in such a mixture is simply taken to be the Gibbs function of the pure component.

Intensive properties of a nonreacting ideal-or real-gas mixture are obtained by dividing the extensive properties by the mass or the mole number of the mixture in the gas mixture. The internal energy, enthalpy, and entropy of a gas mixture per unit mass or per unit mole of the mixture can be determined summing the products of the mass fractions and the specific property or summing the products of the mole fractions and the molar specific property. That is, the intensive properties of a gas mixture are determined by either a mass weighted average of the properties or a mole weighted average of the properties.

Kay's rule, proposed by W. B. Kay in 1936, predicts the P-v-T behavior of a gas mixture by determining the compressibility factor for a gas mixture at the reduced pressure and reduced temperature defined in terms of the pseudocritical pressure (the sum of the products of the mole fraction and critical pressure of each component) and pseudocritical temperature (the sum of the products of the mole fraction and critical temperature of each component).

Mass fraction is the ratio of the mass of one component in a mixture to the total mass of the mixture.

Molar analysis is one way to describe the composition of a mixture that is accomplished by specifying the number of moles of each component.

Mole fraction is the ratio of the number of moles of one component in a mixture to the total moles of the mixture. Note that for an ideal-gas mixture, the mole fraction, the pressure fraction, and the volume fraction of a component are identical.

Nonreacting gas mixture is a mixture of gases not undergoing a chemical reaction and can be treated as a pure substance since it is usually a homogeneous mixture of different gases.

Osmotic pressure is the pressure difference across a semipermeable membrane that separates fresh water from the saline water under equilibrium conditions.

Osmotic rise is the vertical distance saline water would rise when separated from the fresh water by a membrane that is permeable to water molecules alone at equilibrium.

Partial pressure of a component in a gas mixture is the product of the mole fraction and the mixture pressure. The partial pressure is identical to the component pressure for ideal gas mixtures.

Partial volume of a component in a gas mixture is the product of the mole fraction and the mixture volume. The partial volume is identical to the component volume for ideal gas mixtures.

Pressure fraction of a gas component in a gas mixture is the ratio of the component pressure to the mixture pressure. Note that for an ideal-gas mixture, the mole fraction, the pressure fraction, and the volume fraction of a component are identical.

Volume fraction of a gas component in a gas mixture is the ratio of the component volume to the mixture volume. Note that for an ideal-gas mixture, the mole fraction, the pressure fraction, and the volume fraction of a component are identical.

EXAMPLE 12-1 PROPERTIES OF PRODUCTS OF COMBUSTION

The combustion of a hydrocarbon fuel with air results in a mixture of products of combustion having the composition on a volume basis as follows: 4.89% carbon dioxide, 6.50% water vapor, 12.20% oxygen and 76.41% nitrogen. Determine the average molar mass of the mixture; the average specific heat at constant pressure of the mixture at 600 K, in kJ/kmol-K, and the partial pressure of the water vapor in the mixture for a mixture pressure of 200 kPa.

Equations

GIVEN

$$T_{Mix} = 600 \ [\text{K}] \tag{1}$$

$$P_{Mix} = 200 \ [\text{kPa}] \tag{2}$$

Assume the mixture is an ideal gas mixture and there are 100 kmol of mixture. Note that volume fractions equal mole fractions in ideal gas mixtures.

ANALYSIS

Molar mass of the mixture

$$MM_{Mix} = \frac{4.89 \cdot \text{MW (CO2)} + 6.50 \cdot \text{MW (H2O)} + 12.20 \cdot \text{MW (O2)} + 76.41 \cdot \text{MW (N2)}}{4.89 + 6.50 + 12.20 + 76.41} \tag{3}$$

Average specific heat at constant pressure of the mixture

$$Cp_{Mix} = \frac{A + B}{4.89 + 6.50 + 76.41 + 12.20} \tag{4}$$

$$A = (4.89 \cdot c_p \, (\text{CO2}, \, T = T_{Mix}) + 6.50 \cdot c_p \, (\text{H2O}, \, T = T_{Mix}) + 76.41 \cdot c_p \, (\text{N2}, \, T = T_{Mix})) \tag{5}$$

$$B = (12.20 \cdot c_p \, (\text{O2}, \, T = T_{Mix})) \tag{6}$$

Partial pressure of the water in the mixture

$$y_v = \frac{6.50}{4.89 + 6.50 + 12.20 + 76.41} \tag{7}$$

$$P_v = y_v \cdot P_{Mix} \tag{8}$$

Solution

$A = 2772 \ [\text{kJ/kmol-K}]$
$B = 392.3 \ [\text{kJ/kmol-K}]$
$\boxed{Cp_{Mix} = 31.65 \ [\text{kJ/kmol-K}]}$
$\boxed{MM_{Mix} = 28.63 \ [\text{kg/kmol}]}$
$P_{Mix} = 200 \ [\text{kPa}]$
$P_v = 13.00 \ [\text{kPa}]$
$T_{Mix} = 600 \ [\text{K}]$
$\boxed{y_v = 0.0650}$

EXAMPLE 12-2 DETERMINE MASS FRACTIONS, ENTHALPY CHANGE PER UNIT MASS

A mixture that is 20% carbon dioxide, 10% oxygen, and 70% nitrogen by volume undergoes a process from 300 K, 100 kPa to 500 K, 400 kPa. Determine the makeup of the mixture on a mass basis and the enthalpy change per unit mass of mixture.

Equations

GIVEN

$$T_{MIx,1} = 300 \ [K] \tag{1}$$

$$P_{Mix,1} = 100 \ [kPa] \tag{2}$$

$$T_{Mix,2} = 500 \ [K] \tag{3}$$

$$P_{Mix,2} = 400 \ [kPa] \tag{4}$$

ANALYSIS

Assume the mixture is an ideal gas mixture. Note that volume fractions equal mole fractions in ideal gas mixtures

$y_{CO2} = 0.2$ **CO_2 mole fraction** $\tag{5}$

$y_{O2} = 0.1$ **O_2 mole fraction** $\tag{6}$

$y_{N2} = 0.7$ **N_2 mole fraction** $\tag{7}$

$MM_{Mix} = (y_{CO2} \cdot \text{MW} \,(\text{CO2}\,) + y_{O2} \cdot \text{MW}\,(\text{O2}\,) + y_{N2} \cdot \text{MW}\,(\text{N2}\,))$ **Molar mass of the mixture** $\tag{8}$

$mf_{CO2} = y_{CO2} \cdot \dfrac{\text{MW}\,(\text{CO2}\,)}{MM_{Mix}}$ **CO_2 mass fraction** $\tag{9}$

$mf_{O2} = y_{O2} \cdot \dfrac{\text{MW}\,(\text{O2}\,)}{MM_{Mix}}$ **O_2 mass fraction** $\tag{10}$

$mf_{N2} = y_{N2} \cdot \dfrac{\text{MW}\,(\text{N2}\,)}{MM_{Mix}}$ **N_2 mass fraction** $\tag{11}$

$\Delta h_{CO2} = \text{h}\,(\text{CO2},\ T = T_{Mix,2}) - \text{h}\,(\text{CO2},\ T = T_{Mix,1})$ **The specific enthalpy change of CO_2** $\tag{12}$

$\Delta h_{O2} = \text{h}\,(\text{O2},\ T = T_{Mix,2}) - \text{h}\,(\text{O2},\ T = T_{Mix,1})$ **The specific enthalpy change of O_2** $\tag{13}$

$\Delta h_{N2} = \text{h}\,(\text{N2},\ T = T_{Mix,2}) - \text{h}\,(\text{N2},\ T = T_{Mix,1})$ **The specific enthalpy change of N_2** $\tag{14}$

$\Delta h_{Mix} = mf_{CO2} \cdot \Delta h_{CO2} + mf_{O2} \cdot \Delta h_{O2} + mf_{N2} \cdot \Delta h_{N2}$ **The specific enthalpy change of the mixture** $\tag{15}$

Solution

$\Delta h_{CO2} = 187 \; [\text{kJ/kg}]$

$\boxed{\Delta h_{Mix} = 200.7 \; [\text{kJ/kg}]}$

$\Delta h_{N2} = 208.9 \; [\text{kJ/kg}]$

$\Delta h_{O2} = 188.4 \; [\text{kJ/kg}]$

$\boxed{mf_{CO2} = 0.2784}$

$\boxed{mf_{N2} = 0.6203}$

$\boxed{mf_{O2} = 0.1012}$

$MM_{Mix} = 31.61 \; [\text{kg/kmol}]$

$y_{CO2} = 0.2$

$y_{N2} = 0.7$

$y_{O2} = 0.1$

Arrays

Row	$P_{Mix,i}$ [kPa]	$T_{MIx,i}$ [K]
1	100	300
2	400	500

EXAMPLE 12-3 CONSTANT PRESSURE ADIABATIC MIXING

A process requires a mixture that is 21% oxygen, and 78% nitrogen and 1% argon by volume. All three gases are supplied from separate tanks to an adiabatic, constant pressure mixing chamber at 200 kPa but at different temperatures. The oxygen enters at 10°C, the nitrogen at 60°C and the argon at 200°C. Determine the total entropy change for the mixing process per unit mass of mixture.

Equations

GIVEN

$$P_{Mix} = 200 \ [\text{kPa}] \tag{1}$$

$$T_{O2,1} = 10 \ [\text{C}] \tag{2}$$

$$P_{O2,1} = P_{Mix} \tag{3}$$

$$T_{N2,1} = 60 \ [\text{C}] \tag{4}$$

$$P_{N2,1} = P_{Mix} \tag{5}$$

$$T_{Ar,1} = 200 \ [\text{C}] \tag{6}$$

$$P_{Ar,1} = P_{Mix} \tag{7}$$

ANALYSIS

Assume the mixture is an ideal gas mixture. Note that volume fractions equal mole fractions in ideal gas mixtures.

$$y_{O2} = 0.21 \quad \textbf{O}_2 \textbf{ mole fraction} \tag{8}$$

$$y_{N2} = 0.78 \quad \textbf{N}_2 \textbf{ mole fraction} \tag{9}$$

$$y_{Ar} = 0.01 \quad \textbf{Ar mole fraction} \tag{10}$$

$$P_{O2,2} = y_{O2} \cdot P_{Mix} \quad \textbf{P}_{O2} \textbf{ partial pressure} \tag{11}$$

$$P_{N2,2} = y_{N2} \cdot P_{Mix} \quad \textbf{P}_{N2} \textbf{ partial pressure} \tag{12}$$

$$P_{Ar,2} = y_{Ar} \cdot P_{Mix} \quad \textbf{P}_{Ar} \textbf{ partial pressure} \tag{13}$$

Molar mass of the mixture

$$MM_{Mix} = (y_{O2} \cdot \text{MW (O2)} + y_{N2} \cdot \text{MW (N2)} + y_{Ar} \cdot \text{MW (Argon)}) \tag{14}$$

$$mf_{O2} = y_{O2} \cdot \frac{\text{MW (O2)}}{MM_{Mix}} \quad \textbf{O}_2 \textbf{ mass fraction} \tag{15}$$

$$mf_{N2} = y_{N2} \cdot \frac{\text{MW (N2)}}{MM_{Mix}} \quad \textbf{N}_2 \textbf{ mass fraction} \tag{16}$$

$$mf_{Ar} = y_{Ar} \cdot \frac{\text{MW (Argon)}}{MM_{Mix}} \quad \textbf{Ar mass fraction} \tag{17}$$

The final temperature of the mixture is needed. The conservation of energy on a unit mass basis for steady flow mixing with no heat transfer or work, $\dot{E}_{in} = \dot{E}_{out}$, allows calculation of T_{Mix}. All components of the exit mixture have the same common temperature, T_{Mix}

$$\dot{E}_{in} = \dot{E}_{out} \tag{18}$$

$$Cp_{Ar} = c_p \left(\text{Argon}, \ T = 27, \ P = 100 \right) \qquad \text{Specific heat at constant pressure for Ar} \tag{19}$$

$$\dot{E}_{in} = mf_{O2} \cdot h \left(O2, \ T = T_{O2,1} \right) + mf_{N2} \cdot h \left(N2, \ T = T_{N2,1} \right) + mf_{Ar} \cdot Cp_{ar} \cdot T_{Ar,1} \tag{20}$$

$$\dot{E}_{out} = mf_{O2} \cdot h \left(O2, \ T = T_{Mix} \right) + mf_{N2} \cdot h \left(N2, \ T = T_{Mix} \right) + mf_{Ar} \cdot Cp_{ar} \cdot T_{Mix} \tag{21}$$

$$\Delta s_{O2} = s \left(O2, \ T = T_{Mix}, \ P = P_{O2,2} \right) - s \left(O2, \ T = T_{O2,1}, \ P = P_{O2,1} \right) \qquad \text{O}_2 \text{ specific entropy change} \tag{22}$$

$$\Delta s_{N2} = s \left(N2, \ T = T_{Mix}, \ P = P_{N2,2} \right) - s \left(N2, \ T = T_{N2,1}, \ P = P_{N2,1} \right) \qquad \text{N}_2 \text{ specific entropy change} \tag{23}$$

Air specific entropy change

$$\Delta s_{Ar} = Cp_{Ar} \cdot \ln \left(\frac{ConvertTemp \left(C, \ K, \ T_{Mix} \right)}{ConvertTemp \left(C, \ K, \ T_{Ar,1} \right)} \right) - 8.314 \ [\text{kJ/kmol} \cdot \text{K}] \, / MW \left(\text{Argon} \right) \cdot \ln \left(P_{Ar,2} / P_{Ar,1} \right) \tag{24}$$

$$\Delta s_{total} = mf_{O2} \cdot \Delta s_{O2} + mf_{N2} \cdot \Delta s_{N2} + mf_{Ar} \cdot \Delta s_{Ar} \qquad \text{Total specific entropy change of the mixture} \tag{25}$$

Solution

$Cp_{Ar} = 0.5215 \ [\text{kJ/kg-C}]$
$\Delta s_{Ar} = 0.7602 \ [\text{kJ/kg-K}]$
$\Delta s_{N2} = 0.04321 \ [\text{kJ/kg-K}]$
$\Delta s_{O2} = 0.5284 \ [\text{kJ/kg-K}]$
$\boxed{\Delta s_{total} = 0.1657 \ [\text{kJ/kg-K}]}$
$\dot{E}_{in} = 25.74 \ [\text{kJ/kg}]$
$\dot{E}_{out} = 25.74 \ [\text{kJ/kg}]$
$mf_{Ar} = 0.01379$
$mf_{N2} = 0.7542$
$mf_{O2} = 0.232$
$MM_{Mix} = 28.97 \ [\text{kg/kmol}]$
$P_{Mix} = 200 \ [\text{kPa}]$
$T_{Mix} = 50.38 \ [\text{C}]$
$y_{Ar} = 0.01$
$y_{N2} = 0.78$
$y_{O2} = 0.21$

Arrays

Row	$P_{Ar,i}$ [kPa]	$P_{N2,i}$ [kPa]	$P_{O2,i}$ [kPa]	$T_{Ar,i}$ [C]	$T_{N2,i}$ [C]	$T_{O2,i}$ [C]
1	200	200	200	200	60	10
2	2	156	42			

Chapter 12 Supplemental Problems

Supplement 12.1 Determine Mass Fractions

A mixture that is 15% carbon dioxide, 5% carbon dioxide, 10% oxygen, and 70% nitrogen by volume undergoes a an adiabatic compression process having a compression ratio of 8:1. If the initial state of the mixture is 300 K, 100 kPa, determine the makeup of the mixture on a mass basis and the internal energy change per unit mass of mixture. Answer: 0.2143, 0.0454, 0.1039, 0.6364, 251.8 kJ/kg

Supplement 12.2 Mixture Flow Through a Converging Nozzle

A mixture of carbon dioxide and nitrogen flows through a converging nozzle. The mixture leaves the nozzle at a temperature of 500 K with a velocity 360 m/s. If the velocity is equal to the speed of sound at the exit temperature, determine the required make up of the mixture on a mass basis. Answer: 0.8377, 0.1623

Supplement 12.3 Work Done By Products of Combustion in a Piston-Cylinder

A piston-cylinder device contains products of combustion from the combustion of a hydrocarbon fuel with air. The combustion process results in a mixture that has the composition on a volume basis as follows: 4.89% carbon dioxide, 6.50% water vapor, 12.20% oxygen, and 76.41% nitrogen. This mixture is initially at 1800 K, 1 MPa and expands in an adiabatic, reversible process to 200 kPa. Determine the work done on the piston by the gas, in kJ/kg of mixture. Treat the water vapor as an ideal gas. Answer: 547.8 kJ/kg

Supplement 12.4 Work to Compress Fuel-Air Mixture

Propane and air are supplied to an internal combustion engine such that the air-to-fuel ratio is 16:1 when the pressure is 95 kPa and the temperature is 30C. The compression ratio of the engine is 9.5:1. If the compression process is isentropic, determine the required work input for this compression process, in kJ/kg of mixture. Answer: 292.2 kJ/kg

Supplement 12.5 Work Done By Mixture Expanding In Turbine

A mixture of 60% carbon dioxide and 40% methane on a mole basis expands through a turbine from 1600 K, 800 kPa to 100 kPa. The volume flow rate at the turbine entrance is 10 liters per second. Determine the rate of work done by the mixture using (a) ideal-gas approximation and (b) Kay's rule. Answer: 14.72 kW, 14.71 kW.

Supplement 12.6 Mixing Between Tanks

A pipe fitted with a closed valve connects two tanks. One tank contains a 5 kg mixture of 62.5% CO_2 and 37.5% O_2 on a mole basis at 30°C, 125 kPa. The second tank contains 10 kg of N_2 at 15°C, 200 kPa. The valve in the pipe is opened and the gases are allowed to mix. During the mixing process 100 kJ of heat energy is supplied to the combined tanks. Determine the final pressure and temperature of the mixture and the total volume of the mixture. Answers: 113.1 kPa, 312.4 K, 11.1 m3.

Chapter 13 Educational Objectives and Glossary

The Educational Objectives of Chapter 13 are to:

- Explain the meaning of the terms dry air and atmospheric air.
- Define and calculate the specific and relative humidity of atmospheric air.
- Calculate the dew-point temperature of atmospheric air.
- Relate the adiabatic saturation temperature and wet-bulb temperatures of atmospheric air.
- Use the psychrometric chart as a tool to determine the properties of atmospheric air.
- Relate the desire for human comfort to air-conditioning requirements.
- Solve problems associated with the conservation of mass and energy for various air-conditioning processes.

Chapter 13 Glossary

Absolute or **specific humidity** (also called humidity ratio) is the mass of water vapor present in a unit mass of dry air; that is, it is the ratio of the mass of water vapor to the mass of dry air in atmospheric air.

Adiabatic saturation process is the process in which a steady stream of unsaturated air of unknown specific humidity is passed through a long insulated channel that contains a pool of water. As the air flows over the water, some water will evaporate and mix with the airstream. The moisture content of air will increase during this process, and its temperature will decrease, since part of the latent heat of vaporization of the water that evaporates will come from the air. If the channel is long enough, the airstream will exit as saturated air (100 percent relative humidity) at the exit temperature.

Adiabatic saturation temperature is the exit temperature that air attains in the adiabatic saturation process.

Atmospheric air is the air in the atmosphere, which normally contains some water vapor (or moisture).

Cooling pond is a large lake open to the atmosphere into which warm water containing waste heat is pumped. Heat transfer from the pond surface to the atmosphere is very slow, thus about 20 times the area of a spray pond is needed in this case to achieve the same cooling.

Dehumidifying is the process of removing moisture from atmospheric air.

Dew-point temperature is defined as the temperature at which condensation begins when the air is cooled at constant pressure.

Dry air is air that contains no water vapor.

Dry-bulb temperature is the ordinary temperature of atmospheric air.

Evaporative coolers, also known as swamp coolers, use evaporative cooling based on the principle that as water evaporates, the latent heat of vaporization is absorbed from the water body and the surrounding air. As a result, both the water and the air are cooled during the process.

Forced-draft cooling tower, or induced-draft cooling tower, is a wet cooling tower in which the air is drawn through the tower by fans.

Humidifying is the process of adding moisture to atmospheric air.

Natural-draft cooling tower uses the naturally occurring density gradients between the inside air-water vapor mixture and the outside air which create an airflow from the bottom to the top of a wet cooling tower.

Psychrometric chart presents the properties of atmospheric air at a specified pressure and two independent intensive properties. The psychrometric chart is a plot of absolute humidity versus dry-bulb temperature and shows lines of constant relative humidity, wet-bulb temperature, specific volume, and enthalpy for the atmospheric air.

Relative humidity is a measure of the amount of moisture the air holds relative to the maximum amount the air can hold at the same temperature. The relative humidity can be expressed as the ratio of the vapor pressure to the saturation pressure of water at that temperature.

Saturated air is air which can hold no more moisture. Any moisture introduced into saturated air will condense.

Simple cooling is the process of lowering the temperature of atmospheric air when no moisture is removed.

Simple heating is the process of raising the temperature of atmospheric air when no moisture is added.

Sling psychrometer is a device with both a dry-bulb thermometer and a wet-bulb temperature mounted on the frame of the device so that when it is swung through the air both the wet-and dry-bulb temperatures can be read simultaneously.

Spray pond is a pond where warm water is sprayed into the air and is cooled by the air as it falls into the pond. Spray ponds require 25 to 50 times the area of a cooling tower because water loss due to air drift is high.

Vapor pressure is usually considered to be the partial pressure of water vapor in atmospheric air.

Waste heat is energy that must be dissipated to the atmosphere from a process such as the heat transferred from condensing steam in the condenser of a steam power plant.

Wet-bulb temperature is temperature measured by using a thermometer whose bulb is covered with a cotton wick saturated with water and blowing air over the wick.

Wet cooling tower is essentially a semienclosed evaporative cooler.

EXAMPLE 13-1 DETERMINE PROPERTIES OF ATMOSPHERIC AIR

An 8 m^3 tank contains saturated air at 30°C, 105 kPa. Determine (a) the mass of dry air, (b) the specific humidity, and (c) the enthalpy of the air per unit mass of the dry air.

Equations

GIVEN

$$P_1 = 105 \ [\text{kPa}] \tag{1}$$

$$T_1 = 30 \ [\text{C}] \tag{2}$$

$$RH_1 = 100/100 \quad \textbf{Relative humidity for saturated air} \tag{3}$$

$$Vol = 8 \ [\text{m}^3] \tag{4}$$

PROPERTIES

$$h = \text{h} \, (\text{AirH2O}, \ T = T_1, \ P = P_1, \ w = w) \quad \textbf{Specific enthalpy} \tag{5}$$

$$v = \text{v} \, (\text{AirH2O}, \ T = T_1, \ P = P_1, \ R = RH_1) \quad \textbf{Specific volume} \tag{6}$$

$$w = \omega \, (\text{AirH2O}, \ T = T_1, \ P = P_1, \ R = RH_1) \quad \textbf{Humidity ratio} \tag{7}$$

ANALYSIS

$$v = Vol/m_a \tag{8}$$

Solution

$\boxed{h = 97.2 \ [\text{kJ/kg}]}$ $\boxed{m_a = 9.263 \ [\text{kg}]}$ $v = 0.8636 \ [\text{m}^3/\text{kg}]$ $Vol = 8 \ [\text{m}^3]$ $\boxed{w = 0.02622 \ [\text{kg/kg}]}$

Arrays

Row	P_i [kPa]	RH_i	T_i [C]
1	105	1	30

EXAMPLE 13-2 AUTOMOBILE AIR CONDITIONER

Atmospheric air from the inside of an automobile enters the evaporator section of the air conditioner at 1 atm, 27 °C, 50% relative humidity. The air returns to the automobile at 10 °C, 90% relative humidity. The passenger compartment has a volume of 2 m^3 and 5 air changes per minute are required to maintain the inside of the automobile at the desired comfort level. Sketch the psychrometric diagram for the atmospheric air flowing through the air conditioning process. Determine the dew point and wet bulb temperatures at the inlet to the evaporator section, in °C. Determine the required heat transfer rate from the atmospheric air to the evaporator fluid, in kW. Determine rate of condensation of water vapor in the evaporator section, in kg/min.

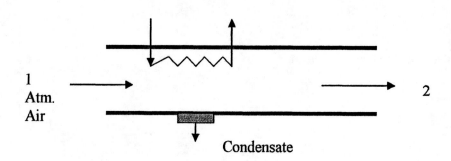

Equations

GIVEN

$$P_1 = 101.32 \text{ [kPa]} \tag{1}$$

$$T_1 = 27 \text{ [C]} \tag{2}$$

$$RH_1 = 50/100 \tag{3}$$

$$P_2 = 101.32 \text{ [kPa]} \tag{4}$$

$$T_2 = 10 \text{ [C]} \tag{5}$$

$$RH_2 = 90/100 \tag{6}$$

PROPERTIES

$T_{dp,1} = \text{DP} \left(\text{AirH2O}, \, T = T_1, \, P = P_1, \, w = w_1 \right)$ **Dew point temperature at inlet**   (7)

$T_{wb,1} = \text{wb} \left(\text{AirH2O}, \, T = T_1, \, P = P_1, \, R = RH_1 \right)$ **Wet-bulb temperature at inlet**   (8)

$v_1 = \text{v} \left(\text{AirH2O}, \, T = T_1, \, P = P_1, \, R = RH_1 \right)$ **Specific volume at inlet**   (9)

$w_1 = \omega \left(\text{AirH2O}, \, T = T_1, \, P = P_1, \, R = RH_1 \right)$ **Humidity ratio at inlet**   (10)

$h_1 = \text{h} \left(\text{AirH2O}, \, T = T_1, \, P = P_1, \, w = w_1 \right)$ **Specific enthalpy at inlet**   (11)

$w_2 = \omega\,(\text{AirH2O},\ T = T_2,\ P = P_2,\ R = RH_2)$ **Humidity ratio at exit**   (12)

$h_2 = \text{h}\,(\text{AirH2O},\ T = T_2,\ P = P_2,\ w = w_2)$ **Specific enthalpy at exit**   (13)

$h_{liq,2} = \text{h}\,(\text{Water},\ T = T_2,\ x = 0)$ **Specific enthalpy of the condensate**   (14)

ANALYSIS

$\dot{Vol}_1 = 2\ \left[\text{m}^3/\text{change}\right] \cdot 5\ [\text{changes/min}]$ **Volume flow rate at inlet**   (15)

$v_1 = \dfrac{\dot{Vol}_1}{\dot{m}_a}$ **Mass flow rate of dry air, $\text{m}_{dot,a}$**   (16)

$w_1 = \dfrac{\dot{m}_{v,1}}{\dot{m}_a}$ **Mass flow rate of vapor at inlet, $\text{m}_{dot,v,1}$**   (17)

$w_2 = \dfrac{\dot{m}_{v,2}}{\dot{m}_a}$ **Mass flow rate of vapor at exit, $\text{m}_{dot,v,2}$**   (18)

$\dot{m}_a \cdot h_1 = \dot{Q}_{out} \cdot \left|60\,\dfrac{kJ/min}{kw}\right| + \dot{m}_a \cdot h_2 + \dot{m}_w \cdot h_{liq,2}$ **Steady flow conservation of energy for the air**   (19)

$\dot{m}_{v,1} = \dot{m}_{v,2} + \dot{m}_w$ **Mass balance**   (20)

Solution

$h_{liq,2} = 41.99\ [\text{kJ/kg}]$ $\dot{m}_a = 11.55\ [\text{kg/min}]$ $\boxed{\dot{m}_w = 0.04954\ [\text{kg/min}]}$ $\boxed{\dot{Q}_{out} = 5.407\ [\text{kW}]}$

$\boxed{T_{dp,1} = 15.7\ [\text{C}]}$ $\boxed{T_{wb,1} = 19.53\ [\text{C}]}$

Arrays

Row	$\dot{m}_{v,i}$ [kg/min]	P_i [kPa]	RH_i	T_i [C]	$\dot{Vol}_i$ [m³/min]	h_i [kJ/kg]	v_i [m³/kg]	w_i
1	0.1288	101.3	0.5	27	10	55.6	0.8655	0.01115
2	0.07926	101.3	0.9	10		27.35		0.00686

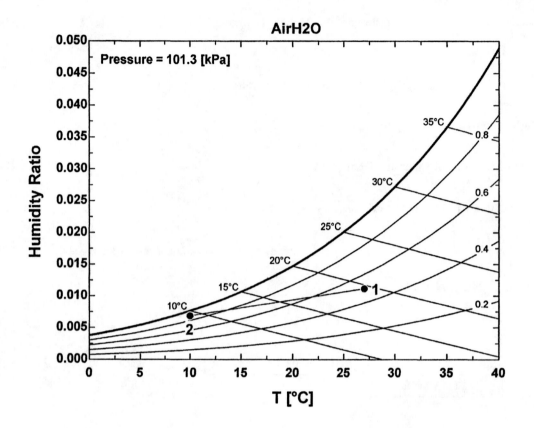

EXAMPLE 13-3 AIR CONDITIONER REFRIGERANT FLOW RATE

Atmospheric air enters an air-conditioning system at 30°C and 70% relative humidity with a volume flow rate of 4 m³/min and is cooled to 20°C at a pressure of 1 atm. The system uses refigerant-134a as the cooling fluid that enters the cooling section at 350 kPa with a quality of 20 percent and leaves as a saturated vapor. Sketch the hardware for this process. Sketch the psychrometric diagram for the process. What is the heat transfer from the air to the cooling coils, in kW? If any water is condensed from the air, how much water will be condensed from the atmospheric air per min? Determine the mass flow rate of the refrigerant, in kg/min.

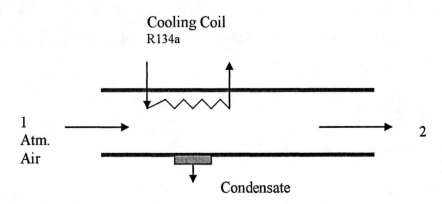

Equations

GIVEN

$$P_1 = 1 \text{ [atm]} \cdot \left| 101.325 \, \frac{\text{kPa}}{\text{atm}} \right| \tag{1}$$

$$T_1 = 30 \text{ [C]} \tag{2}$$

$$RH_1 = 70/100 \tag{3}$$

$$\dot{Vol}_1 = 4 \text{ [m}^3/\text{min]} \tag{4}$$

$$P_2 = P_1 \tag{5}$$

$$T_2 = 20 \text{ [C]} \tag{6}$$

$$RH_2 = 20/100 \tag{7}$$

$$P_{R134a} = 350 \text{ [kPa]} \tag{8}$$

$$x_{R134a} = 0.2 \tag{9}$$

PROPERTIES

$$v_1 = v \left(\text{AirH2O}, \, T = T_1, \, P = P_1, \, R = RH_1\right) \quad \text{Specific volume at inlet} \tag{10}$$

$w_1 = \omega\,(\text{AirH2O},\ T = T_1,\ P = P_1,\ R = RH_1)$ **Humidity ratio at inlet**   (11)

$h_1 = \text{h}\,(\text{AirH2O},\ T = T_1,\ P = P_1,\ w = w_1)$ **Specific enthalpy at inlet**   (12)

$w_2 = \omega\,(\text{AirH2O},\ T = T_2,\ P = P_2,\ R = RH_2)$ **Humidity ratio at exit**   (13)

$h_2 = \text{h}\,(\text{AirH2O},\ T = T_2,\ P = P_2,\ w = w_2)$ **Specific enthalpy at exit**   (14)

$h_{liq,2} = \text{h}\,(\text{Water},\ T = T_2,\ x = 0)$ **Specific enthalpy of the condensate**   (15)

$h_{R,1} = \text{h}\,(\text{R134a},\ x = x_{R134a},\ P = P_{R134a})$ **Specific enthalpy of R134a at cooling coil inlet**   (16)

$h_{R,2} = \text{h}\,(\text{R134a},\ x = 1,\ P = P_{R134a})$ **Specific enthalpy of R134a at cooling coil exit**   (17)

ANALYSIS

$v_1 = \dfrac{\dot{Vol}_1}{\dot{m}_a}$ **Mass flow rate of dry air, m$_{dot,a}$**   (18)

$w_1 = \dfrac{\dot{m}_{v,1}}{\dot{m}_a}$ **Mass flow rate of vapor at inlet, m$_{dot,v,1}$**   (19)

$w_2 = \dfrac{\dot{m}_{v,2}}{\dot{m}_a}$ **Mass flow rate of vapor at exit, m$_{dot,v,2}$**   (20)

$\dot{m}_a \cdot h_1 = \dot{Q}_{out} \cdot \left| 60\,\dfrac{kJ/min}{kW} \right| + \dot{m}_a \cdot h_2 + \dot{m}_w \cdot h_{liq,2}$ **Steady flow conservation of energy for the air**   (21)

$\dot{m}_{v,1} = \dot{m}_{v,2} + \dot{m}_w$ **Mass balance**   (22)

$\dot{m}_R \cdot h_{R,1} + \dot{Q}_{out} \cdot \left| 60\,\dfrac{kJ/min}{kW} \right| = \dot{m}_R \cdot h_{R,2}$ **Steady flow conservation of energy for R 134a**   (23)

Solution

$h_{liq,2} = 83.84\ [\text{kJ/kg}]$ $\dot{m}_a = 4.521\ [\text{kg/min}]$ $\dot{m}_R = 1.435\ [\text{kg/min}]$ $\dot{m}_w = 0.07196\ [\text{kg/min}]$

$P_{R134a} = 350\ [\text{kPa}]$ $\dot{Q}_{out} = 3.727\ [\text{Kw}]$ $x_{R134a} = 0.2$

Arrays

Row	$\dot{m}_{v,i}$ [kg/min]	w_i	P_i [kPa]	RH_i	T_i [C]	$\dot{Vol}_i$ [m³/min]	h_i [kJ/kg]	$h_{R,i}$ [kJ/kg]	v_i [m³/kg]
1	0.085	0.0188	101.3	0.7	30	4	78.24	97.56	0.8847
2	0.01304	0.002885	101.3	0.2	20		27.45	253.3	

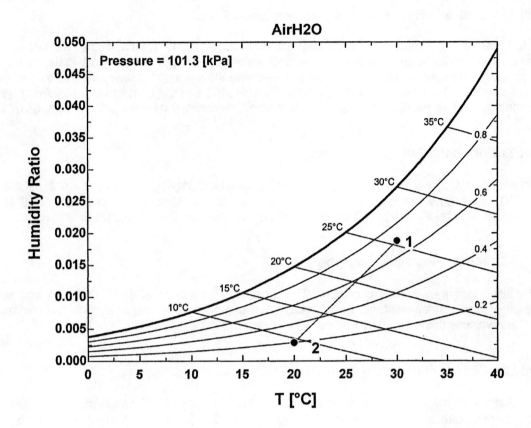

Supplement 13.1 Unsteady Flow of Air-vapor Mixture into a Tank

An uninsulated tank having a volume of 0.5 m³ contains air at 35°C, 130 kPa, 20% relative humidity. The tank is connected to a water supply line in which water flows at 50°C. Water is sprayed into the tank until the relative humidity of the air-vapor mixture is 90%. Determine the amount of water supplied to the tank, in kg, the final pressure of the air-vapor mixture in the tank, in kPa, and the heat transfer required during the process maintain the air-vapor mixture in the tank at 35°C. Answer: 0.01386 kg, 133.9 kPa, 64.07 kJ

Supplement 13.2 Adiabatic Saturation Process

Atmospheric air at 35°C flows steadily into an adiabatic saturation device and leaves as a saturated mixture at 25°C. Makeup water is supplied to the device at 25°C. Atmospheric pressure is 98 kPa. Determine the relative humidity and specific humidity of the air. Answer: 0.4511, 0.01655.

Supplement 13.3 Nozzle Flow with Atmospheric Air

Air flows steadily through an isentropic nozzle. The air enters the nozzle at 35°C, 200 kPa and 50% relative humidity. If no condensation is to occur during the expansion process, determine the pressure, temperature, and velocity of the air at the nozzle exit. Answer: 293.2 K, 168.2 kPa, 173.2 m/s.

Supplement 13.4 Cooling of Atmospheric Air in a Workspace

Air from a workspace enters an air conditioner unit at 30 °C dry bulb and 25 °C wet bulb. The air leaves the air conditioner and returns to the space at 25 °C dry bulb and 6.5°C dew point temperature. If there is any, the condensate leaves the air conditioner at the temperature of the air leaving the cooling coils. The volume flow rate of the air returned to the workspace is 1000 m³/min. Atmospheric pressure is 98 kPa. Determine the heat transfer rate from the air, in kW, and the mass flow rate of condensate water, if any, in kg/h. Answer: 672.9 kW, 847.1 kg/h.

Supplement 13.5 Determine Chilled Water Flow Rate for Air Conditioner

Two thousand cubic meters per hour of atmospheric air at 28ºC with a dew point temperature of 25ºC flows into an air conditioner that uses chilled water as the cooling fluid. The atmospheric air is to be cooled to 18ºC. Sketch the system hardware and the psychrometric diagram for the process. Determine the mass flow rate of the condensate water, if any, leaving the air conditioner, in kg/h. If the cooling water has a 10°C temperature rise while flowing through the air conditioner, determine the volume flow rate of chilled water supplied to the air conditioner heat exchanger, in gal/min. The air conditioning process takes place at 100 kPa. : 16.24 kg/h, 6.669 gal/min.

Supplement 13.6 Determine Volume Flow Rate of Air to Auto A/C

An automobile air conditioner uses refrigerant 134a as the cooling fluid. The evaporator operates at 275 kPa gage and the condenser operates at 1.7 MPa gage. The compressor requires a power input of eight horsepower and has an isentropic efficiency of 85%. Atmospheric air at 22°C, 50% relative humidity enters the evaporator and leaves at 8°C, 90% relative humidity. Determine the volume flow rate of the atmospheric air entering the evaporator of the air conditioner, in m³/min. Answer: 44.6 m3/min

Supplement 13.7 Cooling Tower

A natural-draft cooling tower is to remove waste heat from the cooling water flowing through the condenser of a steam power plant. The turbine in the steam power plant receives 42 kg/s of steam from the steam generator. Eighteen percent of the steam entering the turbine is extracted for various feedwater heaters. The condensate of the higher pressure feedwater heaters is trapped to the next lowest pressure feedwater heater. The last feedwater heater operates at 0.2 MPa and all of the steam extracted for the feedwater heaters is throttled from the last feedwater heater exit to the condenser operating at a pressure of 10 kPa. The remainder of the steam produces work in the turbine and leaves the lowest pressure stage of the turbine at 10 kPa with an entropy of 7.962 kJ/kg-K. The cooling tower supplies the cooling water at 26 C to the condenser, and cooling water returns from the condenser to the cooling tower at 40 C. Atmospheric air enters the tower at 1 atm with dry- and wet-bulb temperatures of 23 and 18 C, respectively, leaves saturated at 37 C. Determine (a) the mass flow rate of the cooling water, (b) the volume flow rate of air into the cooling tower, and (c) the mass flow rate of the required makeup water. Answer: 1412 kg/s, 47696 m3/min, 28.19 kg/s.

Chapter 14 Educational Objectives and Glossary

The Educational Objectives of Chapter 14 are to:

- Introduce the concepts of fuels and combustion.
- Apply the conservation of mass to reacting systems to determine balanced reaction equations.
- Define the parameters used in combustion analysis, such as air-fuel ratio, percent theoretical air, and dew point temperature.
- Apply energy balances to reacting systems for both steady-flow control volumes and fixed mass systems.
- Calculate the enthalpy of reaction, enthalpy of combustion, and the heating values of fuels.
- Determine the adiabatic flame temperature for reacting mixtures.
- Evaluate the entropy change of reacting systems.
- Analyze reacting systems from the second-law perspective.

Chapter 14 Glossary

Absolute entropy is the entropy value relative to the absolute base established by the third law of thermodynamics.

Adiabatic flame or **adiabatic combustion temperature** is the maximum temperature the products of combustion will reach in the limiting case of no heat loss to the surroundings during the combustion process. The adiabatic flame temperature attains its maximum value when complete combustion occurs with the theoretical amount of air.

Air–fuel ratio AF is a frequently used quantity in the analysis of combustion processes to quantify the amounts of fuel and air. It is usually expressed on a mass basis and is defined as the ratio of the mass of air to the mass of fuel for a combustion process.

Chemically correct amount of air is the stoichiometric or theoretical air, or 100 percent theoretical air.

Combustion is a chemical reaction during which a fuel is oxidized and a large quantity of energy is released.

Combustion air is dry air which can be approximated as 21 percent oxygen and 79 percent nitrogen by mole numbers. Therefore, each mole of oxygen entering a combustion chamber will be accompanied by $0.79/0.21 = 3.76$ mol of nitrogen. To supply one mole of oxygen to a combustion process, 4.76 mol of combustion air are required.

Complete combustion is a combustion process in which all the carbon in the fuel burns to CO_2, all the hydrogen burns to H_2O, and all the sulfur (if any) burns to SO_2. That is, all the combustible components of a fuel are burned to completion during a complete combustion process.

Conservation of mass principle (or the **mass balance**) is the principle used to balance chemical reaction equations. It can be stated as follows: The total mass of each element is conserved during a chemical reaction. The total mass of each element on the right-hand side of the reaction equation (the products) must be equal to the total mass of that element on the left-hand side (the reactants) even though the elements exist in different chemical compounds in the reactants and products. Even though the mass must be conserved, the total number of moles is not conserved during a chemical reaction.

Deficiency of air results when the amounts of air are less than the stoichiometric amount.

Enthalpy of a chemical component at a specified state is the sum of the enthalpy of formation of the component at 25°C, 1 atm, and the sensible enthalpy of the component relative to 25°C, 1 atm, which is the difference between the sensible enthalpy at the specified state ad the sensible enthalpy at the standard reference state of 25°C and 1 atm. This definition enables us to use enthalpy values from tables regardless of the reference state used in their construction.

Enthalpy of combustion h_C is the enthalpy of reaction during a steady-flow combustion process when 1 kmol (or 1 kg) of fuel is burned completely at a specified temperature and pressure and represents the amount of heat released.

Enthalpy of formation is the enthalpy of a substance at a specified state due to its chemical composition. The enthalpy of formation of all stable elements (such as O_2, N_2, H_2, and C) has a value of zero at the standard reference state of 25°C and 1 atm.

Enthalpy of reaction h_R is defined as the difference between the enthalpy of the products at a specified state and the enthalpy of the reactants at the same state for a complete reaction.

Equivalence ratio is the ratio of the actual fuel–air ratio to the stoichiometric fuel–air ratio.

Excess air is the amount of air in excess of the stoichiometric amount.

Exothermic reaction is a reaction during which chemical energy is released in the form of heat.

Fuel is any material that can be burned to release energy.

Fuel–air ratio is the reciprocal of air–fuel ratio.

Fuel cells operate on the principle of electrolytic cells in which the chemical energy of the fuel is directly converted to electric energy, and electrons are exchanged through conductor wires connected to a load. Fuel cells are not heat engines, and thus their efficiencies are not limited by the Carnot efficiency. They convert chemical energy to electric energy essentially in an isothermal manner.

Heating value of a fuel is defined as the amount of heat released when a fuel is burned completely in a steady-flow process and the products are returned to the state of the reactants. In other words, the heating value of a fuel is equal to the absolute value of the enthalpy of combustion of the fuel.

Higher heating value (HHV) is the heating value when the H_2O in the products is in the liquid form.

Hydrocarbon fuels are the most familiar fuels and consist primarily of hydrogen and carbon. They are denoted by the general formula C_nH_m. Hydrocarbon fuels exist in all phases, some examples being coal, gasoline, and natural gas.

Ignition temperature is the minimum temperature to which a fuel must be brought to start the combustion.

Incomplete combustion is a combustion process in which the combustion products contain any unburned fuel or components such as C, H_2, CO, or OH.

Liquefied petroleum gas (LPG) is a byproduct of natural gas processing or crude oil refining. It consists mainly of propane (over 90 percent), and thus LPG is usually referred to as propane. However, it also contains varying amounts of butane, propylene, and butylenes.

Lower heating value (LHV) is the heating value when the H_2O in the products is in the vapor form.

Natural gas is produced from gas wells or oil wells rich in natural gas. It is composed mainly of methane, but it also contains small amounts of ethane, propane, hydrogen, helium, carbon dioxide, nitrogen, hydrogen sulfate, and water vapor. It is stored either in the gas phase at pressures of 150 to 250 atm as CNG (compressed natural gas) or in the liquid phase at 162°C as LNG (liquefied natural gas).

Orsat gas analyzer is a commonly used device to analyze the composition of combustion gases. The amounts of carbon dioxide, carbon monoxide, and oxygen are measured on a percent by volume and are based on a dry analysis.

Percent deficiency of air is the deficiency of air expressed as a percent of stoichiometric air. For example, 90 percent theoretical air is equivalent to 10 percent deficiency of air.

Percent excess air or **percent theoretical air** is the amount of excess air usually expressed in terms of the stoichiometric air. For example, 50 percent excess air is equivalent to 150 percent theoretical air.

Products are the components that exist after the reaction in a combustion process.

Reactants are the components that exist before the reaction in a combustion process.

Stable form of an element is the chemically stable form of that element at 25°C and 1 atm. Nitrogen, for example, exists in diatomic form (N_2) at 25°C and 1 atm. Therefore, the stable form of nitrogen at the standard reference state is diatomic nitrogen N_2, not monatomic nitrogen N.

Standard reference state for the properties of chemical components is chosen as 25°C (77°F) and 1 atm. Property values at the standard reference state are indicated by a superscript (°) (such as $h°$ and $u°$).

Stoichiometric air or **theoretical air** is the minimum amount of air needed for the complete combustion of a fuel. When a fuel is completely burned with theoretical air, no uncombined oxygen will be present in the product gases.

Stoichiometric combustion or **theoretical combustion** is the ideal combustion process during which a fuel is burned completely with theoretical air.

Third law of thermodynamics is stated as the entropy of a pure crystalline substance at absolute zero temperature is zero.

EXAMPLE 14-1 COMBUSTION OF AN ALCOHOL

Propal alcohol C_3H_7OH is burned with 50 percent excess air. Write the balanced reaction equation for complete combustion and determine the air-to-fuel ratio, in kg air/kg fuel.

Equations

PROPERTIES

$MM_{air} = MW(air)$ **Molar mass of air**   (1)

$MM_{fuel} = 3 \cdot 12 + 8 \cdot 1 + 1 \cdot 16$ **Molar mass of fuel**   (2)

ANALYSIS

The reaction equation for 50% excess air is:

C3H7OH + 1.5*A$_{th}$ (O2 +3.76N2)=B CO2 + D H2O + E O2 + F N2

$3 = B$ **Carbon Balance**   (3)

$8 = 2 \cdot D$ **Hydrogen Balance**   (4)

$1 + 1.5 \cdot A_{th} \cdot 2 = B \cdot 2 + D + E \cdot 2$ **Oxygen Balance**   (5)

$0.5 \cdot A_{th} = E$ **Nitrogen Balance**   (6)

$1.5 \cdot A_{th} \cdot 3.76 = F$ (7)

$$AF = \frac{1.5 \cdot A_{th} \cdot 4.76 \cdot MM_{air}}{(MM_{fuel})} \quad \textbf{Air-fuel ratio} \qquad (8)$$

Solution

$\boxed{AF = 15.51}$	$A_{th} = 4.5$	$B = 3$	$D = 4$ $E = 2.25$
$F = 25.38$	$MM_{air} = 28.97\ [\text{kg/kmol}]$	$MM_{fuel} = 60\ [\text{kg/kmol}]$	

EXAMPLE 14-2 WATER SUPPLY TO COMBUSTION PROCESS

Butane C_4H_{10} is burned in 200 percent theoretical air. For complete combustion how many kmol of water must be sprayed into the combustion chamber per kmol of fuel if the products of combustion are to have a dew point temperature of 60°C when the product pressure is 100 kPa?

Equations

GIVEN

$$T_{DP} = 60 \ [C] \tag{1}$$

$$P_{prod} = 100 \ [kPa] \tag{2}$$

ANALYSIS

The reaction equation for 200% theroetical air without the additional water is:

C4H10 + 2*A$_{th}$ (O2 +3.76N2)=B CO2 + D H2O + E O2 + F N2

$4 = B$ **Carbon Balance** $\tag{3}$

$10 = 2 \cdot D$ **Hydrogen Balance** $\tag{4}$

$2 \cdot A_{th} \cdot 2 = B \cdot 2 + D + E \cdot 2$ **Oxygen Balance** $\tag{5}$

$1 \cdot A_{th} = E$ $\tag{6}$

$2 \cdot A_{th} \cdot 3.76 = F$ **Nitrogen Balance** $\tag{7}$

With additional water (N_v) sprayed into the combustion chamber, the balanced reaction equation is:

C4H10 + 2*A$_{th}$ (O2 +3.76N2) + N$_v$ H2O =B CO2 + (D+N$_v$) H2O + E O2 + F N2

The partial pressure of the water in the saturated product mixture at the dew point is:

$$P_{v,prod} = P \ (steam, \ T = T_{DP}, \ x = 1) \tag{8}$$

$$y_v = P_{v,prod}/P_{prod} \tag{9}$$

The additional moles of water required are determined from the vapor mole fraction in the products:

$$y_v = \frac{D + N_v}{B + D + N_v + E + F} \tag{10}$$

Solution

$A_{th} = 6.5$	$B = 4$	$D = 5$	$E = 6.5$	$F = 48.88$
$\boxed{N_v = 9.782}$	$P_{prod} = 100 \ [kPa]$	$P_{v,prod} = 19.93 \ [kPa]$	$T_{DP} = 60 \ [C]$	$y_v = 0.1993$

EXAMPLE 14-3 FIND REQUIRED VOLUME FLOW RATE OF A FUEL

Liquid ethyl alcohol (C_2H_5OH(**liq**)) at 25 °C is burned in a steady-flow combustion chamber with 40 percent excess air that also enters at 25 °C. The products leave the combustion chamber at 600 K. Assuming combustion is complete, determine the required volume flow rate of the liquid ethyl alcohol, in liter/min, to supply heat at a rate of 2000 kJ/s. At 25°C the density of liquid ethyl alcohol is 790 kg/m^3, the specific heat a constant pressure is 114.08 kJ/kmol-K, and the enthalpy of vaporization is 42340 kJ/kmol.

Equations

GIVEN

$$T_P = 600 \ [K] \tag{1}$$

$$T_R = ConvertTemp\,(C, \ K, \ 25) \tag{2}$$

$$\dot{Q}_{out} = 2000 \ [kW] \tag{3}$$

$$\bar{h}_{fg} = 42340 \ [kJ/kmol] \tag{4}$$

$$\rho_{fuel} = 790 \ \left[kg/m^3\right] \tag{5}$$

PROPERTIES

$$\bar{h}_{f,C2H5OH,gas} = -235310 \ [kJ/kmol] \quad \textbf{Enthalpy of formation} \tag{6}$$

$$MM_{fuel} = 2 \cdot 12 + 6 \cdot 1 + 16 \quad \textbf{Molar mass of fuel} \tag{7}$$

ANALYSIS

The reaction equation for 40% excess air is

C2H5OH(liq)+ 1.4*A$_{th}$ (O2 +3.76N2)=B CO2 + D H2O + E O2 + F N2

$$2 = B \quad \textbf{Carbon Balance} \tag{8}$$

$$6 = 2 \cdot D \quad \textbf{Hydrogen Balance} \tag{9}$$

$$1 + 1.4 \cdot A_{th} \cdot 2 = B \cdot 2 + D + E \cdot 2 \quad \textbf{Oxygen Balance} \tag{10}$$

$$0.4 \cdot A_{th} = E \quad \textbf{Excess oxygen in the products} \tag{11}$$

$$1.4 \cdot A_{th} \cdot 3.76 = F \quad \textbf{Nitrogen Balance} \tag{12}$$

$$\dot{N}_{fuel} \cdot H_R = \dot{Q}_{out} + \dot{N}_{fuel} \cdot H_P \quad \textbf{The steady-flow energy balance} \tag{13}$$

$$H_R = 1 \cdot \left(\bar{h}_{f,C2H5OH,gas} - \bar{h}_{fg}\right) + 1.4 \cdot A_{th} \cdot h\,(O2, \ T = T_R) + 1.4 \cdot A_{th} \cdot 3.76 \cdot h\,(N2, \ T = T_R) \tag{14}$$

$$H_P = B \cdot h\,(CO2, \ T = T_P) + D \cdot h\,(H2O, \ T = T_P) + E \cdot h\,(O2, \ T = T_P) + F \cdot h\,(N2, \ T = T_P) \tag{15}$$

$$\dot{m}_{fuel} = \dot{N}_{fuel} \cdot MM_{fuel} \quad \textbf{Fuel mass flow rate} \tag{16}$$

$$\dot{V}_{fuel} = (\dot{m}_{fuel}/\rho_{fuel}) \cdot \left|60000\,\frac{L/min}{m^3/s}\right| \quad \textbf{Fuel volume flow rate} \tag{17}$$

Solution

$A_{th} = 3$

$B = 2$

$D = 3$

$E = 1.2$

$F = 15.79$

$\bar{h}_{fg} = 42340 \text{ [kJ/kmol]}$

$\bar{h}_{f,C2H5OH,gas} = -235310 \text{ [kJ/kmol]}$

$H_P = -1.304 \times 10^6 \text{ [kJ/kmol]}$

$H_R = -277650 \text{ [kJ/kmol]}$

$MM_{fuel} = 46 \text{ [kg/kmol]}$

$\dot{m}_{fuel} = 0.08966 \text{ [kg/s]}$

$\dot{N}_{fuel} = 0.001949 \text{ [kmol/s]}$

$\dot{Q}_{out} = 2000 \text{ [kW]}$

$\rho_{fuel} = 790 \text{ [kg/m}^3\text{]}$

$T_P = 600 \text{ [K]}$

$T_R = 298.1 \text{ [K]}$

$\boxed{\dot{V}_{fuel} = 6.81 \text{ [L/min]}}$

Supplement 14.1 Mass Flow Rate of Air for Combustion of Fuel Mixture

A fuel mixture of 20% by mass methane, CH_4, and 80% by mass ethanol, C_2H_6O, is burned completely with theoretical air. If the total flow rate of the fuel is 31 kg/s, determine the required flow rate of air, in kg/s. Answer: 367 kg/s

Supplement 14.2 Water Condensed in High Efficiency Gas Furnace

To supply heated air to a house, a high efficiency gas furnace burns gaseous propane C_3H_8 with a combustion efficiency of 96 percent. Both the fuel and 140 percent theoretical air are supplied to the combustion chamber at 25 °C and 100 kPa, and the combustion is complete. Because this is a high efficiency furnace, the product gases are cooled to 40 °C and 100 kPa before leaving the furnace. To maintain the house at the desired temperature, a heat transfer rate of 31650 kJ/h is required from the furnace. Determine the volume flow rate of water condensed from the product gases in gallons of water per day. Answer: 2.3 gal/day

Supplement 14.3 Water Condensed during Combustion Process

A mixture of 40% by volume methane, CH_4, and 60% by volume propane, C_3H_8, is burned completely with theoretical air and leaves the combustion chamber at 100°C. The products have a pressure of 100 kPa and are cooled at constant pressure to 39°C. Sketch the T-s diagram for the water vapor that does not condense, if any. How much of the water formed during combustion process will be condensed, in kmol-H_2O/kmol-fuel? Answer: 1.96

Supplement 14.4 Properties of Products of Combustion

Liquid propane (C_3H_8 (liq)) enters a combustion chamber at 25°C and 1 atm at a rate of 0.4 kg/min where it is mixed and burned with 150 percent excess air that enters the combustion chamber at 25°C. The heat transfer from the combustion process is 53 kW. Write the balanced combustion equation and determine the mass flow rate of air, in kg/min; the average molar mass (molecular weight) of the product gases; the average specific heat at constant pressure of the product gases, in kJ/kmol-K; and the temperature of the products of combustion. Answers: 15.63 kg/min, 28.63 kg/kmol, 36.06 kJ/kmol-K, 1282 K

Supplement 14.5 Determine Moles of Gas Components in Combustion Process

A gaseous fuel mixture of 30% propane, C_3H_8, and 70% butane, C_4H_{10}, on a volume basis is burned in air such that the air-fuel ratio is 20 kg air/kg-fuel when the combustion process is complete. Determine the moles of nitrogen in the air supplied to the combustion process, in kmol/kmol-fuel. Determine the moles of water formed in the combustion process, in kmol/kmol-fuel. Determine the moles of oxygen in the product gases. Ans.: 29.41, 4.1, 2.67

Supplement 14.6 Lower Heating Value of a Fuel Mixture

A liquid gas fuel mixture consists of 90% octane, C_8H_{18}, and 10% alcohol, C_2H_5OH, by moles. This fuel is burned with 200% theoretical dry air. Write the balanced reaction equation for complete combustion of this fuel mixture. Determine the theoretical air-fuel ratio for this reaction, in kg-air/kg-fuel. Determine the product-fuel ratio for this reaction, in kg-product/kg-fuel. For a fuel mixture flow rate of 5 kg/s, determine the air-flow rate, in kg/s. Determine the lower heating value of the fuel mixture with 200% theoretical air at 25°C, in kJ/kg. Ans.: 14.83 kg air/kg-fuel, 30.54 kg prod/kg-fuel, 148.3 kg air/s, 43672 kJ/kg-fuel.

Chapter 15 Educational Objectives and Glossary

The Educational Objectives of Chapter 15 are to:

- Develop the equilibrium criterion for reacting systems based on the second law of thermodynamics; more specifically, the increase of entropy principle.
- Develop a general criterion for chemical equilibrium applicable to any reacting system based on minimizing the Gibbs function for the system.
- Define and evaluate the chemical equilibrium constant.
- Apply the general criterion for chemical equilibrium analysis to reacting ideal-gas mixtures.
- Apply the general criterion for chemical equilibrium analysis to simultaneous reactions.
- Relate the chemical equilibrium constant to the enthalpy of reaction.
- Establish the phase equilibrium for nonreacting systems in terms of the specific Gibbs function of the phases of a pure substance.
- Apply the Gibbs phase rule to determine the number of independent variables associated with a multi-component, multiphase system
- Identify Henry's law and Raoult's law for gases dissolved in liquids.

Chapter 15 Glossary

Chemical equilibrium reactions are chemical reactions in which the reactants are depleted at exactly the same rate as they are replenished from the products by the reverse reaction. At equilibrium the reaction proceeds in both directions at the same rate.

Criterion for chemical equilibrium is the equation set equal to zero that involves the stoichiometric coefficients and the molar Gibbs functions of the reactants and the products in the equilibrium reaction.

Equilibrium constant for an equilibrium reaction is the ratio of the product of the product component's partial pressure raised to their stoichiometric coefficients and the product of the reactant component's partial pressure raised to their stoichiometric coefficients. The equilibrium constant of an ideal-gas mixture at a specified temperature can be determined from knowledge of the standard-state Gibbs function change at the same temperature. The number of equilibrium constant relations needed to determine the equilibrium composition of a reacting mixture is equal to the number of chemical species minus the number of elements present in equilibrium.

Gibbs phase rule provides the number of independent variables associated with a multicomponent, multiphase system.

Henry's law states that the mole fraction of a weakly soluble gas in the liquid is equal to the partial pressure of the gas outside the liquid divided by Henry's constant.

Inert gas is a gaseous component in a chemical reaction that does not react chemically with the other components. The presence of inert gases affects the equilibrium composition (although it does not affect the equilibrium constant).

Phase equilibrium is the condition that the two phases of a pure substance are in equilibrium when each phase has the same value of specific Gibbs function. Also, at the triple point (the state at which all three phases coexist in equilibrium), the specific Gibbs function of each one of the three phases is equal.

Raoult's law applies to a gas-liquid mixture when a gas is highly soluble in a liquid (such as ammonia in water) and relates the mole fractions of the species of a two-phase mixture in the liquid and gas phases in an approximate manner.

Simultaneous reactions are chemical reactions that involve two or more reactions occurring at the same time.

Solubility represents the maximum amount of solid that can be dissolved in a liquid at a specified temperature.

Standard-state Gibbs function change is the difference between the sum products of the stoichiometric coefficients and the Gibbs function of a component at 1 atm pressure and temperature T for the products and reactants in the stoichiometric reaction.

Stoichiometric coefficients are the mole numbers in the stoichiometric (theoretical) reaction.

Stoichiometric (theoretical) reaction is the balance reaction equation for a chemical equilibrium reaction.

van't Hoff equation is the expression of the variation of the equilibrium constant with temperature in terms of the enthalpy of reaction at temperature T.

EXAMPLE 15-1 EQUILIBRIUM CONSTANT

Determine the equilibrium constant K_p for the process $CO + 1/2\ O_2 = CO_2$ at (a) 298 K and (b) 2000 K. Compare your results with the values for K_p listed in Table A-28.

Equations

GIVEN

$$Tprod_1 = 298\ [K] \tag{1}$$

$$Tprod_2 = 2000\ [K] \tag{2}$$

$$R_u = 8.314\ [kJ/kmol \cdot K] \qquad \textbf{Universal gas constant} \tag{3}$$

ANALYSIS

The following equations provide the molar specific Gibbs function (g=h-Ts) for each component in the product gases as a function of its temperature, Tprod, at 1 atm pressure, 101.3 kPa

For $Tprod_1$:

$$g_{CO} = h\,(CO,\ T = Tprod_1) - Tprod_1 \cdot s\,(CO,\ T = Tprod_1,\ P = 101.3) \tag{4}$$

$$g_{O2} = h\,(O2,\ T = Tprod_1) - Tprod_1 \cdot s\,(O2,\ T = Tprod_1,\ P = 101.3) \tag{5}$$

$$g_{CO2} = h\,(CO2,\ T = Tprod_1) - Tprod_1 \cdot s\,(CO2,\ T = Tprod_1,\ P = 101.3) \tag{6}$$

The standard-state Gibbs function is

$$\Delta G = 1 \cdot g_{CO2} - 1 \cdot g_{CO} - 0.5 \cdot g_{O2} \tag{7}$$

The equilibrium constant is given by:

$$K_{p,1} = \exp\left(-\frac{\Delta G}{R_u \cdot Tprod_1}\right) \tag{8}$$

$$lnK_{p,1} = \ln\,(k_{p,1}) \tag{9}$$

For $Tprod_2$:

$$g_{CO,2} = h\,(CO,\ T = Tprod_2) - Tprod_2 \cdot s\,(CO,\ T = Tprod_2,\ P = 101.3) \tag{10}$$

$$g_{O2,2} = h\,(O2,\ T = Tprod_2) - Tprod_2 \cdot s\,(O2,\ T = Tprod_2,\ P = 101.3) \tag{11}$$

$$g_{CO2,2} = h\,(CO2,\ T = Tprod_2) - Tprod_2 \cdot s\,(CO2,\ T = Tprod_2,\ P = 101.3) \tag{12}$$

The standard-state Gibbs function is

$$\Delta G_2 = 1 \cdot g_{CO2,2} - 1 \cdot g_{CO,2} - 0.5 \cdot g_{O2,2} \tag{13}$$

The equilibrium constant is given by:

$$K_{p,2} = \exp\left(-\frac{\Delta G_2}{R_u \cdot Tprod_2}\right) \tag{14}$$

$$lnK_{p,2} = \ln(k_{P,2}) \tag{15}$$

Compare the value of $\ln K_p$ calculated by EES with the value of $\ln K_p$ from table A-28 in the text.

Note: The equilibrium equation is the reverse of that in Table A-28. Therefore, K_p is the inverse of the value obtained from Table A-28 and the $\ln(K_p)$ is the negative of the value in Table A-28

$$lnK_{p,1,TableA28} = 103.762 \tag{16}$$

$$lnK_{p,2,TableA28} = 6.635 \tag{17}$$

Solution

$\Delta G = -257266 \text{ [kJ/kmol]}$ $\Delta G_2 = -110402 \text{ [kJ/kmol]}$ $g_{CO} = -169366 \text{ [kJ/kmol]}$

$g_{CO2} = -457166 \text{ [kJ/kmol]}$ $g_{CO2,2} = -920121 \text{ [kJ/kmol]}$ $g_{CO,2} = -570781 \text{ [kJ/kmol]}$

$g_{O2} = -61068 \text{ [kJ/kmol]}$ $g_{O2,2} = -477876 \text{ [kJ/kmol]}$ $K_{p,1} = 1.248 \times 10^{45}$

$K_{p,2} = 764.8$ $lnK_{p,1} = 103.8$ $lnK_{p,1,TableA28} = 103.8$

$lnK_{p,2} = 6.640$ $lnK_{p,2,TableA28} = 6.635$ $R_u = 8.314 \text{ [kJ/kmol-K]}$

$Tprod_1 = 298 \text{ [K]}$ $Tprod_2 = 2000 \text{ [K]}$

EXAMPLE 15-2 SINGLE CHEMICAL EQUILIBRIUM REACTION

Study the effect of varying the percent excess air during the steady-flow combustion of hydrogen at a pressure of 1 atm. At what temperature will 97 percent of H2 burn into H2O? Assume the equilibrium mixture consists of H2O, H2, O2, and N2.

Equations

To solve this problem, we need to give EES a guess value for T_{prop} other than the default value of 1. Set the guess value of T_{prod} to 1000 K by selecting Variable Infromation in the Options menu. Be sure to select the molar basis for properties. Then press F2 or click the Calculator icon.

GIVEN

$$Ex = PercentEx \cdot \left| 0.01 \, \frac{1}{\%} \right| \tag{1}$$

$$P_{prod} = 101.3 \; [\text{kPa}] \tag{2}$$

$$R_u = 8.314 \; [\text{kJ/kmol} \cdot \text{K}] \quad \textbf{Universal gas constant} \tag{3}$$

ANALYSIS

The combustion equation of H2 with stoichiometric amount of air is
H2 + 0.5(O2 + 3.76N2)=H2O +0.5(3.76)N2

For the incomplete combustion with 100% excess air, the combustion equation is
H2 + (1+EX)(0.5)(O2 + 3.76N2)=0.97 H2O +aH2 + bO2+cN2

$$2 = 0.97 \cdot 2 + a \cdot 2 \quad \textbf{Hydrogen balance} \tag{4}$$

$$(1 + Ex) \cdot 0.5 \cdot 2 = 0.97 + b \cdot 2 \quad \text{Oxygen balance} \tag{5}$$

$$(1 + Ex) \cdot 0.5 \cdot 3.76 \cdot 2 = c \cdot 2 \quad \textbf{Nitrogen balance} \tag{6}$$

$$N_{tot} = 0.97 + a + b + c \quad \textbf{Total kilomoles of products at equilibrium} \tag{7}$$

The assumed equilibrium reaction is
H2O=H2+0.5O2

The following equations provide the specific Gibbs function (g=h-Ts) for each H2 component in the product gases as a function of its temperature, T_{prod}, at 1 atm pressure, 101.3 kPa

$$g_{H2O} = \text{h}(\text{H2O}, \, T = T_{prod}) - T_{prod} \cdot \text{s}(\text{H2O}, \, T = T_{prod}, \, P = 101.3) \tag{8}$$

$$g_{H2} = \text{h}(\text{H2}, \, T = T_{prod}) - T_{prod} \cdot \text{s}(\text{H2}, \, T = T_{prod}, \, P = 101.3) \tag{9}$$

$$g_{O2} = \text{h}(\text{O2}, \, T = T_{prod}) - T_{prod} \cdot \text{s}(\text{O2}, \, T = T_{prod}, \, P = 101.3) \tag{10}$$

$$\Delta G = 1 \cdot g_{H2} + 0.5 \cdot g_{O2} - 1 \cdot g_{H2O} \quad \textbf{The standard-state Gibbs function} \tag{11}$$

The equilibrium constant is given by Eq. 15-14.

$$K_P = \exp\left(-\frac{\Delta G}{R_u \cdot T_{prod}}\right) \tag{12}$$

$$P = \frac{P_{prod}}{101.3 \ [\text{kPa}]} \tag{13}$$

The equilibrium constant is also given by Eq. 15-15.

KP = (P/N$_{tot}$)$^{1+0.5-1}$*(a^1*b$^{0.5}$)/(0.97^1)

$$\sqrt{(P/N_{tot})} \cdot a \cdot \sqrt{(b)} = K_P \cdot 0.97 \tag{14}$$

$$lnK_p = \ln(k_P) \tag{15}$$

Compare the value of lnK_p calculated by EES with the value of lnK_p from table A-28 in the text.

Solution

$a = 0.03$	$b = 0.515$	$c = 3.76$	$\Delta G = 100373 \ [\text{kJ/kmol}]$
$Ex = 1 \ [1]$	$g_{H2} = -439931 \ [\text{kJ/kmol}]$	$g_{H2O} = -861686 \ [\text{kJ/kmol}]$	$g_{O2} = -642762 \ [\text{kJ/kmol}]$
$K_P = 0.009664$	$lnK_p = -4.639$	$N_{tot} = 5.275$	$P = 1$
$PercentEx = 100 \ [\%]$	$P_{prod} = 101.3 \ [\text{kPa}]$	$R_u = 8.314 \ [\text{kJ/kmol-K}]$	$T_{prod} = 2602 \ [\text{K}]$

Table 1

Run	lnK_p	PercentEx [%]	T_{prod} [K]
1	-5.414	10	2440
2	-5.165	20	2490
3	-5.019	30	2520
4	-4.918	40	2542
5	-4.844	50	2557
6	-4.786	60	2570
7	-4.739	70	2580
8	-4.7	80	2589
9	-4.667	90	2596
10	-4.639	100	2602

Plot 1

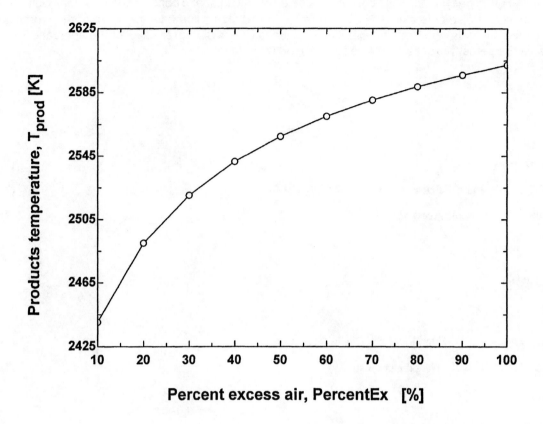

EXAMPLE 15-3 ADIABATIC FLAME TEMPERATURE, SINGLE EQUILIBRIUM REACTION

Ethyl alcohol (C_2H_5OH(**gas**)) at 25 °C is burned in a steady-flow adiabatic combustion chamber with 40 percent excess air that also enters at 25 °C. Determine the adiabatic flame temperature of the products at 1 atm assuming the only significant equilibrium reaction is $CO_2 = CO + 1/2$ O2. Plot the adiabatic flame temperature as the percent excess air varies from 10 to 100 percent.

Equations

GIVEN

$$T_{reac} = ConvertTemp\,(C,\ K,\ 25) \tag{1}$$

$$Q_{out} = 0\ [\text{kJ/kmol}] \quad \textbf{For adiabatic combustion of 1 kmol of fuel} \tag{2}$$

$$PercentEx = 40\ [\%] \quad \textbf{Percent excess air} \tag{3}$$

$$Ex = PercentEx \cdot \left|0.01\,\frac{1}{\%}\right| \tag{4}$$

$$P_{prod} = 101.3\ [\text{kPa}] \tag{5}$$

PROPERTIES

$$\bar{h}_{f,C2H5OH,gas} = -235310\ [\text{kJ/kmol}] \quad \textbf{Enthalpy of formation} \tag{6}$$

$$R_u = 8.314\ [\text{kJ/kmol·K}] \quad \textbf{Universal gas constant} \tag{7}$$

ANALYSIS

The complete combustion reaction equation for excess air is:

C2H5OH(gas)+ (1+Ex)*A$_{th}$ (O2 +3.76N2)=2 CO2 + 3 H2O +Ex*A$_{th}$ O2 + f N2

$$1 + (1 + Ex) \cdot A_{th} \cdot 2 = 2 \cdot 2 + 3 \cdot 1 + Ex \cdot A_{th} \cdot 2 \quad \textbf{Oxygen Balance for complete combustion} \tag{8}$$

The reaction equation for excess air and products in equilibrium is:

C2H5OH(gas)+ (1+Ex)*A$_{th}$ (O2 +3.76N2)=a CO2 + b CO+ d H2O + e O2 + f N2

$$2 = a + b \quad \textbf{Carbon Balance} \tag{9}$$

$$6 = 2 \cdot d \quad \textbf{Hydrogen Balance} \tag{10}$$

$$1 + (1 + Ex) \cdot A_{th} \cdot 2 = a \cdot 2 + b + d + e \cdot 2 \quad \textbf{Oxygen Balance} \tag{11}$$

$$(1 + Ex) \cdot A_{th} \cdot 3.76 = f \quad \textbf{Nitrogen Balance} \tag{12}$$

$$N_{tot} = a + b + d + e + f \quad \textbf{Total kilomoles of products at equilibrium} \tag{13}$$

The assumed equilibrium reaction is CO2=CO+0.5O2

The following equations provide the specific Gibbs function (g=h-Ts) for each component in the product gases as a function of its temperature, T$_{prod}$, at 1 atm pressure, 101.3 kPa

$$g_{CO2} = h\,(CO2,\ T = T_{prod}) - T_{prod} \cdot s\,(CO2,\ T = T_{prod},\ P = 101.3) \tag{14}$$

$$g_{CO} = \text{h}\left(\text{CO}, \, T = T_{prod}\right) - T_{prod} \cdot \text{s}\left(\text{CO}, \, T = T_{prod}, \, P = 101.3\right) \tag{15}$$

$$g_{O2} = \text{h}\left(\text{O2}, \, T = T_{prod}\right) - T_{prod} \cdot \text{s}\left(\text{O2}, \, T = T_{prod}, \, P = 101.3\right) \tag{16}$$

$$\Delta G = 1 \cdot g_{CO} + 0.5 \cdot g_{O2} - 1 \cdot g_{CO2} \qquad \text{The standard-state Gibbs function} \tag{17}$$

The equilibrium constant is given by Eq. 15-14.

$$K_P = \exp\left(-\frac{\Delta G}{R_u \cdot T_{prod}}\right) \tag{18}$$

$$P = \frac{P_{prod}}{101.3 \, [\text{kPa}]} \tag{19}$$

The equilibrium constant is also given by Eq. 15-15.

$$\text{KP} = (\text{P/N}_{tot})^{1+0.5-1} * (\text{b}^1 * \text{e}^{0.5})/(\text{a}^1)$$

$$\sqrt{(P/N_{tot})} \cdot b \cdot \sqrt{(e)} = K_P \cdot a \tag{20}$$

$$H_R = Q_{out} + H_P \qquad \text{Steady-flow energy balance} \tag{21}$$

$$H_R = 1 \cdot \left(\bar{h}_{f,C2H5OH,gas}\right) + (1 + Ex) \cdot A_{th} \cdot \text{h}\left(\text{O2}, \, T = T_{reac}\right) + (1 + Ex) \cdot A_{th} \cdot 3.76 \cdot \text{h}\left(\text{N2}, \, T = T_{reac}\right) \tag{22}$$

$$H_P = a \cdot \text{h}\left(\text{CO2}, \, T = T_{prod}\right) + b \cdot \text{h}\left(\text{CO}, \, T = T_{prod}\right) + d \cdot \text{h}\left(\text{H2O}, \, T = T_{prod}\right) + e \cdot \text{h}\left(\text{O2}, \, T = T_{prod}\right) + f \cdot \text{h}\left(\text{N2}, \, T = T_{prod}\right) \tag{23}$$

Solution

$a = 1.995$	$A_{th} = 3$	$b = 0.004938$
$d = 3$	$\Delta G = 118197 \, [\text{kJ/kmol}]$	$e = 1.202$
$Ex = 0.4 \, [1]$	$f = 15.79$	$g_{CO} = -546839 \, [\text{kJ/kmol}]$
$g_{CO2} = -891538 \, [\text{kJ/kmol}]$	$g_{O2} = -453003 \, [\text{kJ/kmol}]$	$\bar{h}_{f,C2H5OH,gas} = -235310 \, [\text{kJ/kmol}]$
$H_P = -235310 \, [\text{kJ/kmol}]$	$H_R = -235310 \, [\text{kJ/kmol}]$	$K_P = 0.0005787$
$N_{tot} = 21.99$	$P = 1$	$PercentEx = 40 \, [\%]$
$P_{prod} = 101.3 \, [\text{kPa}]$	$Q_{out} = 0 \, [\text{kJ/kmol}]$	$R_u = 8.314 \, [\text{kJ/kmol-K}]$
$T_{prod} = 1907 \, [\text{K}]$	$T_{reac} = 298.1 \, [\text{K}]$	

Table 1

Run	a	A_{th}	b	d	e	f	PercentEx [%]	T_{prod} [K]
1	1.922	3	0.07809	3	0.339	12.41	10	2191
2	1.97	3	0.03017	3	0.6151	13.54	20	2093
3	1.988	3	0.01201	3	0.906	14.66	30	1996
4	1.995	3	0.004933	3	1.202	15.79	40	1907
5	1.998	3	0.002089	3	1.501	16.92	50	1826
6	1.999	3	0.0009089	3	1.8	18.05	60	1752
7	2	3	0.000405	3	2.1	19.18	70	1685
8	2	3	0.0001843	3	2.4	20.3	80	1625
9	2	3	0.0000855	3	2.7	21.43	90	1569
10	2	3	0.00004036	3	3	22.56	100	1518

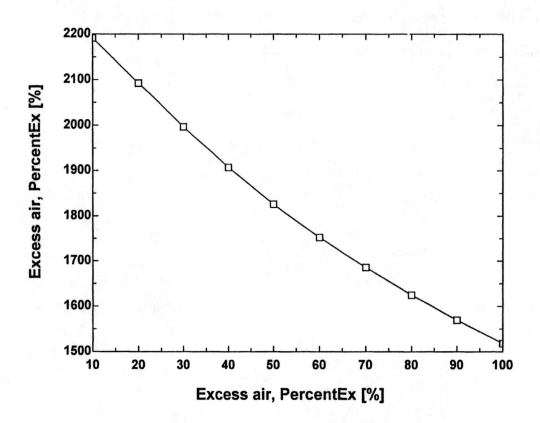

Chapter 15 Supplemental Problems

Supplement 15.1 Tabulate lnKp

Tabulate the natural log of the equilibrium constant as a function of temperature between 298 to 3000 K for the equilibrium reaction $CO + H_2O = CO_2 + H_2$. Compare your results to those obtained by combining the ln Kp values for the two equilibrium reactions $CO_2 = CO + 1/2\ O_2$ and $H_2O = H_2 + 1/2\ O_2$ in given in Table A-28.

Supplement 15.2 Estimate equilibrium constant

Estimate Kp for the following equilibrium reaction at 2500 K.
$CO + H2O = CO2 + H2$
At 2000K it is known that the enthalpy of reaction is -26176 kJ/kmol and Kp is 0.2209. Compare your result with the value obtained from the definition of the equilibrium constant. Answers: 0.1612, 0.1644.

Supplement 15.3 Estimate Enthalpy of Reaction

Estimate the enthalpy of reaction for the equilibrium reaction
$CH_4 + 2\ O_2 = CO_2 + 2\ H_2O$
at 2500 K, using (a) enthalpy data and (b) Kp data. Answers: -810845 kJ/kmol, : -810845 kJ/kmol

Supplement 15.4 Adiabatic flame temperature, simultaneous equilibrium reactions

Ethyl alcohol (C_2H_5OH(gas)) at 25 °C is burned in a steady-flow adiabatic combustion chamber with 40 percent excess air that also enters at 25 °C. Determine the adiabatic flame temperature of the products at 1 atm assuming the significant equilibrium reactions are $CO_2 = CO + 1/2\ O_2$ and $1/2\ N_2 + 1/2\ O_2 = NO$. Plot the adiabatic flame temperature and kmoles of CO_2, CO and NO at equilibrium for values of percent excess air between 10 and 100%.

Supplement 15.5 Constant volume adiabatic combustion and equilibrium

A constant volume tank contains a mixture of 1 kmol H_2 and 1 kmol O_2 at 25°C and 1 atm. The contents are ignited. Determine the final temperature and pressure in the tank when the combustion gases are H_2O, H_2, and O_2. Answers: 3857 K, 1043 kPa

Supplement 15.6 Control CO in products of combustion

It is desired to control the amount of CO in the products of combustion of octane C8H18 so that the volume fraction of CO in the products is less than 0.1%. Determine the percent theoretical air required for the combustion of octane at 5 atm such that the reactant and product temperatures are 298K and 2000 K, respectively. Determine the heat transfer per kmol of octane for this process if the combustion occurs in a steady-flow combustion chamber. Plot the percent theoretical air required for 0.1% CO in the products as a function of product pressures between 100 and 2300 kPa.

Chapter 16 Educational Objectives and Glossary

The Educational Objectives of Chapter 16 are to:

- Develop the general relations for the thermodynamics of high-speed gas flow.
- Introduce the concepts of stagnation state, velocity of sound, and Mach number for a compressible fluid.
- Develop the relationships between the static and stagnation fluid properties for isentropic flows of ideal gases.
- Derive the relationships between the static and stagnation fluid properties as functions of specific-heat ratios and Mach number.
- Derive the effects of area changes for one-dimensional isentropic subsonic and supersonic flows.
- Solve problems of isentropic flow through converging and converging-diverging nozzles.
- Develop the concept of the normal shock wave and the variation of flow properties across the shock wave.
- Explain the influence of nozzle and diffuser efficiencies on the flow parameters for the flow of ideal gases and vapors through these devices.

Chapter 16 Glossary

Back pressure is the pressure applied at the nozzle discharge region.

Bernoulli's equation is a form of the conservation of momentum principle for steady-flow control volumes.

Choked flow occurs in a nozzle when the mass flow reaches a maximum value for the minimum flow area. This happens when the flow properties are those required to increase the fluid velocity to the velocity of sound at the minimum flow area location.

Converging–diverging nozzles are ducts in which the flow area first decreases and then increases in the direction of the flow.

Critical properties are the properties of a fluid at a location where the Mach number is unity.

Critical ratios are the ratios of the stagnation to static properties when the Mach number is unity.

Diffuser efficiency is a measure of a diffuser's ability to increase the pressure of the fluid. It is expressed in terms of the ratio of the kinetic energy that can be converted to pressure rise if the fluid is discharged at the actual exit stagnation pressure to the maximum kinetic energy available for converting to pressure rise. These two quantities are identical for an isentropic diffuser since the actual exit stagnation pressure in this case becomes equal to the inlet stagnation pressure, yielding an efficiency of 100 percent.

Discharge coefficient, a parameter that is used to express the performance of a nozzle, is defined as the ratio of the mass flow rate through the nozzle to the mass flow rate through the nozzle for isentropic flow from the same inlet state to the same exit pressure.

Dynamic temperature is the kinetic energy per unit mass divided by the constant pressure specific heat and corresponds to the temperature rise during the stagnation process.

Fanno line is the locus of all states for frictionless adiabatic flow in a constant-area duct plotted on a T-s diagram.

Hypersonic flow occurs when a flow has a Mach number $M \gg 1$.

Isentropic stagnation state is the stagnation state when the stagnation process is reversible as well as adiabatic (i.e., isentropic). The entropy of a fluid remains constant during an isentropic stagnation process.

Mach number, named after the Austrian physicist Ernst Mach (1838–1916), is the ratio of the actual velocity of the fluid (or an object in still air) to the velocity of sound in the same fluid at the same state.

Normal shock wave is an abrupt change over a very thin section normal to the direction of flow in which the flow transitions from supersonic to subsonic flow. This abrupt change in the flow causes a sudden drop in velocity to subsonic levels and a sudden increase in pressure. Flow through the shock is highly irreversible, and thus it cannot be approximated as isentropic.

Pressure recovery factor, a measure of a diffuser's ability to increase the pressure of the fluid, is expressed in terms of the ratio of the actual stagnation pressure of a fluid at the diffuser exit relative to the maximum possible stagnation pressure.

Pressure rise coefficient, a measure of a diffuser's ability to increase the pressure of the fluid, is defined as the ratio of the actual pressure rise in the diffuser to the pressure rise that would be realized if the process were isentropic.

Rayleigh line is the locus of all states for frictionless flow in a constant-area duct with heat transfer plotted on a T-s diagram.

Sonic flow occurs when a flow has a Mach number $M = 1$.

Stagnation enthalpy represents the total energy of a flowing fluid stream per unit mass and represents the enthalpy of a fluid when it is brought to rest adiabatically with no work. The stagnation enthalpy equals the static enthalpy when the kinetic energy of the fluid is negligible.

Stagnation pressure is the pressure a fluid attains when brought to rest isentropically. For ideal gases with constant specific heats, the stagnation pressure is related to the static pressure of the fluid through the isentropic process equation relating pressure and temperature.

Stagnation properties are the properties of a fluid at the stagnation state. These properties are called stagnation temperature, stagnation pressure, stagnation density, etc. The stagnation state and the stagnation properties are indicated by the subscript 0.

Stagnation (or **total**) **temperature** is the temperature an ideal gas will attain when it is brought to rest adiabatically.

Subsonic flow occurs when a flow has a Mach number $M < 1$.

Supersaturated steam is steam that exists in the wet region without containing any liquid. This phenomenon would exist due to the supersaturation process.

Supersaturation is the phenomenon owing to steam flowing through a nozzle with the high velocities and exiting the nozzle in the saturated region. Since the residence time of the steam in the nozzle is small, and there may not be sufficient time for the necessary heat transfer and the formation of liquid droplets, the condensation of the steam may be delayed for a little while.

Supersonic flow occurs when a flow has a Mach number $M > 1$.

Throat of a converging-diverging nozzle is located at smallest flow area.

Transsonic flow occurs when a flow has a Mach number $M \cong 1$.

Velocity coefficient, a parameter that is used to express the performance of a nozzle, is defined as the ratio of the actual velocity at nozzle exit to the velocity at nozzle exit for isentropic flow from the same inlet state to the same exit pressure.

Velocity of sound (or the **sonic velocity**) is the velocity at which an infinitesimally small pressure wave travels through a medium.

Wilson line is the locus of points where condensation will take place regardless of the initial temperature and pressure as steam flows through a high-velocity nozzle. The Wilson line is often approximated by the 4 percent moisture line on the *h-s* diagram for steam. Therefore, steam flowing through a high-velocity nozzle is assumed to begin condensation when the 4 percent moisture line is crossed.

EXAMPLE 16-1 Inlet Temperature for Choked Converging Nozzle

Air enters a converging nozzle with a velocity of 30 m/s. The nozzle is choked and the exit velocity is determined to be 366 m/s. Determine the temperature of the air at the inlet to the nozzle, in K.

Equations

GIVEN

$$V_{inlet} = 30 \ [m/s] \tag{1}$$

$$V_{exit} = 366 \ [m/s] \tag{2}$$

PROPERTIES

$$Gas\$ = \text{'Air'} \tag{3}$$

$$C_p = c_p \, (Gas\$, \ T = T_{av}) \quad \textbf{Specific heat at constant presssure} \tag{4}$$

$$T_{av} = \text{Average}(T_{inlet}, \ T_{exit}) \quad \textbf{Average of the inlet and exit temperatures} \tag{5}$$

$$C_p - C_v = R \tag{6}$$

$$k = C_p/C_v \tag{7}$$

$$MM = \text{MW} \, (Gas\$) \quad \textbf{Molar mass} \tag{8}$$

$$R_u = 8.314 \ [kJ/kmol \cdot K] \quad \textbf{Universal gas constant} \tag{9}$$

$$R = R_u/MM \quad \textbf{Gas constant} \tag{10}$$

ANALYSIS

$$V_{exit} = \sqrt{\left(k \cdot R \cdot T_{exit} \cdot \left| 1000 \, \frac{m^2/s^2}{kJ/kg} \right| \right)} \quad \textbf{Choked nozzle, V}_{exit} \textbf{ = speed of sound} \tag{11}$$

$$T_o = T_{exit} + \left(\frac{V_{exit}^2}{2} \cdot \left| 0.001 \, \frac{kJ/kg}{m^2/s^2} \right| \right) /C_p \quad \textbf{The stagnation temperature T}_o \tag{12}$$

$$T_o = T_{inlet} + \frac{V_{inlet}^2}{2 \cdot C_p} \cdot \left| 0.001 \, \frac{kJ/kg}{m^2/s^2} \right| \tag{13}$$

Solution

$C_p = 1.009 \ [kJ/kg\text{-}K]$	$C_v = 0.7217 \ [kJ/kg\text{-}K]$	$Gas\$ = \text{'Air'}$	$k = 1.398$
$MM = 28.97 \ [kg/kmol]$	$R = 0.287 \ [kJ/kg\text{-}K]$	$R_u = 8.314 \ [kJ/kmol\text{-}K]$	$T_{av} = 366.9 \ [K]$
$T_{exit} = 333.9 \ [K]$	$\boxed{T_{inlet} = 399.9 \ [K]}$	$T_o = 400.3 \ [K]$	$V_{exit} = 366 \ [m/s]$
$V_{inlet} = 30 \ [m/s]$			

EXAMPLE 16-2 Converging -Diverging Nozzle

Air at 900 kPa, 1000 K enters a converging-diverging nozzle with a velocity of 180 m/s. The throat area of the nozzle is 15 cm² and the mass flow rate is 1.6 kg/s when the nozzle is not choked. The back pressure for the nozzle is 100 kPa. Assuming isentropic flow, calculate the throat temperature, pressure, and velocity when the nozzle is not choked. What will be the throat temperature, pressure, velocity, and mass flow rate when the nozzle is choked?

Equations

GIVEN

$A_{cm2} = 15 \ [\text{cm}^2]$ **Throat area** (1)

$P_{inlet} = 900 \ [\text{kPa}]$ (2)

$T_{inlet} = 1000 \ [\text{K}]$ (3)

$V_{inlet} = 180 \ [\text{m/s}]$ (4)

$P_{back} = 100 \ [\text{kPa}]$ (5)

$\dot{m}_{unchoked} = 1.6 \ [\text{kg/s}]$ (6)

PROPERTIES

$Gas\$ = \text{'Air'}$ (7)

$C_p = \text{c}_\text{p} \, (Gas\$, \ T = T_{inlet})$ **Specific heat at constant presssure** (8)

$C_p - C_v = R$ (9)

$k = C_p/C_v$ (10)

$MM = \text{MW} \, (Gas\$)$ **Molar mass** (11)

$R_u = 8.314 \ [\text{kJ/kmol} \cdot \text{K}]$ **Universal gas constant** (12)

$R = R_u/MM$ **Gas constant** (13)

ANALYSIS

$A_t = A_{cm2} \cdot \left| 1 \times 10^{-4} \ \dfrac{m^2}{cm^2} \right|$ (14)

$T_o = T_{inlet} + \left(\dfrac{V_{inlet}^2}{2} \cdot \left| 0.001 \ \dfrac{kJ/kg}{m^2/s^2} \right| \right) / C_p$ **Stagnation temperature** (15)

$P_o/P_{inlet} = (T_o/T_{inlet})^{\frac{k}{k-1}}$ **Stagnation pressure, P$_o$** (16)

$$P_{crit}/P_o = \left(\frac{2}{k+1}\right)^{k/(k-1)} \qquad \text{Critical pressure from Eq. 16-22} \tag{17}$$

Unchoked flow conditions assume $P_{back} > P_{crit}$

$$T_{t,unck}/T_o = (P_{t,unck}/P_o)^{\frac{k-1}{k}} \qquad \text{Throat temperature for unchoked flow} \tag{18}$$

$$V_{t,unck}\frac{2}{2} = \left(C_p \cdot \left|1000\,\frac{J/kg\text{-}K}{kJ/kg\text{-}K}\right|\right) \cdot (T_o - T_{t,unck}) \qquad \text{Throat velocity for unchoked flow} \tag{19}$$

$$\rho_{t,unck} = \frac{P_{t,ck}}{(R \cdot T_{t,unck})} \qquad \text{Throat density for choked flow} \tag{20}$$

$$\dot{m}_{unchoked} = \rho_{t,unck} \cdot V_{t,unck} \cdot A_t \qquad \text{Nozzle mass flow rate for choked flow} \tag{21}$$

Choked flow conditions $P_{back} <= P_{crit}$

$$P_{t,ck} = P_{crit} \tag{22}$$

$$T_{t,ck}/T_o = (P_{t,ck}/P_o)^{\frac{k-1}{k}} \qquad \text{Throat temperature for choed flow, } T_{t,ck} \tag{23}$$

$$V_{t,ck}\frac{2}{2} = C_p \cdot \left|1000\,\frac{J/kg\text{-}K}{kJ/kg\text{-}K}\right| \cdot (T_o - T_{t,ck}) \qquad \text{Throat velocity for choked flow, } V_{t,ck} \tag{24}$$

$$\rho_{t,ck} = \frac{P_{t,ck}}{(R \cdot T_{t,ck})} \qquad \text{Throat density for choked flow} \tag{25}$$

$$\dot{m}_{choked} = \rho_{t,ck} \cdot V_{t,ck} \cdot A_t \qquad \text{Nozzle mass flow rate for choked flow} \tag{26}$$

Solution

$A_{cm2} = 15\ [\text{cm}^2]$ $A_t = 0.0015\ [\text{m}^2]$ $C_p = 1.14\ [\text{kJ/kg-K}]$ $C_v = 0.8532\ [\text{kJ/kg-K}]$

$Gas\$ = \text{'Air'}$ $k = 1.336$ $MM = 28.97\ [\text{kg/kmol}]$ $\boxed{\dot{m}_{choked} = 1.783\ [\text{kg/s}]}$

$\dot{m}_{unchoked} = 1.6\ [\text{kg/s}]$ $P_{back} = 100\ [\text{kPa}]$ $P_{crit} = 513.3\ [\text{kPA}]$ $P_{inlet} = 900\ [\text{kPa}]$

$P_o = 951.9\ [\text{kPa}]$ $\boxed{P_{t,ck} = 513.3\ [\text{kPA}]}$ $\boxed{P_{t,unck} = 567.7\ [\text{kPa}]}$ $R = 0.287\ [\text{kJ/kg-K}]$

$\rho_{t,ck} = 2.06\ [\text{kg/m3}]$ $\rho_{t,unck} = 2.008\ [\text{kg/m3}]$ $R_u = 8.314\ [\text{kJ/kmol-K}]$ $T_{inlet} = 1000\ [\text{K}]$

$T_o = 1014\ [\text{K}]$ $\boxed{T_{t,ck} = 868.2\ [\text{K}]}$ $\boxed{T_{t,unck} = 890.5\ [\text{K}]}$ $V_{inlet} = 180\ [\text{m/s}]$

$\boxed{V_{t,ck} = 577.1\ [\text{m/s}]}$ $\boxed{V_{t,unck} = 531.1\ [\text{m/s}]}$

EXAMPLE 16-3 Normal Shock Wave

A mixture that is 20% nitrogen and 80% carbon dioxide by volume flows into a nozzle with a velocity of 200 m/s, a temperature of 1000 K, and a pressure of 800 kPa. At a location in the nozzle the flow experiences a normal shock, and after the shock the flow has a Mach number of 0.45. Determine the temperature, pressure, and velocity before and after the shock and Mach number before the shock.

Equations

The equations relating the flow parameters across the shock use the following notation:

M_x = Mach Number up stream of normal shock

M_y = Mach Number down stream of normal shock

PyOverPx= P_y/P_x Pressue ratio across normal shock

TyOverTx = T_y/T_x Temperature ratio across normal shock

RhoyOverRhox= ρ_y/ρ_x Density ratio across normal shock

PoyOverPox = P_{oy}/P_{ox} Stagantion pressure ratio across normal shock

PoyOverPx = P_{oy}/P_x Stagnation pressure after normal shock ratioed to pressure before shock

The isentropic flow equations use the following notation:

M = flow Mach Number

M^{star} = ratio of the local velocity to the velocity of sound where M = 1

P= P/P_o for compressible, isentropic flow

T= T/T_o for compressible, isentropic flow

$\rho\$\rho_o$= ρ/ρ_o for compressible, isentropic flow

A^{star}=A/A* for compressible, isentropic flow

GIVEN

$$M_y = 0.45 \tag{1}$$

$$T_{Prod} = 1000 \ [K] \tag{2}$$

$$P_{Prod} = 800 \ [kPa] \tag{3}$$

$$V_{prod} = 200 \ [m/s] \tag{4}$$

$$y_{N2} = 0.2 \tag{5}$$

$$y_{CO2} = 0.8 \tag{6}$$

$$R_u = 8.324 \ [kJ/kmol \cdot K] \tag{7}$$

ANALYSIS

$$MM_{prod} = y_{CO2} \cdot MW \ (CO2 \ ) + y_{N2} \cdot MW \ (N2 \ ) \qquad \textbf{Molar mass of the products} \tag{8}$$

Specific heat at constant pressure of the products on a kmol basis

$$Cp_{prod} = y_{CO2} \cdot c_p \left(CO2,\ T = T_{prod} \right) + y_{N2} \cdot c_p \left(N2,\ T = T_{prod} \right) \tag{9}$$

$$Cv_{prod} = Cp_{prod} - R_u \quad \text{Specific heat at constant volume of the products on a kmol basis} \tag{10}$$

$$k = Cp_{prod}/Cv_{prod} \tag{11}$$

$$Cp_{mass} = Cp_{prod}/MM_{prod} \quad \text{Convert } Cp_{prod} \text{ to a mass basis} \tag{12}$$

$$R = R_u/MM_{prod} \quad \text{Gas constant} \tag{13}$$

$$T_o = T_{prod} + \left(\frac{V_{prod}^2}{2} \cdot \left| 0.001\ \frac{kJ/kg}{m^2/s^2} \right| \right) /Cp_{mass} \quad \text{Stagnation temperature} \tag{14}$$

$$P_o = P_{prod} \cdot \left(T_o/T_{prod} \right)^{\frac{k}{k-1}} \quad \text{Stagnation pressure, } P_o \tag{15}$$

The isentropic Mach number relations given in Table A-15 follow.

$$M = M_x \tag{16}$$

$$T/To = \left(1 + \frac{k-1}{2} \cdot M^2 \right)^{-1} \tag{17}$$

$$P/Po = T/To^{\frac{k}{k-1}} \tag{18}$$

$$rho/rho_o = T/To^{\frac{1}{k-1}} \tag{19}$$

$$M^* = M \cdot \sqrt{\left(\frac{k+1}{2 + (k-1) \cdot M^2} \right)} \tag{20}$$

$$A/A^* = \left(\frac{2}{k+1} \cdot \left(1 + (k-1)/2 \cdot M^2 \right) \right)^{(k+1)/(2 \cdot (k-1))} /M \tag{21}$$

$$T_x = T_o \cdot T/To \tag{22}$$

$$P_x = P_o \cdot P/Po \tag{23}$$

$$V_x = M \cdot \sqrt{\left(k \cdot R \cdot T_x \cdot \left| 1000\ \frac{m^2/s^2}{kJ/kg} \right| \right)} \tag{24}$$

The Normal shock relations given in Table A-16 follow.

$$M_y = \sqrt{\left(\left(M_x^2 + \frac{2}{k-1} \right) / \left(2 \cdot M_x^2 \cdot k/(k-1) - 1 \right) \right)} \tag{25}$$

$$Py/Px = \frac{1 + k \cdot M_x^2}{1 + k \cdot M_y^2} \tag{26}$$

$$Ty/Tx = \left(1 + M_x^2 \cdot \frac{k-1}{2} \right) / \left(1 + M_y^2 \cdot (k-1)/2 \right) \tag{27}$$

$$Rhoy/Rhox = Py/Px/Ty/Tx \tag{28}$$

$$Poy/Pox = M_x/M_y \cdot \left(\left(1 + M_y^2 \cdot \frac{k-1}{2} \right) / \left(1 + M_x^2 \cdot (k-1)/2 \right) \right)^{(k+1)/(2 \cdot (k-1))} \tag{29}$$

$$Poy/Px = \left(1 + k \cdot M_x^2 \right) \cdot \left(1 + M_y^2 \cdot \frac{k-1}{2} \right)^{k/(k-1)} / \left(1 + k \cdot M_y^2 \right) \tag{30}$$

$$T_y = T_x \cdot Ty/Tx \tag{31}$$

$$P_y = P_x \cdot Py/Px \tag{32}$$

$$V_y = M_y \cdot \sqrt{\left(k \cdot R \cdot T_y \cdot \left| 1000 \, \frac{m^2/s^2}{kJ/kg} \right| \right)} \tag{33}$$

Solution

$A/A^* = 4.287$
$k = 1.2$
$\boxed{M_y = 0.45}$
$Py/Px = 7.696$
$\boxed{P_x = 34.81 \text{ [kPa]}}$
$\rho/\rho_o = 0.06769$
$\boxed{T_o = 1016 \text{ [K]}}$
$V_{prod} = 200 \text{ [m/s]}$
$y_{N2} = 0.2$

$Cp_{mass} = 1.223 \text{ [kJ/kg-K]}$
$M = 2.672$
$M^* = 2.14$
$P/Po = 0.03948$
$\boxed{P_y = 267.9 \text{ [kPa]}}$
$R_u = 8.324 \text{ [kJ/kmol-K]}$
$T_{Prod} = 1000 \text{ [K]}$
$\boxed{V_x = 1018 \text{ [m/s]}}$

$Cp_{prod} = 49.9 \text{ [kJ/kmol-K]}$
$MM_{prod} = 40.81 \text{ [kg/kmol]}$
$Poy/Pox = 0.3427$
$P_o = 881.7 \text{ [kPa]}$
$R = 0.204 \text{ [kJ/kg-K]}$
$Ty/Tx = 1.68$
$\boxed{T_x = 592.8 \text{ [K]}}$
$\boxed{V_y = 222.2 \text{ [m/s]}}$

$Cv_{prod} = 41.58 \text{ [kJ/kmol-K]}$
$M_x = 2.672$
$Poy/Px = 8.68$
$P_{Prod} = 800 \text{ [kPa]}$
$Rhoy/Rhox = 4.58$
$T/To = 0.5833$
$\boxed{T_y = 996.2 \text{ [K]}}$
$y_{CO2} = 0.8$

Chapter 16 Supplemental Problems

Supplement 16.1 Inlet Temperature, Pressure for Choked Converging Nozzle

Air enters a converging nozzle with a velocity of 40 m/s. If the nozzle is choked and the exit velocity and pressure are determined to be 420 m/s, 120 kPa, respectively. Determine the temperature (in K) and pressure (in kPa) of the air at the inlet to the nozzle. Answer: 527.8 K, 225.2 kPa

Supplement 16.2 Turbojet with Converging Nozzle

A turbojet aircraft is flying with a velocity of 300 m/s at an altitude of 8000 m. The pressure ratio across the compressor is 12, and the temperature at the turbine inlet is 1500 K. Air enters the compressor at a rate of 50 kg/s, and the jet fuel has a heating value of 42,700 kJ/kg. The turbojet is equipped with a converging nozzle. Determine the velocity of the exhaust gases, the nozzle exit area, in m^2, and the rate of fuel consumption. Answer: 641.3 m/s, 0.1189 m2, 1.245 kg/s

Supplement 16.3 Turbojet with Converging-Diverging Nozzle

A turbojet aircraft is flying with a velocity of 300 m/s at an altitude of 9000 m. The pressure ratio across the compressor is 12, and the temperature at the turbine inlet is 1500 K. Air enters the compressor at a rate of 50 kg/s, and the jet fuel has a heating value of 42,700 kJ/kg. The turbojet is equipped with a converging-diverging nozzle. Determine the nozzle throat area, in m^2; the nozzle exit area, in m^2; the velocity of the exhaust gases; and the rate of fuel consumption. Answer: 0.2782 m2, 0.133 m2, 1.26 kg/s, 1145 m/s.

Supplement 16.4 Non-Isentropic Converging Nozzle

Air at 900 kPa, 400 K enters a converging nozzle with a negligible velocity.
The exit area of the nozzle is 10 cm^2. The critical-to-stagnation pressure ratio for irreversible adiabatic flow is given by Pcrit/Po = (1-1/N*(k-1)/(k+1))^(k/(k-1)), where N is the nozzle isentropic efficiency. Assuming the nozzle has isentropic efficiencies of 100% and 95%, calculate and plot the exit pressure versus the back pressure Pb for 0.9>= Pb >=0.1 MPa.

Supplement 16.5 Non-Isentropic Converging-Diverging Nozzle

Air at 900 kPa, 1000 K enters a converging-diverging nozzle with an inlet velocity of 180 m/s. The nozzle throat area is 15 cm^2, and the mass flow rate is 1.6 kg/s when the nozzle is not choked. The back pressure for the nozzle is 100 kPa. The critical-to-stagnation pressure ratio for irreversible adiabatic flow is given by:

Pcrit/Po = (1-1/N*(k-1)/(k+1))^(k/(k-1)),

where N is the nozzle isentropic efficiency. Assuming the nozzle has an isentropic efficiency of 95%, calculate the throat temperature, pressure, and velocity when the nozzle is not choked. What will be the throat temperature, pressure, velocity, and mass flow rate when the nozzle is choked? Answer: 895.6 K, 563.3 kPa, 530.1 m/s, 869.9 K, 517.3 kPa, 595.3 m/s, 1.85 kg/s.

Supplement 16.6 Normal Shock Wave

The products of complete combustion of kerosene C10H22 with 50% excess air flows through a converging-diverging nozzle. At a location in the nozzle where the flow Mach number reaches 3, the flow experiences a normal shock wave. The flow enters the nozzle with a velocity of 200 m/s, a temperature of 1200 K, and a pressure of 1000 kPa. Determine the temperature, pressure, and velocity before and after the shock and Mach number after the shock. Answer: 524.2 K, 25.9 kPa, 1330 m/s, 1181 K, 259.6 kPa, 298.9 m/s, 0.4492